Block 2

Contents

The Open University, Walton Hall, Milton Keynes, MK7 6AA.

First published 2005. Second edition 2008.

Edited, designed and typeset by The Open University, using the Open University TEX System.

Printed and bound in the United Kingdom by Charlesworth Press, Wakefield.

ISBN 978 0 7492 5282 3

1.1

UNIT 5   Statics

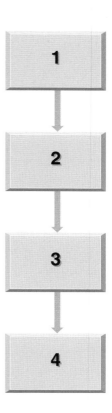

Study guide for Unit 5

This unit and *Unit 6* lay the foundations of the subject of mechanics, which has a large part to play in this course. Mechanics is concerned with how and why objects stay put, and how and why they move. This unit considers how and why objects stay put, while *Unit 6* and the later mechanics units consider how and why they move. The material in this unit and in *Unit 6* lays the foundations of mechanics.

This unit assumes a good working knowledge of vectors, which you should have obtained from *Unit 4*.

The recommended study pattern is to study one section per study session, in the order in which they appear. There are only four sections in this unit, so for the fifth study session you might like to look at the multimedia package designed to support this unit, which is described in the media guide.

Introduction

This unit and the next lay the foundations of mechanics that will be used throughout the course. Mechanics can itself be divided into three distinct areas.

Quantum mechanics deals with the motion of very *small* objects (such as atoms, which have diameters of about 10^{-10} metres).

Relativistic mechanics deals with the motion of very *fast* objects (such as the electrons in a television tube, which travel at speeds of about 10^8 metres per second).

Newtonian mechanics is concerned with the more familiar everyday world of objects which are larger than atoms, and which move at speeds less than a few million metres per second.

In this course only *Newtonian mechanics* is considered, but this still leaves a vast range of phenomena to discuss. Isaac Newton (1642–1727) was the great English mathematician whose name is given to this subject. His *Philosophiae Naturalis Principia Mathematica* of 1687 (Mathematical Principles of Natural Philosophy, known as *Principia* for short) incorporates one of the most celebrated examples of mathematical modelling. It was in *Principia* that Newton laid down the foundations of Newtonian mechanics. This great book, which showed for the first time how earthly and heavenly movements obey the same laws, is cast in the form of a set of propositions all deriving from three axioms, or *laws of motion*. It is these, here translated into modern English from the original Latin, that still provide the basis for Newtonian mechanics.

Sir Isaac Newton (courtesy of Mansell/Time Inc./Katz)

Law I Every body continues in a state of rest, or moves with constant velocity in a straight line, unless a force is applied to it.

Law II The rate of change of velocity of a body is proportional to the resultant force applied to the body, and is made in the direction of the resultant force.

Law III To every action (i.e. force) by one body on another there is always opposed an equal reaction (i.e. force) — i.e. the actions of two bodies upon each other are always equal in magnitude and opposite in direction.

These laws did not spring fully formed from Newton's imagination. Earlier investigators, notably the Italian mathematician and scientist Galileo Galilei (1564–1642) and the French polymath René Descartes (1596–1650), had formulated some similar results. But it was Newton who perceived that these three laws were sufficient for the foundations of mechanics.

It is perhaps surprising that these seminal laws of mathematical modelling were written entirely in prose, with no hint of a mathematical symbol. Symbolic forms were developed during the eighteenth century. Newton himself followed through the complicated chains of reasoning arising from the laws with far less recourse to symbolism, or indeed to calculus, than later mathematicians have found necessary. In this course, the laws themselves will be explained and the arguments based on them simplified by using the vector notation developed in *Unit 4*.

One of the central concepts in Newtonian mechanics is that of a *force*. The word 'force' is used in everyday conversation in a variety of ways: he *forced* his way in; the *force* of destiny; to put into *force*; the labour *force*. In mathematics and science, the word 'force' has a precise definition. However, this definition relies on the movement of objects and so is deferred until the next unit. Essentially, though, this definition says that a **force** either changes the shape of the object on which it acts, or causes movement of the object. When we experience a force, in the mathematical sense of the word, we feel it through contact: pulling on a rope, lifting a shopping bag, pushing against a car, holding a child aloft. In each case, the force that we experience has a magnitude and a direction, so we model a force as a vector quantity.

Mathematical representation of a force

A force is represented mathematically by a vector. The magnitude of the vector represents the magnitude of the force, and the direction of the vector specifies the direction in which the force is applied.

Sometimes we can see the effect of a force, such as when a mattress depresses under the weight of someone sitting on it, a washing line sags under the weight of the washing, a rubber band is stretched over some packages, a door is pulled open, or a bag of shopping is lifted. In each case there is an obvious deformation or movement that indicates that a force is present. Sometimes, however, the presence of a force is not so obvious, in situations such as a ladder leaning against a wall (though you could appreciate the presence of a force in this situation were *you* to replace the wall and hold the ladder steady yourself), a box resting on a shelf, or a cable holding up a ceiling lamp (consider holding up the lamp by the cable yourself).

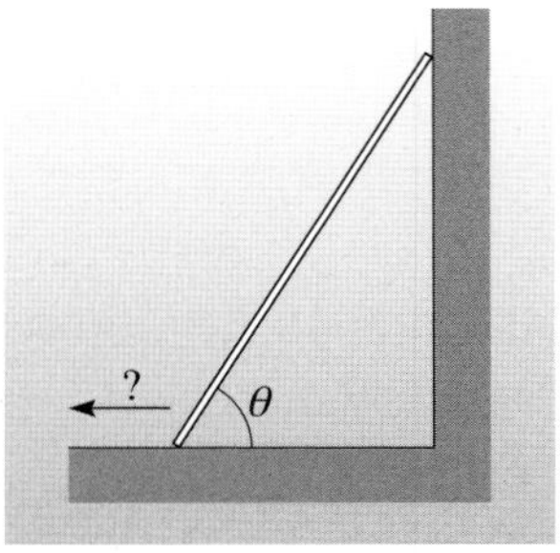

This unit considers the conditions under which objects remain stationary when subjected to forces, which is a topic known as **statics**. For example, what is the minimum angle θ that a ladder leaning against a wall can make with the ground before the ladder slides to the ground (see Figure 0.1)? Cases where forces cause motion are discussed in *Unit 6* and elsewhere in the course. The study of motion is called **dynamics**.

Figure 0.1

Before forces and their effects can be analysed mathematically, they and the objects on which they act have to be modelled mathematically. In Section 1 objects are modelled as particles, and the section shows how various forces such as the forces of gravity, tension and friction can be modelled. It also shows how to analyse one-particle systems in equilibrium. Section 2 extends the ideas to systems involving two or more particles. Section 3 goes on to consider situations where an object needs to be modelled as a solid body rather than as a particle. Section 3 also discusses the turning effect of a force (known as *torque*), which happens only if a force acts on a solid body rather than a particle. Section 4 describes the application to statics problems of the concepts and principles described in the earlier sections.

1 Modelling forces

This section shows how four common types of force can be modelled: the force of gravity, the force exerted by a surface on an object in contact with it, the tension force due to a string, and the friction force between two surfaces. These forces and the situations in which they occur are modelled and analysed in Subsections 1.2–1.5. First, however, we look at one way of modelling the objects on which forces act.

1.1 Particles

When we create a mathematical model, the aim is to simplify the real situation being modelled so that only the essential features are included. This enables us to analyse the situation mathematically. In mechanics, the most important things to model are the forces acting on objects, and throughout this unit and the other mechanics units you will see how to do this. However, we also need to model the objects on which the forces act.

Sometimes, such as when the length, breadth, depth, orientation or internal structure of an object is important, the object needs to be modelled as a *solid body*, which possesses both mass and size. An example is provided by a ladder leaning against a wall, where the length of the ladder is important. At other times, when the size and structure of the object are not important, the object may be modelled as a *particle*, which possesses mass but no size. An example is provided by a pallet of bricks hanging on the end of a cable from a crane, where the pallet of bricks can be modelled as a particle if we are interested only in the forces acting on the cable.

The modelling of solid bodies is discussed in Section 3.

Definition

A **particle** is a material object whose size and internal structure may be neglected. It has mass but no size, and so occupies a single point in space. A particle is often represented in diagrams by a black dot •.

Observation has shown that each force acting on an object can be modelled as acting *at a particular point* on the object, this point being referred to as the **point of action** of the force. In situations where a particle model is appropriate, all the forces acting on the object are modelled as acting through the point in space occupied by the particle. It is conventional to show these forces in diagrams, known as **force diagrams**, by vector arrows whose tails coincide with the particle and whose directions correspond to the directions in which the forces act, as Figure 1.1 illustrates.

Figure 1.1

Note that in force diagrams arrows are usually drawn with arbitrary lengths. This contrasts with the usual convention for vectors where length indicates magnitude.

When several forces are acting on a particle, observation has shown that the overall effect of these forces can be represented by a single vector given by the sum of the vectors representing the individual forces. In this unit, we deal with objects that do not move, i.e. objects in **equilibrium**. For a particle in equilibrium, the forces acting on it must balance each other (or else it would move), so we have the following important condition.

Equilibrium condition for particles

A particle subjected to forces $\mathbf{F}_1, \mathbf{F}_2, \ldots, \mathbf{F}_n$ is in equilibrium if the forces sum to the zero vector, i.e.

$$\sum_{i=1}^{n} \mathbf{F}_i = \mathbf{0}.$$

This condition was first stated by Isaac Newton as part of his first law of motion.

We often say that the sum of the forces is zero, with the implication that this means the zero vector.

1.2 Weight

When you hold a shoe, your fingers experience a force. The shoe, like all objects, has a force associated with it, and if you do not provide opposition to this force in holding the shoe, the shoe will fall to the ground. But what is the source of the force exerted by the shoe?

This force is due to the attraction of the shoe to the Earth. The force of attraction of objects to the Earth is called the **force of gravity** or the **gravitational force**. The gravitational force acting on a particular object is not constant, but depends on the position of the object relative to the Earth: there is a small variation of this force with height above ground (or depth below ground), and there is an even smaller variation with latitude and longitude. When applied to a particular object, this force is called the **weight** of the object. In this course, we shall assume that the weight of a particular object is constant near the Earth's surface.

In everyday speech, the words *mass* and *weight* are interchangeable. Mathematically, however, they are different. The **mass** of an object is the amount of matter in the object and is independent of the object's position in the universe; it is a *scalar* quantity, measured in *kilograms* (kg) in the SI system. The **weight** of an object is the gravitational force on the object, and is dependent on where the object is situated; it is a *vector* quantity, whose magnitude is measured in *newtons* (N) in the SI system and whose direction is downwards towards the centre of the Earth.

The newton is defined formally in *Unit 6*.

Mass and weight are, however, related in that an object of mass m has weight of magnitude mg, where g is a constant known as the **acceleration due to gravity**. Near the Earth's surface, g has the value of approximately $9.81\,\mathrm{m\,s^{-2}}$, and we shall assume this value for g throughout this course. If the Cartesian unit vector $\mathbf{k}$ points vertically upwards from the surface of the Earth, then the weight $\mathbf{W}$ of an object of mass m is $-mg\mathbf{k}$ (where we need the negative sign because the force of gravity acts vertically downwards, i.e. the weight acts vertically downwards).

The relationship between mass and weight is based on Newton's second law of motion, which is discussed in *Unit 6*.

Weight

An object of mass m has weight $\mathbf{W}$ of magnitude $|\mathbf{W}| = mg$, where g is the acceleration due to gravity, with direction towards the centre of the Earth. If the object is modelled as a particle, the force of gravity on the object can be illustrated by the force diagram in Figure 1.2.

Figure 1.2

Exercise 1.1

What is the weight of a particle of mass $3\,\mathrm{kg}$ in a coordinate system where the $\mathbf{k}$-direction is vertically downwards?

When modelling forces acting on objects, it is often convenient to define Cartesian unit vectors and to express the force vectors in component form, i.e. to resolve the vectors into their components. These Cartesian unit vectors define the directions of the axes in a Cartesian coordinate system, so we often refer to the process of defining Cartesian unit vectors as **choosing axes**.

*Exercise 1.2 _____

Later in this unit we shall find it convenient to use axes which are not horizontal and vertical. Express the weight **W** of a particle of mass 15 kg in terms of the Cartesian unit vectors **i** and **j**, where **i** and **j** both lie in a vertical plane and are oriented as shown in Figure 1.3.

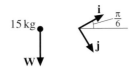

Figure 1.3

In the previous exercise, nice angles (i.e. multiples of $\frac{\pi}{6}$ ($30°$)) were chosen in order to help you evaluate the cosines involved without having to use a calculator. Another convenient angle is $\frac{\pi}{4}$ ($45°$). The cosines of all these angles are given in the Handbook. Sometimes, as in the above exercise, obtuse angles are used; cosines of such angles can be derived from the addition formulae, which are also given in the Handbook. For example,

$$\cos \tfrac{2\pi}{3} = \cos(\tfrac{\pi}{2} + \tfrac{\pi}{6}) = \cos \tfrac{\pi}{2} \cos \tfrac{\pi}{6} - \sin \tfrac{\pi}{2} \sin \tfrac{\pi}{6} = -\tfrac{1}{2}.$$

1.3   Normal reaction

Consider an empty coffee mug resting on a table. Let us model the mug as a particle. We know that one force, the mug's weight, is acting on the mug. But, since the mug is at rest (i.e. not moving), the equilibrium condition for particles tells us that some other force(s) must be acting on the mug (so that all the forces acting on the mug sum to zero). The only possible source for another force on the mug is the table. So, in order for the mug to remain at rest, the equilibrium condition tells us that the table must exert a force on the mug, which must be equal in magnitude to the weight of the mug and opposite in direction. The force exerted by the table on the mug, and indeed exerted by any surface on an object in contact with it, is called the **normal reaction force** or simply the **normal reaction**.

The situation is illustrated in Figure 1.4, which shows not only the mug and table, but the corresponding force diagram (plus the Cartesian unit vector **k** pointing vertically upwards). The normal reaction force is denoted by **N** and the weight of the mug by **W**. Using the equilibrium condition for particles, we have

$$\mathbf{W} + \mathbf{N} = \mathbf{0}.$$

If the mug has mass m, then $\mathbf{W} = -mg\mathbf{k}$, and hence

$$\mathbf{N} = -\mathbf{W} = mg\mathbf{k}$$

is a force acting vertically upwards with the same magnitude as the weight of the mug.

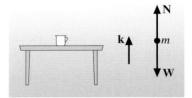

Figure 1.4

The normal reaction force is remarkable in that it adjusts itself to the magnitude required. For example, if the coffee mug is replaced by a full pot of coffee, then the normal reaction increases (unless the weight of the coffee pot is too much for the table, in which case the table collapses and the pot is no longer at rest). Contrast this with the weight of an object, which is fixed and constant, regardless of what is happening to the object. Our basic modelling assumption is that the magnitude of the normal reaction force is potentially unlimited.

There is a normal reaction force whenever one object (e.g. a mug) presses on another (e.g. a table). Observation has shown that this force acts _normally_ (i.e. at a right angle) to the common tangent at the point of contact between the objects. It therefore need not act vertically upwards.

This explains the name _normal_ reaction force.

For example, if the table on which the mug is resting is on an uneven floor, so that the table top makes an angle θ with the horizontal, then the normal reaction force makes an angle θ with the vertical, as shown in Figure 1.5. (In such a case there must be other forces acting on the mug if it is to remain in equilibrium. These other forces are discussed later.)

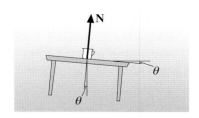

Figure 1.5

1.4 Tension

Consider a lamp hanging from a ceiling on an electric cable. Let us model the lamp as a particle. As in the case of the mug and the table in the previous subsection, we know that there is a weight associated with the lamp, and that since the lamp is at rest, by the equilibrium condition some other force(s) must be acting on it. The only possible source for another force is the cable, so the cable must exert a force on the lamp. The force exerted by the cable on the lamp is called the **tension force**.

Tension forces occur whenever objects are tautly joined, e.g. by cables, ropes, strings or threads. These cables and ropes can be modelled in different ways. For example, if we want to model the ceiling lamp and are interested only in the force in the cable, then we can model the cable as a **model string**, defined as an object possessing length, but no area, volume or mass, and which does not stretch (i.e. it is inextensible). On the other hand, if we are interested in how much the cable stretches under the weight of the lamp, then we can model the cable as a *model spring*, which has properties similar to those of a model string (i.e. it has no area, volume or mass), but allows extension. In this unit we consider only strings.

Springs are discussed in *Unit 7.*

The ceiling lamp example is illustrated in Figure 1.6. The tension force due to the model string is denoted by $\mathbf{T}$, and the weight of the lamp by $\mathbf{W}$. In a manner similar to the case of normal reaction forces, the equilibrium condition for particles gives

$$\mathbf{W} + \mathbf{T} = \mathbf{0}.$$

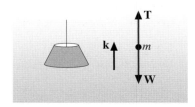

If the lamp has mass m, then $\mathbf{W} = -mg\mathbf{k}$, and hence

$$\mathbf{T} = -\mathbf{W} = mg\mathbf{k}$$

is a force acting vertically upwards (along the length of the model string) with the same magnitude as the weight of the lamp.

Figure 1.6

We assume that the tension force due to a model string acts along the length of the string and away from the point of its attachment to an object. As in the case of a normal reaction, the magnitude of this force (often referred to as the *tension in the string* — a scalar quantity) depends on the requirements necessary to maintain equilibrium, so it is potentially unlimited. (In reality, a string can exert only a certain tension force before it breaks, but a *model* string supports an unlimited tension force.)

Definitions

(a) A **model string** is an object with a fixed finite length, and no area, volume or mass, that exerts a force at the point of attachment.

(b) The **tension force due to a string** is directed along the length of the string away from the point of attachment.

As in the case of normal reaction forces, the tension force due to a string need not be vertically upwards, as the following example illustrates.

Example 1.1

A hanging flower basket of mass 4 kg is suspended by one cord from a porch and tied by another cord to the wall, as shown in Figure 1.7. Model the basket as a particle and the cords as model strings. What are the magnitudes of the tension forces due to the cords?

Solution

We choose axes as shown in Figure 1.7. Note that we need choose only two axes because all the forces act in the same vertical plane. Denoting the tension forces by $\mathbf{T}_1$ and $\mathbf{T}_2$, and the weight of the basket by $\mathbf{W}$, we have the force diagram shown in Figure 1.8.

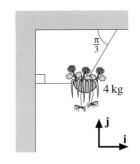

Figure 1.7

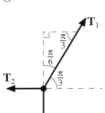

Figure 1.8

In the diagram, the angle between the vector $\mathbf{T}_1$ and the unit vector $\mathbf{j}$ is calculated by imagining the right-angled triangle shown, and using the fact that the angles of a triangle sum to π radians. The angle between the vectors $\mathbf{T}_1$ and $\mathbf{i}$ is calculated using the fact that the angle between the unit vectors $\mathbf{i}$ and $\mathbf{j}$ is a right angle (so the required angle is $\frac{\pi}{2} - \frac{\pi}{6} = \frac{\pi}{3}$).

The equilibrium condition for particles tells us that

$$\mathbf{T}_1 + \mathbf{T}_2 + \mathbf{W} = \mathbf{0}. \tag{1.1}$$

To progress further, we need to express the three forces in terms of the unit vectors $\mathbf{i}$ and $\mathbf{j}$. To do this, we apply the technique of resolving vectors described in *Unit 4*. Starting with the weight $\mathbf{W}$, we have

$$\begin{aligned}
\mathbf{W} &= (\mathbf{W} \cdot \mathbf{i})\,\mathbf{i} + (\mathbf{W} \cdot \mathbf{j})\,\mathbf{j} \\
&= |\mathbf{W}| \cos \tfrac{\pi}{2}\,\mathbf{i} + |\mathbf{W}| \cos \pi\,\mathbf{j} \\
&= -|\mathbf{W}|\,\mathbf{j}.
\end{aligned}$$

Similarly, the tension force $\mathbf{T}_1$ can be expressed as

$$\begin{aligned}
\mathbf{T}_1 &= (\mathbf{T}_1 \cdot \mathbf{i})\,\mathbf{i} + (\mathbf{T}_1 \cdot \mathbf{j})\,\mathbf{j} \\
&= |\mathbf{T}_1| \cos \tfrac{\pi}{3}\,\mathbf{i} + |\mathbf{T}_1| \cos \tfrac{\pi}{6}\,\mathbf{j} \\
&= \tfrac{1}{2}|\mathbf{T}_1|\,\mathbf{i} + \tfrac{\sqrt{3}}{2}|\mathbf{T}_1|\,\mathbf{j}.
\end{aligned}$$

Finally, the tension force $\mathbf{T}_2$ can be written as

$$\begin{aligned}
\mathbf{T}_2 &= (\mathbf{T}_2 \cdot \mathbf{i})\,\mathbf{i} + (\mathbf{T}_2 \cdot \mathbf{j})\,\mathbf{j} \\
&= |\mathbf{T}_2| \cos \pi\,\mathbf{i} + |\mathbf{T}_2| \cos \tfrac{\pi}{2}\,\mathbf{j} \\
&= -|\mathbf{T}_2|\,\mathbf{i}.
\end{aligned}$$

In later examples and solutions, this process of resolving vectors will not be done explicitly for forces aligned with the axes. The components will be written down *by inspection of the diagram*.

Using the components of the three forces in Equation (1.1) gives two scalar equations for the $\mathbf{i}$- and $\mathbf{j}$-components, respectively:

$$\tfrac{1}{2}|\mathbf{T}_1| - |\mathbf{T}_2| + 0 = 0, \tag{1.2}$$

$$\tfrac{\sqrt{3}}{2}|\mathbf{T}_1| + 0 - |\mathbf{W}| = 0. \tag{1.3}$$

But $|\mathbf{W}| = 4g$, so Equation (1.3) gives

$$|\mathbf{T}_1| = 2|\mathbf{W}|/\sqrt{3} = 8g/\sqrt{3} \simeq 45.31.$$

Substituting this into Equation (1.2) gives

$$|\mathbf{T}_2| = 4g/\sqrt{3} \simeq 22.66.$$

So the model predicts that the tension force due to the cord from the porch has magnitude about 45.3 N and that the tension force due to the cord from the wall has magnitude about 22.7 N. ■

The procedure that was used in Example 1.1 can be used to solve many problems in statics, and may be summarized as follows.

Procedure 1.1   Solving statics problems

Given a statics problem, perform some or all of the following steps.

(a) Draw a sketch of the physical situation, and annotate it with any relevant information.

◄Draw picture►

(b) Choose axes, and mark them on your sketch.

◄Choose axes►

(c) Draw a force diagram or diagrams.

◄Draw force diagram►

(d) Use the equilibrium condition and any other appropriate law(s) to obtain equation(s).

◄Apply law(s)►

(e) Solve the equation(s).

◄Solve equation(s)►

(f) Interpret the solution in terms of the original problem.

◄Interpret solution►

In this unit, the steps in this procedure will often be identified (using the marginal abbreviations above) in the solutions to examples and exercises. The procedure is intended to be a guide rather than a rigid set of rules. For example, if it is not obvious which set of axes to choose, then draw the force diagram first, and the best choice may become more apparent. Try using the procedure in the following exercise.

*Exercise 1.3

During December, a large plastic Christmas tree of mass 10 kg is suspended by its apex using two ropes attached to buildings either side of the high street of Trappendorf. The ropes make angles of $\frac{\pi}{6}$ and $\frac{\pi}{4}$ with the horizontal. Model the Christmas tree as a particle and the ropes as model strings. What are the magnitudes of the tension forces due to the two ropes?

1.5 Friction

Consider a book resting on a horizontal surface. There are two forces acting on the book: the weight downwards and the normal reaction upwards. Suppose that you push the book gently sideways (see Figure 1.9). If you do not push hard enough, the book will not move; it will remain in equilibrium. We know that the vertical forces, i.e. the weight and the normal reaction, balance each other (i.e. they are equal in magnitude and opposite in direction), so they cannot be preventing the book from moving sideways. Therefore there must be another force present. This force is known as the **friction force**. It is considered to act parallel to the surface, i.e. at right angles to the normal reaction, and in a direction that opposes any (possible) motion along that surface. Modelling the book as a particle, and denoting the pushing force by $\mathbf{P}$, the friction force by $\mathbf{F}$, the weight by $\mathbf{W}$ and the normal reaction by $\mathbf{N}$, the force diagram for this example is shown in Figure 1.10.

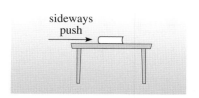

Figure 1.9

Figure 1.10

Friction forces are caused by the roughness of even seemingly very smooth surfaces — a roughness that serves to inhibit the smooth movement of one surface over another. So friction forces are present only where there is movement or the possibility of movement. There is no friction force present when an object is resting on a horizontal surface, where the only two forces acting on the object are its weight and the normal reaction. But when an object is being pushed or pulled, or is resting on a sloping surface, then a friction force is present (see Figure 1.11).

In this unit we consider only cases where objects remain at rest, so that there is only the *possibility* of movement. Friction in cases where there *is* movement is considered in *Unit 6*.

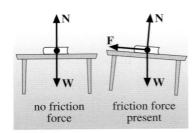

Figure 1.11

Unlike the normal reaction, which is potentially unlimited in magnitude, there is a limit to the magnitude of the friction force; if this limit is reached, then slipping occurs. The limiting value of the magnitude of the friction force depends almost entirely on the materials of the two surfaces and on the magnitude of the normal reaction force between them. It does not usually depend on the area of contact between the two surfaces, or on the angle at which the two surfaces are inclined to the horizontal. Experiments show that the limiting value of the magnitude of the friction force $\mathbf{F}$ (which *just* prevents slipping for two given surfaces) is approximately proportional to the magnitude of the normal reaction force $\mathbf{N}$ between the two surfaces. So, on the verge of slipping, we have $|\mathbf{F}| = \mu|\mathbf{N}|$, where μ is the **coefficient of static friction**, which depends on the materials of the two surfaces. Some approximate values of μ for different materials are given in Table 1.1.

Table 1.1 Approximate coefficients of static friction

Surface	μ
Steel on steel (dry)	0.58
Steel on steel (oiled)	0.1
Plastic on plastic	0.8
Rubber on tarmac	1.3
Steel on wood	0.4
Wood on wood	0.35

Example 1.2

A steel fork of mass 0.05 kg rests on a horizontal wooden table. Model the fork as a particle. What is the maximum sideways force that can be applied before the fork starts to move?

Solution

The situation is illustrated in Figure 1.12. Since all the forces act in a vertical plane, we can choose axes as shown. The force diagram is also shown in the figure, where $\mathbf{F}$ is the friction force, $\mathbf{P}$ is the sideways force, $\mathbf{W}$ is the weight, and $\mathbf{N}$ is the normal reaction.

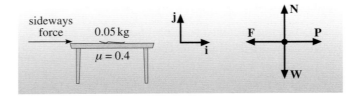

Figure 1.12

◄Draw picture►

◄Choose axes►

◄Draw force diagram►

The equilibrium condition for particles gives

$$\mathbf{F} + \mathbf{N} + \mathbf{P} + \mathbf{W} = \mathbf{0}. \qquad (1.4)$$

◀Apply law(s)▶

When the fork is on the point of moving (slipping), we have

$$|\mathbf{F}| = \mu|\mathbf{N}|,$$

where $\mu = 0.4$ is the coefficient of static friction of steel on wood.

To be able to use Equation (1.4), we need to express the forces in terms of the unit vectors $\mathbf{i}$ and $\mathbf{j}$. Looking at Figure 1.12, the forces can be written in component form as

◀Solve equation(s)▶

$$\mathbf{F} = -|\mathbf{F}|\,\mathbf{i}, \quad \mathbf{N} = |\mathbf{N}|\,\mathbf{j}, \quad \mathbf{P} = |\mathbf{P}|\,\mathbf{i}, \quad \mathbf{W} = -|\mathbf{W}|\,\mathbf{j}.$$

Resolving Equation (1.4) in the $\mathbf{i}$-direction gives

$$-|\mathbf{F}| + 0 + |\mathbf{P}| + 0 = 0,$$

so (as expected)

$$|\mathbf{F}| = |\mathbf{P}|.$$

Resolving (1.4) in the $\mathbf{j}$-direction gives

$$|\mathbf{N}| = |\mathbf{W}|.$$

Therefore, when the fork is on the point of moving,

$$|\mathbf{P}| = |\mathbf{F}| = \mu|\mathbf{N}| = \mu|\mathbf{W}| = 0.4 \times 0.05g = 0.02g \simeq 0.196.$$

So the model predicts that a sideways force of magnitude about 0.196 N can be applied without moving the fork. ■

◀Interpret solution▶

Here is a summary of how we go about modelling problems that involve static friction, i.e. problems involving friction but no motion.

Modelling static friction

Consider two surfaces in contact.

(a) The friction force $\mathbf{F}$ acts in a direction perpendicular to the normal reaction $\mathbf{N}$ between the surfaces and opposite to any possible motion along the common tangent to the surfaces.

(b) $|\mathbf{F}| \leq \mu|\mathbf{N}|$, where μ is a constant called the coefficient of static friction for the two surfaces involved.

$|\mathbf{F}|$ cannot exceed its limiting value $\mu|\mathbf{N}|$. Slipping occurs if a friction force of magnitude greater than $\mu|\mathbf{N}|$ would be needed to prevent it.

(c) $|\mathbf{F}| = \mu|\mathbf{N}|$ when the object is on the verge of slipping. This equality is sometimes referred to as describing a situation of **limiting friction**.

(d) If one of the surfaces is designated as being **smooth**, it may be assumed that there is no friction present when this surface is in contact with another, regardless of the roughness of the other surface.

Let us now apply these ideas to some examples, in which we shall also apply the steps of Procedure 1.1. In most of the situations that we investigate, we shall be concerned with limiting friction.

Exercise 1.4 _____

A wood block of mass 5 kg rests on a horizontal plank of wood. Model the block as a particle. What horizontal force is required to start it moving?

Exercise 1.5

A steel block of mass 0.5 kg rests on a horizontal dry steel surface and is pulled by a horizontal force of 2 N. Model the block as a particle. Does the block move? What is the magnitude of the friction force?

*Exercise 1.6

A shallow box made of a uniform material and without a lid can be placed on a horizontal table in two possible ways (as shown in Figure 1.13):

(a) with its base in contact with the table surface;

(b) with its open top in contact with the table surface.

Which of these two positions requires the smaller sideways force to start the box slipping?

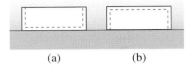

(a)   (b)

Figure 1.13

Inclined planes

Consider now an object resting on a sloping plane surface, often referred to as an **inclined plane**, such as the one shown in Figure 1.14. Provided that the angle of inclination is not large, the object can remain at rest and does not slide down the slope. The forces acting on the object are its weight, the normal reaction and friction. The weight **W** acts vertically downwards. The normal reaction **N** acts normally to the surface between the object and the slope. The friction force **F** is perpendicular to the normal reaction and hence parallel to the slope, and it acts up the slope to counteract the natural tendency of the object to move down the slope.

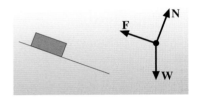

Figure 1.14

Example 1.3

A crate of empty bottles of total mass 30 kg is to be hauled by a rope up a ramp from the cellar of a pub. The rope is parallel to the ramp, and the ramp makes an angle of $\frac{\pi}{6}$ radians with the horizontal. The coefficient of static friction between the plastic crate and the wooden ramp is 0.2.

What is the tension force due to the rope when the crate is on the point of moving upwards?

Solution

The situation is illustrated in Figure 1.15.   ◄Draw picture►

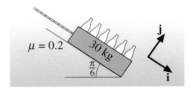

Figure 1.15

All the forces act in a vertical plane, so we need only two axes. We could   ◄Choose axes►
choose **i** to be horizontal and **j** vertical as before, but it makes calculations easier if we choose **i** to be parallel to the slope and **j** perpendicular to it, as shown in Figure 1.15. This is because, when we come to resolve the forces in the **i**- and **j**-directions, three of the four forces (all except **W**) will then act along one or other of the axes, making resolving them much simpler.

Modelling the crate as a particle and the rope as a model string, the force   ◄Draw force diagram►
diagram is as shown in Figure 1.16, where **W** is the weight, **N** the normal reaction, **F** the friction force, and **T** the tension force.

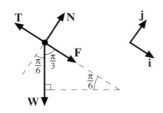

Figure 1.16

The equilibrium condition for particles gives   ◄Apply law(s)►

$$\mathbf{T} + \mathbf{N} + \mathbf{F} + \mathbf{W} = \mathbf{0}. \tag{1.5}$$

When the crate is on the point of moving, we have

$$|\mathbf{F}| = \mu|\mathbf{N}|,$$

where $\mu = 0.2$ is the coefficient of static friction.

As before, the first step in solving the equations involves resolving the force   ◄Solve equation(s)►
vectors into components. In this case, three of the force vectors are aligned
with the axes and can be written down immediately:

$$\mathbf{F} = |\mathbf{F}|\,\mathbf{i}, \quad \mathbf{N} = |\mathbf{N}|\,\mathbf{j}, \quad \mathbf{T} = -|\mathbf{T}|\,\mathbf{i}.$$

To find the weight of the crate in component form, we use the formula
derived in *Unit 4*:

$$\begin{aligned}
\mathbf{W} &= (\mathbf{W}\cdot\mathbf{i})\,\mathbf{i} + (\mathbf{W}\cdot\mathbf{j})\,\mathbf{j} \\
&= |\mathbf{W}|\cos\tfrac{\pi}{3}\,\mathbf{i} + |\mathbf{W}|\cos(\tfrac{\pi}{2} + \tfrac{\pi}{3})\,\mathbf{j} \\
&= \tfrac{1}{2}|\mathbf{W}|\,\mathbf{i} - \tfrac{\sqrt{3}}{2}|\mathbf{W}|\,\mathbf{j}.
\end{aligned}$$

Note that

$$\begin{aligned}
&\cos(\tfrac{\pi}{2} + \tfrac{\pi}{3}) \\
&= \cos\tfrac{\pi}{2}\cos\tfrac{\pi}{3} - \sin\tfrac{\pi}{2}\sin\tfrac{\pi}{3} \\
&= -\tfrac{\sqrt{3}}{2}.
\end{aligned}$$

Now Equation (1.5) can easily be resolved in the **i**-direction, giving

$$-|\mathbf{T}| + 0 + |\mathbf{F}| + \tfrac{1}{2}|\mathbf{W}| = 0,$$

so

$$|\mathbf{T}| = |\mathbf{F}| + \tfrac{1}{2}|\mathbf{W}|. \tag{1.6}$$

Similarly, resolving Equation (1.5) in the **j**-direction gives

$$0 + |\mathbf{N}| + 0 - \tfrac{\sqrt{3}}{2}|\mathbf{W}| = 0,$$

so

$$|\mathbf{N}| = \tfrac{\sqrt{3}}{2}|\mathbf{W}|. \tag{1.7}$$

At the point of moving, $|\mathbf{F}| = 0.2|\mathbf{N}|$ and Equations (1.6) and (1.7) give

$$|\mathbf{T}| = 0.2|\mathbf{N}| + \tfrac{1}{2}|\mathbf{W}| = 0.2 \times \tfrac{\sqrt{3}}{2}|\mathbf{W}| + \tfrac{1}{2}|\mathbf{W}|.$$

Thus, since $|\mathbf{W}| = 30g$,

$$|\mathbf{T}| = (\tfrac{\sqrt{3}}{10} + \tfrac{1}{2}) \times 30g \simeq 198.$$

Therefore, when the crate is on the point of moving, the model predicts that   ◄Interpret solution►
the tension force due to the rope is about 198 N up the ramp. ■

Mathematically, different choices of axes make no difference to the final
solution obtained to a mechanics problem. However, a sensible choice of
axes, as in Example 1.3, can reduce the amount of calculation. You will find   Choice of axes is discussed
that, with experience, you will be able to choose axes that reduce the work   again in *Unit 6*.
involved.

Exercise 1.7

A full crate of bottles of mass 60 kg is at the top of the ramp described in Example 1.3, ready to be lowered into the cellar. What force needs to be applied to the rope to keep the crate from sliding down the ramp?

End-of-section Exercises

Exercise 1.8

On a building site, a pallet of bricks of mass 1800 kg is suspended from the cable of a crane. The length of the cable is 10 m. One of the site workers is pulling with a force of magnitude 800 N horizontally on a rope attached to the pallet, in order to position the pallet over the lorry into which it is to be lowered. How far can the pallet be moved horizontally by the worker?

Exercise 1.9

(a) A box of mass m is resting on a surface inclined at an angle α to the horizontal. If the box is on the point of slipping, what is the coefficient of static friction?

(b) Two identical mugs are placed on a tray. One mug is half full of coffee, the other is empty. The tray is tilted slowly. Use your answer to part (a) to determine which mug will start to move first.

2   Two or more particles

In the previous section we considered the action of forces on one particle and introduced the equilibrium condition for particles. In this section we extend these ideas to situations involving two or more particles. Subsection 2.1 shows how Newton's third law can be applied to such situations. Subsection 2.2 introduces a new modelling device — the model pulley — and Subsection 2.3 considers friction in the two-particle case.

2.1   Newton's third law

The equilibrium condition for particles extends to systems involving two or more particles, in that, if the system is in equilibrium, then each particle must be in equilibrium, so the sum of the forces acting on *each* particle must be zero.

Consider, for example, the simple situation of one book lying on top of another on a desk. Both books are in equilibrium. Let us model each book as a particle. We can apply the equilibrium condition for particles to each book in turn. We therefore need to determine the forces on each book. For the upper book, the situation is similar to the case of an object resting on a surface, discussed in Section 1. There is the weight $\mathbf{W}_1$ of the book acting vertically downwards, and the normal reaction $\mathbf{N}_1$ of the surface (of the lower book) acting vertically upwards. For the lower book, we have its weight $\mathbf{W}_2$ acting vertically downwards, and the normal reaction $\mathbf{N}_2$ of the surface (of the desk) acting vertically upwards, but this time there is also another force — the normal reaction $\mathbf{N}_3$ from the upper book. The situation and the force diagrams are shown in Figure 2.1.

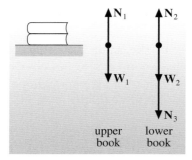

Figure 2.1

You may find the presence of the force $\mathbf{N}_3$ surprising, because in Section 1 we considered the normal reaction force as acting from a surface to an object. However, there is also a normal reaction force acting from the object to the surface. So, for example, if we consider the forces acting on the table described in Subsection 1.3, we have to include the normal reaction exerted by the coffee mug on the table. In fact, pairs of normal reactions occur between any pair of surfaces in contact. Such pairs of normal reaction forces can be deduced from **Newton's third law**, a well-established law of mechanics, which says that for each force exerted by one object on another, there is a force of equal magnitude acting in the opposite direction exerted by the second object on the first. This enables us not only to deduce the presence of $\mathbf{N}_3$, but also to deduce that

The two normal reaction forces that constitute an equal and opposite pair act on *different* objects.

$$\mathbf{N}_1 = -\mathbf{N}_3.$$

In addition to this equation, the equilibrium condition for particles applied to each book in turn gives

$$\mathbf{W}_1 + \mathbf{N}_1 = \mathbf{0},$$
$$\mathbf{W}_2 + \mathbf{N}_2 + \mathbf{N}_3 = \mathbf{0}.$$

Solving these three equations for $\mathbf{N}_1$, $\mathbf{N}_2$ and $\mathbf{N}_3$ gives

$$\mathbf{N}_1 = -\mathbf{W}_1, \quad \mathbf{N}_2 = -\mathbf{W}_1 - \mathbf{W}_2, \quad \mathbf{N}_3 = \mathbf{W}_1.$$

If we had considered the two books as one particle, then the normal reaction force $\mathbf{N}_2$ from the table would still be the same, i.e. $-(\mathbf{W}_1 + \mathbf{W}_2)$. So the above argument is physically reasonable in the sense that the normal reaction force $\mathbf{N}_2$ is unchanged whether we model the books as two particles or one.

Now consider the forces acting on the upper book, namely $\mathbf{N}_1$ and $\mathbf{W}_1$. As shown above, these forces are of equal magnitude and opposite directions. It is a common mistake to say that these forces form an equal and opposite pair as described in Newton's third law. This is not correct — they are equal and opposite because the book is in equilibrium. As we have seen above, the force paired with $\mathbf{N}_1$ by Newton's third law is $\mathbf{N}_3$. What force is paired with the force $\mathbf{W}_1$? The answer is the force of gravity that the book exerts on the Earth. (The magnitude of this force is, of course, negligible when compared to the mass of the Earth.)

In summary, solving statics problems involving more than one particle needs these key ideas:

(a) apply Newton's third law;

(b) apply the equilibrium condition for particles to each particle separately.

Exercise 2.1

Consider a pile of four books of equal mass, lying one on top of another on a desk. Draw the force diagrams for this situation, and find the normal reactions acting on each book in terms of the weight of a book.

In the same way that Newton's third law can be applied to the normal reaction forces between objects, so can it be applied to the tension forces due to a string joining two objects. Thus, for example, for two particles A and B joined by a model string, the tension force $\mathbf{T}_A$ on particle A due to the string is equal in magnitude and opposite in direction to the tension force $\mathbf{T}_B$ on particle B due to the string, so $\mathbf{T}_A = -\mathbf{T}_B$. The *magnitude* of the two forces due to a string is often referred to as the **tension in the string**. This is a scalar quantity.

This was remarked upon in Subsection 1.4.

Exercise 2.2

A lamp of mass 1.5 kg is hanging from the ceiling on its cable. A child's toy of mass 0.5 kg is suspended by a string from the lampshade. Model the lamp (plus lampshade) and the toy as particles, and the cable and the string as model strings. Draw force diagrams showing the forces acting on the two particles. What is the magnitude of the tension force due to the cable?

2.2 Pulleys

The pulley is a common device with which you are probably familiar. You may have seen them in use on building sites, for example, as an aid to raising or lowering heavy loads. The idea of a pulley is useful in modelling mechanics problems, as it enables us to model a change in direction of a tension force.

In diagrams, we shall use an idealized pulley as shown in Figure 2.2. In order to keep the model simple, we make simplifying assumptions, which are formally stated in the following definition.

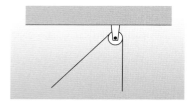

Figure 2.2

Definition

A **model pulley** is an object with no mass or size, over which a model string may pass without any resistance to motion. The tension in a string passing over a model pulley is the same either side of the pulley.

The point to remember is that the result of these assumptions implies that the tension forces due to the string on either side of the model pulley are equal in magnitude, i.e. the tension in the string as it passes over the pulley remains constant.

A model pulley provides a reasonable model of an actual pulley, provided that its dimensions are small compared with the length of the rope or cable passing over it and that its weight is small compared with the other forces involved. Model pulleys can also be used to model a variety of situations that do not involve pulleys at all, but merely involve a change in direction of a tension force (such as when a rope is hanging over the edge of a building). Their use is illustrated by the following example and exercises.

Example 2.1

A sack of flour of mass 50 kg is lying on the floor of a mill, ready to be loaded into a cart. To help with the loading process, a light rope is attached to the sack, passes over a pulley fixed to the ceiling immediately above the sack, and is attached at its other end to a stone of mass 15 kg that hangs without touching the floor. The system is shown in Figure 2.3.

In mechanics problems, if an object is said to be 'light', its mass may be ignored.

Model the sack and the stone as particles, the pulley as a model pulley, and the rope as a model string.

(a) Calculate the normal reaction of the floor on the sack.

(b) What force does the pulley exert on the ceiling?

Solution

All the forces are vertical, so we need only one axis, as shown in Figure 2.3.   ◄Choose axes►

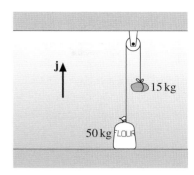

Figure 2.3

(a) The force diagrams for the sack and the stone are shown in Figure 2.4, where $\mathbf{W}_1$ and $\mathbf{W}_2$ represent the weights, $\mathbf{T}_1$ and $\mathbf{T}_2$ represent the tension forces, and $\mathbf{N}$ is the normal reaction of the floor on the sack.   ◄Draw force diagram►

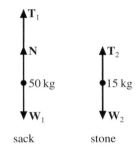

Figure 2.4

The equilibrium condition for particles gives   ◄Apply law(s)►

$$\mathbf{W}_1 + \mathbf{N} + \mathbf{T}_1 = \mathbf{0}, \tag{2.1}$$
$$\mathbf{W}_2 + \mathbf{T}_2 = \mathbf{0}. \tag{2.2}$$

Since the tension forces on either side of a model pulley have the same magnitude, we have

$$|\mathbf{T}_1| = |\mathbf{T}_2|.$$

To solve the equations, the first step is to write the forces in component form as   ◄Solve equation(s)►

$$\mathbf{W}_1 = -|\mathbf{W}_1|\mathbf{j}, \quad \mathbf{N} = |\mathbf{N}|\mathbf{j}, \quad \mathbf{T}_1 = |\mathbf{T}_1|\mathbf{j},$$
$$\mathbf{T}_2 = |\mathbf{T}_2|\mathbf{j} \quad \text{and} \quad \mathbf{W}_2 = -|\mathbf{W}_2|\mathbf{j}.$$

Then resolving Equations (2.1) and (2.2) in the $\mathbf{j}$-direction gives

$$-|\mathbf{W}_1| + |\mathbf{N}| + |\mathbf{T}_1| = 0,$$
$$-|\mathbf{W}_2| + |\mathbf{T}_2| = 0.$$

Therefore $|\mathbf{T}_1| = |\mathbf{T}_2| = |\mathbf{W}_2|$, so

$$|\mathbf{N}| = |\mathbf{W}_1| - |\mathbf{T}_1| = |\mathbf{W}_1| - |\mathbf{W}_2| = 50g - 15g = 35g \simeq 343.$$

So the normal reaction of the floor on the sack has magnitude about 343 N ($35g$) and is directed upwards. In the absence of the stone and the pulley, the magnitude of the normal reaction would have been equal to the magnitude of the weight of the sack ($50g$). The effect of the stone, transmitted via the pulley, is as if the magnitude of the sack's weight were reduced by the magnitude of the weight of the stone ($15g$).   ◄Interpret solution►

(b) To answer this question we need to model the forces on the pulley. We can consider the pulley as a particle of no mass. Modelling the short piece of metal that attaches the pulley to the ceiling as a model string, we have the force diagram shown in Figure 2.5.

◄Draw force diagram►

pulley

Figure 2.5

The equilibrium condition for particles gives

◄Apply law(s)►

$$\mathbf{T}_3 + \mathbf{T}_4 + \mathbf{T}_5 = \mathbf{0}. \tag{2.3}$$

Since the tension in a string around a model pulley remains constant, we have

$$|\mathbf{T}_1| = |\mathbf{T}_2| = |\mathbf{T}_3| = |\mathbf{T}_4|.$$

Resolving Equation (2.3) in the **j**-direction gives

◄Solve equation(s)►

$$-|\mathbf{T}_3| - |\mathbf{T}_4| + |\mathbf{T}_5| = 0.$$

Using the result from part (a) that $|\mathbf{T}_1| = |\mathbf{T}_2| = |\mathbf{W}_2|$, we have

$$|\mathbf{T}_5| = |\mathbf{T}_3| + |\mathbf{T}_4| = 2|\mathbf{W}_2| = 30g \simeq 294.$$

So the model predicts that the force exerted by the short piece of metal (shown in Figure 2.3) on the pulley is about 294 N ($30g$) upwards. Hence, by Newton's third law, the force exerted by this short piece of metal on the ceiling (i.e. the force exerted by the pulley on the ceiling) is about 294 N ($30g$) downwards. This force (which is twice the weight of the stone) balances the weights of the stone ($15g$) and the sack ($50g$), less the normal reaction ($35g$) of the floor on the sack.   ■

◄Interpret solution►

Exercise 2.3

Suppose that the pulley in Example 2.1 is no longer immediately above the sack, so that the rope attached to the sack makes an angle of $\frac{\pi}{4}$ to the vertical, as shown in Figure 2.6.

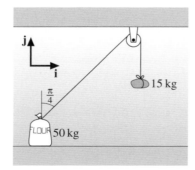

Figure 2.6

(a) What is the magnitude of the normal reaction of the floor on the sack?

(b) What is the magnitude of the friction force on the sack?

(c) What is the smallest value of the coefficient of static friction that would allow the system to remain in equilibrium?

Exercise 2.4

A car engine of mass 120 kg is being held suspended ready for lowering into
a car. The engine is attached to a pulley by a short rope. Another rope,
attached at one end to the ceiling of the garage, passes under the pulley
then up towards the ceiling again, where it passes over another pulley that
is joined to the ceiling. A mechanic holds the end of this rope. The situation
is illustrated in Figure 2.7.

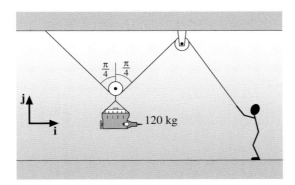

Figure 2.7

Assuming that the components of the system can be modelled as particles,
model strings and model pulleys as appropriate, determine the magnitude
of the force that the mechanic has to exert to keep the engine suspended in
position while the car is pushed underneath it.

2.3 Slipping

You have already investigated slipping in the case of a one-particle system.
In this subsection we examine the phenomenon in systems of more than one
particle.

Example 2.2

Consider a scarf draped over the edge of a table. Model the scarf as two
particles, one of mass m_1 hanging over the edge and the other of mass m_2
resting on the table, with the masses joined by a model string passing over
the edge of the table, which is modelled as a model pulley. Assume that the
scarf's mass is uniformly distributed along its length, so that the masses of
the two particles are proportional to the corresponding lengths of scarf.

If the coefficient of static friction between the scarf and the table surface
is μ, what proportion of the scarf's length can hang over the edge of the
table before the scarf slips off the table?

Solution

We can answer this question if we can find the ratio of m_1 (the mass of scarf
hanging over the edge) to $m_1 + m_2$ (the total mass of scarf) when the scarf
is on the verge of slipping.

The situation is illustrated in Figure 2.8, which also shows a suitable choice
of axes.

◄Draw picture►

◄Choose axes►

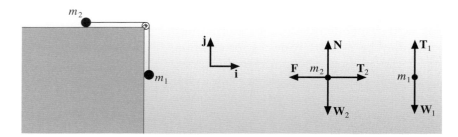

Figure 2.8

There are two forces acting on the hanging particle: its weight $\mathbf{W}_1$ and the tension force $\mathbf{T}_1$. There are four forces acting on the particle on the table: its weight $\mathbf{W}_2$, the tension force $\mathbf{T}_2$, the normal reaction force $\mathbf{N}$, and the friction force $\mathbf{F}$. The force diagrams are shown in Figure 2.8.

◄Draw force diagram►

While the scarf does not slip, we can apply the equilibrium condition for particles to each particle in turn. For the hanging particle, we have

◄Apply law(s)►

$$\mathbf{T}_1 + \mathbf{W}_1 = \mathbf{0}. \tag{2.4}$$

For the particle on the table, we have

$$\mathbf{F} + \mathbf{N} + \mathbf{T}_2 + \mathbf{W}_2 = \mathbf{0}. \tag{2.5}$$

The assumption of a model pulley gives

$$|\mathbf{T}_1| = |\mathbf{T}_2|. \tag{2.6}$$

When the particle is on the verge of slipping, we have

$$|\mathbf{F}| = \mu|\mathbf{N}|, \tag{2.7}$$

where μ is the coefficient of static friction.

From Figure 2.8, the component forms of the force vectors can immediately be written down:

◄Solve equation(s)►

$$\mathbf{T}_1 = |\mathbf{T}_1|\mathbf{j}, \quad \mathbf{W}_1 = -|\mathbf{W}_1|\mathbf{j}, \quad \mathbf{F} = -|\mathbf{F}|\mathbf{i},$$
$$\mathbf{N} = |\mathbf{N}|\mathbf{j}, \quad \mathbf{T}_2 = |\mathbf{T}_2|\mathbf{i} \quad \text{and} \quad \mathbf{W}_2 = -|\mathbf{W}_2|\mathbf{j}.$$

Resolving Equation (2.4) in the $\mathbf{j}$-direction gives

$$|\mathbf{T}_1| - |\mathbf{W}_1| = 0,$$

so

$$|\mathbf{T}_1| = |\mathbf{W}_1| = m_1 g.$$

Resolving Equation (2.5) in the $\mathbf{i}$-direction gives

$$-|\mathbf{F}| + 0 + |\mathbf{T}_2| + 0 = 0,$$

so, using Equation (2.6),

$$|\mathbf{F}| = |\mathbf{T}_2| = |\mathbf{T}_1| = m_1 g.$$

Resolving Equation (2.5) in the $\mathbf{j}$-direction gives

$$0 + |\mathbf{N}| + 0 - |\mathbf{W}_2| = 0,$$

so

$$|\mathbf{N}| = |\mathbf{W}_2| = m_2 g.$$

Using Equation (2.7), we have

$$m_1 g = \mu m_2 g,$$

so

$$m_1 = \mu m_2.$$

Therefore the model predicts that when the scarf is on the verge of slipping, the fraction of its length that hangs over the edge is

◀Interpret solution▶

$$\frac{m_1}{m_1 + m_2} = \frac{\mu m_2}{\mu m_2 + m_2} = \frac{\mu}{\mu + 1}. \quad ■$$

*Exercise 2.5

A gold medallion of mass 0.02 kg is lying on a glass shelf in a bathroom. Attached to the medallion is a gold chain of mass 0.03 kg, half of which is dangling over the edge of the shelf. If the coefficient of static friction between gold and glass is 0.35, will the chain and medallion remain at rest?

End-of-section Exercises

Exercise 2.6

An object of mass 2 kg is suspended from the ceiling by a string. An object of mass 1 kg is suspended from the first object by another string. From this second object is suspended an object of mass 3 kg. Draw the force diagram for each object, and find the tension in each string.

Exercise 2.7

A man of mass 80 kg is about to be lowered into a well from a rope that passes over the horizontal rotating axle of the well. The other end of the rope is held by several men each of mass 80 kg, as shown in Figure 2.9, with the rope between the men and the axle horizontal. Assume that the men can be represented by particles, the rope by a model string and the axle by a model pulley.

If the coefficient of static friction between the men's boots and the ground is 0.35, how many men are required to hold the man at the end of the rope before he is lowered into the well?

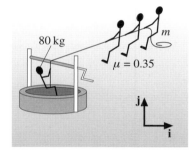

Figure 2.9

Exercise 2.8

An object of mass m_1, resting on a board inclined at an angle α to the horizontal, is attached to an object of mass m_2 by a string hanging over the edge of the board, as shown in Figure 2.10.

Assuming that the objects can be modelled as particles, the string as a model string and the edge of the board as a model pulley, find the condition on the coefficient of static friction μ between the first object and the board for this system to remain in equilibrium.

(*Hint*: There are two ways in which the equilibrium can be disturbed.)

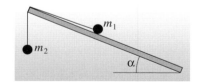

Figure 2.10

3   Torques

This section looks at solid bodies, and in particular at a phenomenon that does not apply to particles: the turning effect of forces. It begins in Subsection 3.1 by introducing ways of modelling objects when their size is important, as it is when the turning effects of forces are considered. Subsection 3.2 goes on to explain what is meant by the turning effect of a force, and to provide a mathematical description of such an effect.

3.1   Extended and rigid bodies

Consider, for example, a tall thin box of cereal on a breakfast table. If you push it near its base, it slides across the table. But if you push it near its top, it tips over. The *position* at which the pushing force acts is important here, so the particle model — which allows forces to act at only one point — is inadequate. In this situation, we model the cereal box as an **extended body**, which is defined to be a material object that has one or more of length, breadth and depth, but whose internal structure may be neglected. So, like a particle, it has mass, but unlike a particle, it has size of some sort and occupies more than a single point in space.

Extended bodies are complicated objects because they can flex or vibrate. To model the slipping or tipping behaviour of the cereal packet, this generality is not needed. So we restrict our attention to *rigid bodies*. A **rigid body** is defined to be an extended body that does not change its shape (so it does not flex or vibrate).

For a particle, all forces are applied at the point represented by the particle; we say that the forces *act* at this point. For extended bodies, we need to be more careful to specify where a force acts. For example, the weight of a body always acts through the **centre of mass** of the body. In this unit we shall consider only symmetric bodies made of uniform material. For such a body, as you would intuitively expect, the centre of mass is at its centre of symmetry (or geometric centre). For example, consider a coin, which can be modelled as a disc. Using symmetry, we can state that the centre of mass of the coin is along the axis of the disc (which runs between the centres of the flat circular faces of the disc), halfway between the flat circular faces.

The shape of an extended body may be one-, two- or three-dimensional (i.e. it may have a length, an area or a volume), depending on the situation.

The formal definition of a rigid body states that the position vector of a point on the rigid body relative to any other point on the rigid body is constant.

A definition of the centre of mass and ways of finding it for a general rigid body are given in *Units 19* and *25*.

3.2   Turning effect of a force

Suppose that you try to balance a ruler on a horizontal extended finger. When the centre of the ruler is over your finger, the ruler should balance. If the centre of the ruler is not over your finger, then the weight of the ruler will cause it to turn about your finger. Although the finger can provide a normal reaction force that is equal in magnitude to the weight of the ruler, if the two forces are not in line, then turning occurs. The weight provides a turning effect if the vertical line of its action (through the centre of mass) does not pass through your finger.

How do we measure the turning effect of a force in terms of what we already know: the magnitude and direction of the force, and the point on the object at which the force acts? In order to begin to answer this question, try a simple experiment. Balance a 30-centimetre (12-inch) ruler on a pencil rubber or a hexagonal pencil, or some other object that is not too wide and so will act as a pivot. Place two identical small coins on either side of the pivot so that each is 10 cm from the pivot (see Figure 3.1).

Figure 3.1

Then experiment with moving one of the coins in steps of 2 cm from its initial position, and see how the other coin has to be moved in order to re-establish balance. The conclusion from this experiment is not, perhaps, a surprising one: coins of equal mass have to be placed at equal distances on either side of the pivot for the ruler to remain balanced.

Next place the two coins together at a point on the ruler, say at 6 cm from the pivot. Where does a third identical coin have to be placed to achieve balance?

You should find that two identical coins placed together at 6 cm from the pivot are balanced by another identical coin placed on the other side of the ruler at 12 cm from the pivot. If you continue to experiment with varying numbers of coins placed at various pairs of positions along the ruler, you will find in each case that if the masses of the two sets of coins are unequal, then, in order to achieve balance, the greater mass has to be placed nearer to the pivot than the smaller one. The turning effect due to the weight of the coins acting at a point depends not only on the mass of the coins, but also on the distance of the point of action from the pivot.

A long symmetrical object, such as the ruler in this experiment, can often be modelled as a rigid body with length, but no breadth or depth. Such a rigid body is known as a **model rod** and is often drawn as a straight line. The pivot on which the object rests is often modelled as a **model pivot**, which has a single point of contact with the rod and is often drawn as a triangle. Using these notions, the above experiments should allow you to believe the following result.

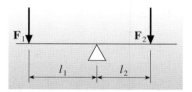

Figure 3.2

> **Balanced rod**
>
> A horizontal rod, pivoted at its centre, will remain horizontal under the action of two forces $\mathbf{F}_1$ and $\mathbf{F}_2$ acting vertically downwards at distances l_1 and l_2, respectively, on either side of the pivot (see Figure 3.2), provided that
>
> $$|\mathbf{F}_1|\,l_1 = |\mathbf{F}_2|\,l_2. \tag{3.1}$$

In other words, the horizontal rod will remain in equilibrium provided that the distances of the forces from the pivot are in inverse ratio to the magnitudes of the forces.

*Exercise 3.1 ⎯⎯⎯⎯⎯⎯⎯⎯⎯⎯⎯⎯⎯⎯⎯⎯⎯⎯⎯⎯⎯⎯

Jack and Jill are sitting on opposite sides of a see-saw. Jill is sitting at a distance of 1.2 m from the pivot, and Jack is 1 m away from the pivot. Jack's mass is 60 kg. If the see-saw is at rest and horizontal, what is Jill's mass?

In the situation described in Exercise 3.1 and in the ruler example, there was an obvious way to measure each distance, i.e. along the see-saw or ruler. We need to generalize this to other situations, where there is not such an obvious way to measure distance. In these two examples the distances along the ruler and see-saw happen to be distances measured perpendicular to the direction of the force and from its point of action, i.e. perpendicular to the *line of action* of the force.

> **Definition**
>
> The **line of action of a force** is a straight line in the direction of the force and through the point of action of the force.

So the turning effect of a force about a fixed point needs to encompass a measure of the force itself and the perpendicular distance of its line of action from the fixed point. It also needs to increase in magnitude if either the force or the distance increases in magnitude, and vice versa.

Consider a force **F** with line of action AB, as shown in Figure 3.3, and some fixed point O. Let R be any point on AB with position vector **r** with respect to O. Then the cross product is

$$\mathbf{r} \times \mathbf{F} = (|\mathbf{r}|\,|\mathbf{F}|\sin\theta)\,\widehat{\mathbf{c}},$$

where $\widehat{\mathbf{c}}$ is a unit vector perpendicular to both **r** and **F**, and with direction out of the page (as given by the screw rule). This cross product satisfies all the above requirements for the turning effect of a force. It includes a measure $|\mathbf{F}|$ of the force and the perpendicular distance $|\mathbf{r}|\sin\theta$ of its line of action AB from the fixed point O. The direction of the cross product, represented by $\widehat{\mathbf{c}}$ and given by the screw rule, corresponds to the direction of the turning effect. In this example, the turning effect of **F** about O is anticlockwise, which corresponds to the anticlockwise motion of a screw pointing out of the page. We refer to the cross product $\mathbf{r} \times \mathbf{F}$ as the *torque* of the force **F** relative to the origin O, and we use it as our measure of the turning effect of the force.

Here **F** is used to denote a general force, rather than a friction force.

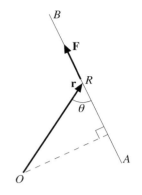

Figure 3.3

Definition

The **torque** $\mathbf{\Gamma}$ of a force **F** about a fixed point O is the cross product

$$\mathbf{\Gamma} = \mathbf{r} \times \mathbf{F},$$

where **r** is the position vector, relative to O, of a point on the line of action of the force.

The symbol $\mathbf{\Gamma}$ is the uppercase Greek letter gamma.

To calculate the magnitude $|\mathbf{r}|\,|\mathbf{F}|\sin\theta$ of a torque, you can find the perpendicular distance $|\mathbf{r}|\sin\theta$ of its line of action from the fixed point, and then multiply this by $|\mathbf{F}|$. However, the component of **F** in the direction perpendicular to OR (in Figure 3.3) is $|\mathbf{F}|\sin\theta$. So another way of calculating the magnitude of a torque is to multiply the length of OR (i.e. $|\mathbf{r}|$) by the component of **F** in the direction perpendicular to OR.

Exercise 3.2

Find the torque of each of the forces in Figure 3.4 relative to the origin O, where each force is of magnitude $3\,\mathrm{N}$.

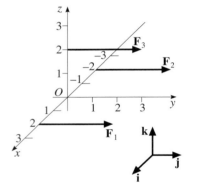

Exercise 3.3

(a) Show that if O is any point on the line of action of a force **F**, and **r** is the position vector, relative to O, of any other point on the line of action, then $\mathbf{r} \times \mathbf{F} = \mathbf{0}$. Deduce that the torque of a force about a point on its line of action is zero.

(b) Suppose now that O is *not* on the line of action of **F**, and let $\mathbf{r}_1$ and $\mathbf{r}_2$ be the position vectors, relative to O, of two points on the line of action. Show that $\mathbf{r}_1 - \mathbf{r}_2$ is parallel to **F**, and hence that $\mathbf{r}_1 \times \mathbf{F} = \mathbf{r}_2 \times \mathbf{F}$. Deduce that the torque of a force about a fixed point O is independent of the choice of the position of the point on the line of action.

Figure 3.4

Let us now convince ourselves that the definition of torque makes sense in terms of the examples of turning forces we have seen so far. To do this, we need an equilibrium condition for rigid bodies that extends the equilibrium condition for particles. You will not be surprised that it requires not only that all the forces on a rigid body sum to zero, but also that all the torques sum to zero.

Equilibrium condition for rigid bodies

A rigid body subjected to forces $\mathbf{F}_1, \mathbf{F}_2, \ldots, \mathbf{F}_n$ is in **equilibrium** if the forces sum to the zero vector and if the torques $\mathbf{\Gamma}_1, \mathbf{\Gamma}_2, \ldots, \mathbf{\Gamma}_n$ corresponding to the forces, relative to the same fixed point O, also sum to the zero vector, i.e.

$$\sum_{i=1}^{n} \mathbf{F}_i = \mathbf{0} \quad \text{and} \quad \sum_{i=1}^{n} \mathbf{\Gamma}_i = \sum_{i=1}^{n} \mathbf{r}_i \times \mathbf{F}_i = \mathbf{0},$$

where $\mathbf{r}_i$ is the position vector, relative to O, of a point on the line of action of $\mathbf{F}_i$.

Let us now apply the definition of a torque and the equilibrium condition for rigid bodies to our see-saw example from Exercise 3.1.

Example 3.1

Jack and Jill are sitting on opposite sides of a see-saw. Jill is sitting at a distance of 1.2 m from the pivot, and Jack is 1 m away from the pivot. Jack's mass is 60 kg. If the see-saw is at rest and horizontal, what is Jill's mass?

Solution

We shall model the see-saw as a model rod resting on a pivot at its centre, and consider Jack and Jill as forces (weights) applied to the rod, as shown in Figure 3.5.

◄Draw picture►

A suitable choice of axes is shown in Figure 3.5. We need three axes since the torques have a direction perpendicular to the directions of the forces and the position vectors. We also need to choose an origin O for the position vectors, and this is conveniently placed at the pivot point of the see-saw.

◄Choose axes►

As you will see below, any choice of origin will do, so we choose one that makes the calculations easy.

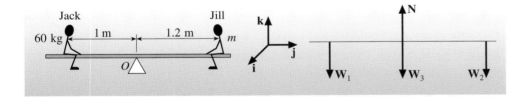

Figure 3.5

In the force diagram for the see-saw, we represent the rod (see-saw) as a straight line with forces applied at the appropriate points, as shown in Figure 3.5, where $\mathbf{W}_1$ is the force applied by Jack's weight, $\mathbf{W}_2$ is the force applied by Jill's weight, $\mathbf{W}_3$ is the weight of the see-saw, and $\mathbf{N}$ is the normal reaction of the pivot on the see-saw.

◄Draw force diagram►

The equilibrium condition for rigid bodies gives

◄Apply law(s)►

$$\mathbf{W}_1 + \mathbf{W}_2 + \mathbf{W}_3 + \mathbf{N} = \mathbf{0},$$
$$\mathbf{\Gamma}_1 + \mathbf{\Gamma}_2 + \mathbf{\Gamma}_3 + \mathbf{\Gamma}_N = \mathbf{0}, \tag{3.2}$$

where $\mathbf{\Gamma}_i$ is the torque corresponding to $\mathbf{W}_i$, for $i = 1, 2, 3$, and $\mathbf{\Gamma}_N$ is the torque corresponding to $\mathbf{N}$, all relative to O.

To solve Equation (3.2), we need position vectors $\mathbf{r}_1$, $\mathbf{r}_2$, $\mathbf{r}_3$ and $\mathbf{r}_N$ of points on the lines of action of $\mathbf{W}_1$, $\mathbf{W}_2$, $\mathbf{W}_3$ and $\mathbf{N}$, relative to O. The position vectors of suitable points on the lines of action of the forces applied by Jack and Jill, relative to O, are $-\mathbf{j}$ and $1.2\mathbf{j}$, respectively. The position vector of a point on the line of action of the two forces acting through the pivot is $\mathbf{0}$. So we have

$$\mathbf{r}_1 = -\mathbf{j}, \quad \mathbf{r}_2 = 1.2\mathbf{j}, \quad \mathbf{r}_3 = \mathbf{0}, \quad \mathbf{r}_N = \mathbf{0}.$$

Using the information on the masses in Figure 3.5, and assuming that the see-saw has mass M and Jill's mass is m, we have

$$\mathbf{W}_1 = -60g\mathbf{k}, \quad \mathbf{W}_2 = -mg\mathbf{k}, \quad \mathbf{W}_3 = -Mg\mathbf{k}, \quad \mathbf{N} = |\mathbf{N}|\mathbf{k}.$$

Therefore

$$\Gamma_1 = (-\mathbf{j}) \times (-60g\mathbf{k}) = 60g(-\mathbf{j} \times -\mathbf{k}) = 60g\mathbf{i},$$
$$\Gamma_2 = (1.2\mathbf{j}) \times (-mg\mathbf{k}) = 1.2mg(\mathbf{j} \times -\mathbf{k}) = 1.2mg(-\mathbf{i}) = -1.2mg\mathbf{i},$$
$$\Gamma_3 = \mathbf{0},$$
$$\Gamma_N = \mathbf{0}.$$

So Equation (3.2) becomes

$$60g\mathbf{i} - 1.2mg\mathbf{i} = \mathbf{0}.$$

Resolving in the $\mathbf{i}$-direction gives

$$60g - 1.2mg = 0,$$

so $m = 50$.

Therefore the model predicts that Jill's mass is 50 kg, as in Exercise 3.1. ■

It is reassuring that the torque approach of Example 3.1 gives the same answer as Exercise 3.1. However, you may well feel that using the torque approach for the see-saw problem is more cumbersome. In this particular situation it is. However, the torque approach is generally applicable to any statics problem involving rigid bodies, whereas the earlier approach is applicable in only very special cases.

Example 3.1 also illustrates that the direction of a torque corresponds to the direction of its turning effect. The two non-zero torques in that example are $\Gamma_1 = 60g\mathbf{i}$ and $\Gamma_2 = -1.2mg\mathbf{i}$. The torque Γ_1, caused by Jack's weight, has the effect of rotating the see-saw in an anticlockwise direction about the pivot. Referring to Figure 3.5, the axis of rotation is along a line perpendicular to the page. Also, this rotation is in an anticlockwise direction from $\mathbf{j}$ to $\mathbf{k}$, which, according to the screw rule, corresponds to the screw moving out of the page in the direction of $\mathbf{i}$, which corresponds to the direction of Γ_1. Similarly, the torque Γ_2, caused by Jill's weight, rotates the see-saw in a clockwise direction from $\mathbf{k}$ to $\mathbf{j}$, and corresponds, by the screw rule, to the screw moving in the direction of $-\mathbf{i}$, which corresponds to the direction of Γ_2. Hence the directions of these torques provide us with information on the axes of rotation of the torques and on the senses of rotation (clockwise or anticlockwise), relative to the chosen fixed point O.

The choice of origin in Example 3.1 certainly made the calculations easy, since it made two of the position vectors zero and hence two of the torques zero. In terms of the answer obtained, however, we could have chosen to place the origin anywhere in space.

◄Solve equation(s)►

We make the obvious choice for these points, namely the points where the lines of action cut the horizontal rod.

Choosing the origin at the pivot has reduced two of the torques to zero, and thus has simplified the torque equilibrium equation considerably.

◄Interpret solution►

Suppose, for example, that in Example 3.1 we had chosen the origin to be at another point, O', and suppose that O in Figure 3.5 has a position vector $\mathbf{a}$ with respect to O'. Then, as Figure 3.6 illustrates, a position vector on the line of action of $\mathbf{W}_1$ is $\mathbf{a} + \mathbf{r}_1$. Similarly, the position vectors corresponding to $\mathbf{W}_2$, $\mathbf{W}_3$ and $\mathbf{N}$ are $\mathbf{a} + \mathbf{r}_2$, $\mathbf{a} + \mathbf{r}_3$ and $\mathbf{a} + \mathbf{r}_N$, respectively. The torque equilibrium equation becomes

$$(\mathbf{a} + \mathbf{r}_1) \times \mathbf{W}_1 + (\mathbf{a} + \mathbf{r}_2) \times \mathbf{W}_2 + (\mathbf{a} + \mathbf{r}_3) \times \mathbf{W}_3 + (\mathbf{a} + \mathbf{r}_N) \times \mathbf{N} = \mathbf{0},$$

which can be rewritten as

$$\mathbf{a} \times (\mathbf{W}_1 + \mathbf{W}_2 + \mathbf{W}_3 + \mathbf{N})$$
$$+ \mathbf{r}_1 \times \mathbf{W}_1 + \mathbf{r}_2 \times \mathbf{W}_2 + \mathbf{r}_3 \times \mathbf{W}_3 + \mathbf{r}_N \times \mathbf{N} = \mathbf{0},$$

which, since $\mathbf{W}_1 + \mathbf{W}_2 + \mathbf{W}_3 + \mathbf{N} = \mathbf{0}$, gives

$$\mathbf{r}_1 \times \mathbf{W}_1 + \mathbf{r}_2 \times \mathbf{W}_2 + \mathbf{r}_3 \times \mathbf{W}_3 + \mathbf{r}_N \times \mathbf{N} = \mathbf{0},$$

as before.

This idea generalizes to forces $\mathbf{F}_1, \mathbf{F}_2, \ldots, \mathbf{F}_n$, in that

$$\sum_{i=1}^{n} (\mathbf{a} + \mathbf{r}_i) \times \mathbf{F}_i = \sum_{i=1}^{n} \mathbf{a} \times \mathbf{F}_i + \sum_{i=1}^{n} \mathbf{r}_i \times \mathbf{F}_i$$

$$= \mathbf{a} \times \sum_{i=1}^{n} \mathbf{F}_i + \sum_{i=1}^{n} \mathbf{r}_i \times \mathbf{F}_i$$

$$= \sum_{i=1}^{n} \mathbf{r}_i \times \mathbf{F}_i \quad \text{if} \sum_{i=1}^{n} \mathbf{F}_i = \mathbf{0}.$$

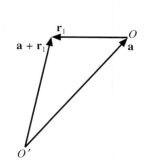

Figure 3.6

So, in terms of the final answer to a problem involving torques, the position of the origin is irrelevant. It makes sense, therefore, as in Example 3.1, to choose the origin to minimize the amount of calculation.

The position of the origin is, however, relevant to the values of the torques.

End-of-section Exercise

Exercise 3.4

A person sits on a park bench which consists of a rigid seat held up by two legs at either end, as shown in Figure 3.7. Model the seat of the bench as a model rod of length l and mass M. Model the person as a particle of mass m sitting at a point x metres from the left-hand end of the bench. Calculate the normal reaction forces on the bench seat due to the legs of the bench.

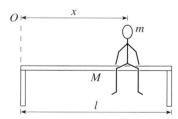

Figure 3.7

4 Applying the principles

This section contains some examples and exercises which use the principles we have developed so far to solve more complicated statics problems. The first example is more complicated than the examples in the previous section because the forces and positions are not conveniently aligned. This is not a fundamental difficulty; it merely makes the calculation of the vector products more complicated.

Example 4.1

During the erection of a marquee, a heavy pole OA of mass m and length l must be held in place by a rope AB, as shown in Figure 4.1. The angle between the pole and the ground is $\frac{\pi}{4}$, and the angle between the rope and the ground is $\frac{\pi}{6}$. Model the pole as a model rod, and the rope as a model string. Assume that the pole is freely hinged at O, i.e. the end of the model rod is fixed at O and is free to pivot about O.

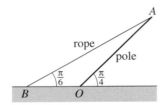

Figure 4.1

If the pole is in equilibrium, find the magnitude of the tension in the rope. Is the magnitude of the tension in the rope bigger or smaller than it would be if the pole were hanging freely on the end of the rope?

Solution

The best choice of axes is not obvious for this problem. So in this case we proceed by drawing the force diagram first, as shown in Figure 4.2.

◀Draw force diagram▶

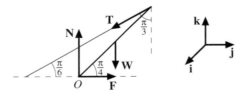

Figure 4.2

From Figure 4.2 we see that three of the forces are either horizontal or vertical, so we choose to orient the axes this way, as shown in the figure. In this problem, the choice of origin is vital, since we are going to take torques about the origin. Choosing the origin at the base of the pole makes two of the torques zero — a great simplification.

◀Choose axes▶

The equilibrium condition for rigid bodies gives

◀Apply law(s)▶

$$\mathbf{N} + \mathbf{F} + \mathbf{W} + \mathbf{T} = \mathbf{0}, \tag{4.1}$$
$$\mathbf{\Gamma}_N + \mathbf{\Gamma}_F + \mathbf{\Gamma}_W + \mathbf{\Gamma}_T = \mathbf{0}. \tag{4.2}$$

where $\mathbf{\Gamma}_N$, $\mathbf{\Gamma}_F$, $\mathbf{\Gamma}_W$ and $\mathbf{\Gamma}_T$ are the torques with respect to O of $\mathbf{N}$, $\mathbf{F}$, $\mathbf{W}$ and $\mathbf{T}$, respectively.

In this case, Equation (4.1) is not very useful since it contains three forces of unknown magnitude, namely $\mathbf{N}$, $\mathbf{F}$ and $\mathbf{T}$. However, by taking torques about O, two of the torques appearing in Equation (4.2) are zero, namely $\mathbf{\Gamma}_N$ and $\mathbf{\Gamma}_F$. Now we proceed by calculating the other two torques.

◄Solve equation(s)►

The position vectors of the points of application of the forces are

$$\mathbf{r}_W = \tfrac{1}{2}l\cos\tfrac{\pi}{4}\mathbf{j} + \tfrac{1}{2}l\sin\tfrac{\pi}{4}\mathbf{k} = \frac{l}{2\sqrt{2}}(\mathbf{j}+\mathbf{k}),$$

$$\mathbf{r}_T = l\cos\tfrac{\pi}{4}\mathbf{j} + l\sin\tfrac{\pi}{4}\mathbf{k} = \frac{l}{\sqrt{2}}(\mathbf{j}+\mathbf{k}).$$

The weight of the pole can be written in component form by inspection of the diagram as $\mathbf{W} = -mg\mathbf{k}$. To resolve the tension force, we use the formula from *Unit 4*. The angle between the direction of the tension force and the vertical is shown in Figure 4.2 to be $\tfrac{\pi}{3}$. The angles to the $\mathbf{j}$- and $\mathbf{k}$-directions can be obtained by adding $\tfrac{\pi}{2}$ and π, respectively. So we have

$$\begin{aligned}\mathbf{T} &= |\mathbf{T}|\cos(\tfrac{\pi}{2}+\tfrac{\pi}{3})\mathbf{j} + |\mathbf{T}|\cos(\pi+\tfrac{\pi}{3})\mathbf{k}\\ &= |\mathbf{T}|(\cos\tfrac{\pi}{2}\cos\tfrac{\pi}{3}-\sin\tfrac{\pi}{2}\sin\tfrac{\pi}{3})\mathbf{j} + |\mathbf{T}|(\cos\pi\cos\tfrac{\pi}{3}-\sin\pi\sin\tfrac{\pi}{3})\mathbf{k}\\ &= |\mathbf{T}|(-\sin\tfrac{\pi}{3})\mathbf{j} + |\mathbf{T}|(-\cos\tfrac{\pi}{3})\mathbf{k}\\ &= -|\mathbf{T}|(\tfrac{\sqrt{3}}{2}\mathbf{j}+\tfrac{1}{2}\mathbf{k}).\end{aligned}$$

There are many ways of computing the components of vectors. It is up to you to choose the way that you feel most comfortable with. For example, this calculation can be done more geometrically straight from the force diagram.

Now that the forces and position vectors are written in component form, we can proceed to calculate the torques:

$$\begin{aligned}\mathbf{\Gamma}_W = \mathbf{r}_W\times\mathbf{W} &= \frac{l}{2\sqrt{2}}(\mathbf{j}+\mathbf{k})\times(-mg\mathbf{k})\\ &= -\frac{lmg}{2\sqrt{2}}\mathbf{i},\end{aligned}$$

$$\begin{aligned}\mathbf{\Gamma}_T = \mathbf{r}_T\times\mathbf{T} &= \frac{l}{\sqrt{2}}(\mathbf{j}+\mathbf{k})\times(-|\mathbf{T}|(\tfrac{\sqrt{3}}{2}\mathbf{j}+\tfrac{1}{2}\mathbf{k}))\\ &= -\frac{l|\mathbf{T}|}{\sqrt{2}}(\tfrac{1}{2}\mathbf{j}\times\mathbf{k}+\tfrac{\sqrt{3}}{2}\mathbf{k}\times\mathbf{j})\\ &= \frac{l|\mathbf{T}|}{2\sqrt{2}}(\sqrt{3}-1)\mathbf{i}.\end{aligned}$$

Note that the terms involving $\mathbf{j}\times\mathbf{j}$ and $\mathbf{k}\times\mathbf{k}$ have been suppressed since they give the zero vector.

Substituting these torques into Equation (4.2) gives

$$-\frac{lmg}{2\sqrt{2}}\mathbf{i} + \frac{l|\mathbf{T}|}{2\sqrt{2}}(\sqrt{3}-1)\mathbf{i} = \mathbf{0}.$$

Resolving in the $\mathbf{i}$-direction and rearranging gives

$$|\mathbf{T}| = \frac{mg}{\sqrt{3}-1}.$$

So the magnitude of the tension in the rope is $mg/(\sqrt{3}-1) \simeq 1.4mg$, which is greater than the magnitude of the weight of the pole, mg. So, rather counter-intuitively, a stronger rope is needed to erect a pole in this way than is needed to lift the pole. ∎

◄Interpret results►

The next example is one of many similar problems that involve ladders. It shows that sometimes both of the equilibrium conditions are needed to solve a problem.

Example 4.2

A ladder of mass M and length l stands on rough horizontal ground, and rests against a smooth vertical wall (see Figure 4.3). The ladder can be modelled as a model rod. Find the minimum angle θ between the ladder and the ground for which the ladder can remain static, if the coefficient of static friction μ between the ladder and the ground is 0.5.

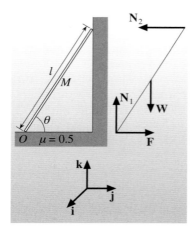

Figure 4.3

Solution

The forces acting on the rod are shown in the force diagram in Figure 4.3, where $\mathbf{W}$ is the weight of the ladder, $\mathbf{N}_1$ is the normal reaction from the ground, $\mathbf{N}_2$ is the normal reaction from the wall, and $\mathbf{F}$ is the friction force at the bottom of the ladder. (The wall is smooth, so we assume that there is no friction force at the top of the ladder.)

◄Draw force diagram►

As two of the three unknown forces act at the bottom of the ladder, this is a convenient point for the origin O. The axes are chosen as shown in Figure 4.3.

◄Choose axes►

The equilibrium condition for rigid bodies gives

◄Apply law(s)►

$$\mathbf{N}_1 + \mathbf{N}_2 + \mathbf{F} + \mathbf{W} = \mathbf{0}, \tag{4.3}$$
$$\boldsymbol{\Gamma}_{N_1} + \boldsymbol{\Gamma}_{N_2} + \boldsymbol{\Gamma}_F + \boldsymbol{\Gamma}_W = \mathbf{0}, \tag{4.4}$$

where $\boldsymbol{\Gamma}_{N_1}$, $\boldsymbol{\Gamma}_{N_2}$, $\boldsymbol{\Gamma}_F$ and $\boldsymbol{\Gamma}_W$ are the torques with respect to O of $\mathbf{N}_1$, $\mathbf{N}_2$, $\mathbf{F}$ and $\mathbf{W}$, respectively.

If the ladder is not going to slip, we must have

$$|\mathbf{F}| \leq \mu\,|\mathbf{N}_1|, \tag{4.5}$$

where μ is the coefficient of static friction.

The position vectors $\mathbf{r}_{N_1}$ and $\mathbf{r}_F$ are both zero, hence the corresponding torques $\boldsymbol{\Gamma}_{N_1}$ and $\boldsymbol{\Gamma}_F$ (relative to O) are also zero. To calculate the non-zero torques, we need the position vectors of the points of application of the forces. These are given by

◄Solve equation(s)►

$$\mathbf{r}_{N_2} = l\cos\theta\,\mathbf{j} + l\sin\theta\,\mathbf{k},$$
$$\mathbf{r}_W = \tfrac{1}{2}l\cos\theta\,\mathbf{j} + \tfrac{1}{2}l\sin\theta\,\mathbf{k}.$$

All of the forces in this example are aligned with the coordinate axes, so the components can be written down by inspection:

$$\mathbf{N}_1 = |\mathbf{N}_1|\,\mathbf{k}, \quad \mathbf{N}_2 = -|\mathbf{N}_2|\,\mathbf{j}, \quad \mathbf{F} = |\mathbf{F}|\,\mathbf{j}, \quad \mathbf{W} = -Mg\mathbf{k}.$$

Now we can calculate the two non-zero torques:

$$\boldsymbol{\Gamma}_{N_2} = (l\cos\theta\,\mathbf{j} + l\sin\theta\,\mathbf{k}) \times (-|\mathbf{N_2}|\mathbf{j})$$
$$= -|\mathbf{N_2}|\,l\sin\theta\,\mathbf{k}\times\mathbf{j}$$
$$= |\mathbf{N_2}|\,l\sin\theta\,\mathbf{i},$$

$$\boldsymbol{\Gamma}_W = (\tfrac{1}{2}l\cos\theta\,\mathbf{j} + \tfrac{1}{2}l\sin\theta\,\mathbf{k}) \times (-Mg\mathbf{k})$$
$$= -\tfrac{1}{2}Mgl\cos\theta\,\mathbf{j}\times\mathbf{k}$$
$$= -\tfrac{1}{2}Mgl\cos\theta\,\mathbf{i}.$$

Substituting these torques into Equation (4.4) gives

$$|\mathbf{N_2}|\,l\sin\theta\,\mathbf{i} - \tfrac{1}{2}Mgl\cos\theta\,\mathbf{i} = \mathbf{0},$$

and resolving this in the **i**-direction gives

$$|\mathbf{N_2}| = \tfrac{1}{2}Mg\cot\theta.$$

Resolving Equation (4.3) in the **j**- and **k**-directions in turn gives

$$-|\mathbf{N_2}| + |\mathbf{F}| = 0, \quad |\mathbf{N_1}| - Mg = 0.$$

Therefore

$$|\mathbf{F}| = |\mathbf{N_2}| = \tfrac{1}{2}Mg\cot\theta, \quad |\mathbf{N_1}| = Mg.$$

Substituting these into the inequality (4.5) gives

$$\tfrac{1}{2}Mg\cot\theta \le \mu Mg,$$

which, on rearrangement and using $\mu = 0.5$, gives

$$\cot\theta \le 1.$$

Note that since M and g are positive, we can safely divide through by them without reversing the inequality.

Therefore the model predicts that the minimum angle the ladder can make with the ground before slipping is $\frac{\pi}{4}$ radians (45°). ◼

◀Interpret results▶

*Exercise 4.1

A model rod OA of length l and mass m is fixed to a wall by a hinge, as shown in Figure 4.4. The rod is free to turn in a vertical plane about the hinge, which is assumed to be smooth (i.e. has no friction force associated with it). The rod is supported in a horizontal position by a string AB inclined at an angle θ to the horizontal.

Find the reaction force at the hinge and the tension force acting on the rod due to the string. Comment on the magnitudes and directions of these two forces.

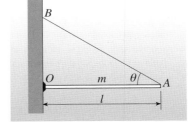

Figure 4.4

Exercise 4.2

A light ladder of length 3.9 m stands on a horizontal floor and rests against a smooth vertical wall, as shown in Figure 4.5. The base of the ladder is 1.5 m from the base of the wall. The coefficient of static friction μ between the ladder and the floor is 0.25. The end rungs are each 0.3 m from an end of the ladder. The ladder may be modelled as a rod, and its mass may be neglected (as it is a light ladder, so its mass is negligible compared with the masses of any people standing on it).

What is the minimum mass of a person standing on the bottom rung that prevents the ladder from slipping when a person of mass 100 kg stands on the top rung?

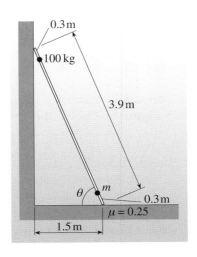

Figure 4.5

End-of-section Exercises

Exercise 4.3

At a building site, a plank of length $2l$ is resting against a large smooth pipe of radius r, as shown in Figure 4.6. The pipe is fixed to the ground, or else it would slide or roll to the left. The angle between the plank and the horizontal is $\frac{\pi}{3}$, so by symmetry the angle between the horizontal and the line between O and the centre of the pipe is $\frac{\pi}{6}$, as shown. In the figure, the distance OA is greater than the distance AB, so the centre of mass of the plank is between O and A.

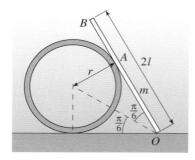

Figure 4.6

What is the least coefficient of static friction between the plank and the ground that will ensure equilibrium?

Exercise 4.4

A gangplank bridges the gap between a quay and a ship, as shown in Figure 4.7. The pulley is directly above the quayside end of the plank. A rope is attached to the end of the plank, then passes over the pulley to an attachment point on the quayside. When the ship is ready to depart, the gangplank is raised by pulling on the rope from the quayside.

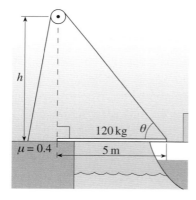

Figure 4.7

Using the information given in Figure 4.7, determine the minimum height of the pulley above the quay that ensures that the gangplank will be raised, rather than slip along the quay, when the rope is pulled. If one man can pull with a force of magnitude $800\,\mathrm{N}$ (and assuming that the pulley is sufficiently high), how many men are needed to raise the gangplank?

Exercise 4.5 _____

A door, of mass 20 kg, height 2 m and breadth 1 m, is supported by two hinges at the top and bottom of the door so that it is hanging in the vertical plane, as shown in Figure 4.8. The force exerted by the top hinge tends to pull the door upwards and towards the doorframe. The force exerted by the bottom hinge tends to push the door upwards and away from the doorframe.

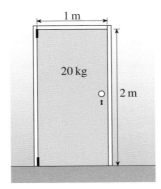

Figure 4.8

If the forces exerted by the hinges have the same magnitude, determine these forces in component form.

_____

Outcomes

After studying this unit you should be able to:

- appreciate the concept of a force;
- understand and model forces of weight, normal reaction, tension and friction;
- recognize and model the forces that act on an object in equilibrium;
- model objects as particles or as rigid bodies;
- use model strings, model rods, model pulleys and model pivots in modelling systems involving forces;
- draw force diagrams, and choose appropriate axes and an origin;
- use the equilibrium conditions for particles and for rigid bodies;
- understand and use torques;
- model and solve a variety of problems involving systems in equilibrium and systems on the verge of leaving equilibrium.

Solutions to the exercises

Section 1

1.1 The weight is $3g\mathbf{k}$.

1.2 Since the weight acts vertically downwards, its direction is in the vertical plane defined by $\mathbf{i}$ and $\mathbf{j}$, so $\mathbf{W}$ has no $\mathbf{k}$-component. To find the $\mathbf{i}$- and $\mathbf{j}$-components, the first step is to draw a diagram and work out the angles involved. In this case we use the two right-angles marked to work out the required angles. (Note that $\frac{\pi}{3} = \frac{\pi}{2} - \frac{\pi}{6}$.)

Resolving the weight following the method from *Unit 4*:
$$\begin{aligned}
\mathbf{W} &= (\mathbf{W} \cdot \mathbf{i})\,\mathbf{i} + (\mathbf{W} \cdot \mathbf{j})\,\mathbf{j} \\
&= (|\mathbf{W}| \times 1 \times \cos\tfrac{2\pi}{3})\,\mathbf{i} + (|\mathbf{W}| \times 1 \times \cos\tfrac{\pi}{6})\,\mathbf{j} \\
&= 15g \times (-\tfrac{1}{2})\,\mathbf{i} + 15g \times (\tfrac{\sqrt{3}}{2})\,\mathbf{j} \\
&= -\tfrac{15}{2}g\,\mathbf{i} + \tfrac{15\sqrt{3}}{2}g\,\mathbf{j}.
\end{aligned}$$
(If you are puzzled as to why $\cos\frac{2\pi}{3} = -\frac{1}{2}$, then see the note in the main text following this exercise.)

1.3 In this and other solutions, you may find that your diagrams and chosen axes are different from those given. You should still be able to check the validity of your solution against the given one, as the basic concepts are unchanged by these differences. Any choice of axes should lead to the same final answers as those given.

◄Draw picture►

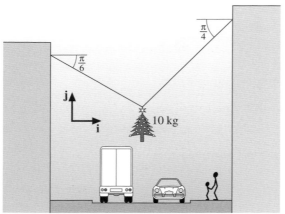

◄Choose axes►

The forces all lie in a vertical plane, so we need only two axes, as shown in the diagram above.

◄Draw force diagram►

The force diagram, where the tension forces are denoted by $\mathbf{T}_1$ and $\mathbf{T}_2$, and the weight of the tree by $\mathbf{W}$, is as follows.

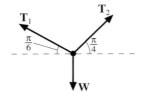

◄Apply law(s)►

The equilibrium condition for particles gives
$$\mathbf{T}_1 + \mathbf{T}_2 + \mathbf{W} = \mathbf{0}. \tag{S.1}$$

◄Solve equation(s)►

From the above force diagram we have
$$\mathbf{W} = -|\mathbf{W}|\,\mathbf{j} = -10g\,\mathbf{j}.$$
The other forces can be expressed in terms of components using the method from *Unit 4*:
$$\begin{aligned}
\mathbf{T}_1 &= (\mathbf{T}_1 \cdot \mathbf{i})\,\mathbf{i} + (\mathbf{T}_1 \cdot \mathbf{j})\,\mathbf{j} \\
&= |\mathbf{T}_1| \cos\tfrac{5\pi}{6}\,\mathbf{i} + |\mathbf{T}_1| \cos\tfrac{\pi}{3}\,\mathbf{j} \\
&= -\tfrac{\sqrt{3}}{2}|\mathbf{T}_1|\,\mathbf{i} + \tfrac{1}{2}|\mathbf{T}_1|\,\mathbf{j}, \\
\mathbf{T}_2 &= (\mathbf{T}_2 \cdot \mathbf{i})\,\mathbf{i} + (\mathbf{T}_2 \cdot \mathbf{j})\,\mathbf{j} \\
&= |\mathbf{T}_2| \cos\tfrac{\pi}{4}\,\mathbf{i} + |\mathbf{T}_2| \cos\tfrac{\pi}{4}\,\mathbf{j} \\
&= \tfrac{1}{\sqrt{2}}|\mathbf{T}_2|\,\mathbf{i} + \tfrac{1}{\sqrt{2}}|\mathbf{T}_2|\,\mathbf{j}.
\end{aligned}$$
Resolving (S.1) in the $\mathbf{i}$-direction gives
$$-\tfrac{\sqrt{3}}{2}|\mathbf{T}_1| + \tfrac{1}{\sqrt{2}}|\mathbf{T}_2| + 0 = 0. \tag{S.2}$$
Similarly, resolving (S.1) in the $\mathbf{j}$-direction gives
$$\tfrac{1}{2}|\mathbf{T}_1| + \tfrac{1}{\sqrt{2}}|\mathbf{T}_2| - 10g = 0. \tag{S.3}$$
Subtracting (S.2) from (S.3) gives
$$(\tfrac{1}{2} + \tfrac{\sqrt{3}}{2})|\mathbf{T}_1| - 10g = 0,$$
so
$$|\mathbf{T}_1| = \tfrac{20}{1+\sqrt{3}}g \simeq 71.81.$$
Substituting this value of $|\mathbf{T}_1|$ into (S.2) gives
$$|\mathbf{T}_2| = \tfrac{20\sqrt{3}}{\sqrt{2}+\sqrt{6}}g \simeq 87.95.$$

◄Interpret solution►

The model predicts that the magnitudes of the tension forces due to the ropes are about $72\,\text{N}$ and $88\,\text{N}$.

1.4

◄Draw picture►

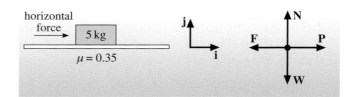

◄Choose axes►

Suitable axes are shown in the diagram.

◄Draw force diagram►

The force diagram, where **F** is the friction force, **P** is the horizontal force, **W** is the weight, and **N** is the normal reaction, is shown above.

◄Apply law(s)►

The equilibrium condition for particles gives

$$\mathbf{F} + \mathbf{N} + \mathbf{P} + \mathbf{W} = \mathbf{0}. \tag{S.4}$$

When the block is about to move, we have

$$|\mathbf{F}| = \mu |\mathbf{N}|,$$

where $\mu = 0.35$ (see Table 1.1 on page 14).

◄Solve equation(s)►

Resolving (S.4) in the **i**-direction gives

$$|\mathbf{F}| = |\mathbf{P}|.$$

Resolving (S.4) in the **j**-direction gives

$$|\mathbf{N}| = |\mathbf{W}|.$$

Therefore, when the block is about to move,

$$|\mathbf{P}| = |\mathbf{F}| = \mu|\mathbf{N}| = \mu|\mathbf{W}|$$
$$= 0.35 \times 5g = 1.75g \simeq 17.2.$$

◄Interpret solution►

The model predicts that a horizontal force in excess of 17 N is required to start the block moving.

1.5 Choose axes as in Solution 1.4. The force diagram is the same as in Solution 1.4. If the object does not move, the equilibrium condition for particles holds, so

$$\mathbf{F} + \mathbf{N} + \mathbf{P} + \mathbf{W} = \mathbf{0}. \tag{S.5}$$

If the block does not move,

$$|\mathbf{F}| \leq \mu|\mathbf{N}|,$$

where μ is the coefficient of static friction.

Resolving (S.5) in the **i**-direction gives

$$|\mathbf{F}| = |\mathbf{P}|.$$

Resolving (S.5) in the **j**-direction gives

$$|\mathbf{N}| = |\mathbf{W}|.$$

Therefore, if the block does not move,

$$|\mathbf{P}| = |\mathbf{F}| \leq \mu|\mathbf{N}| = \mu|\mathbf{W}|.$$

Since $|\mathbf{P}| = 2$ and $|\mathbf{W}| = 0.5g$, the block does not move provided that

$$\mu \geq 2/(0.5g) \simeq 0.41.$$

The coefficient of static friction in Table 1.1 for steel on dry steel is 0.58, so the model predicts that the block does not move.

Since we have $|\mathbf{F}| = |\mathbf{P}|$, the magnitude of the friction force is 2 N.

1.6 Since the friction force does not depend on the area of contact, the sideways force required to start the box slipping is the same in both cases.

1.7

◄Choose axes►

Choose the same axes as in Example 1.3.

◄Draw force diagram►

Modelling the crate as a particle and the rope as a model string, the force diagram is as shown below, where the notation is as in Example 1.3. Both **F** and **T** act in the same direction (on the implied assumption that the crate will slide down the ramp if nothing holds it back).

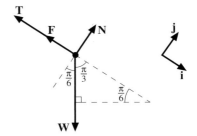

(It is conventional to draw two forces acting in the same direction on a particle as overlapping arrows of different lengths.)

◄Apply law(s)►

The equilibrium condition for particles gives

$$\mathbf{F} + \mathbf{T} + \mathbf{N} + \mathbf{W} = \mathbf{0}. \tag{S.6}$$

If the crate does not move, then

$$|\mathbf{F}| \leq \mu|\mathbf{N}| = 0.2|\mathbf{N}|, \tag{S.7}$$

where μ is the coefficient of static friction.

◄Solve equations►

From the diagram we have

$$\mathbf{N} = |\mathbf{N}|\,\mathbf{j}, \quad \mathbf{T} = -|\mathbf{T}|\,\mathbf{i} \quad \text{and} \quad \mathbf{F} = -|\mathbf{F}|\,\mathbf{i}.$$

Using the formula from *Unit 4* gives

$$\mathbf{W} = |\mathbf{W}| \cos\tfrac{\pi}{3}\,\mathbf{i} + |\mathbf{W}| \cos\tfrac{5\pi}{6}\,\mathbf{j}$$
$$= \tfrac{1}{2}|\mathbf{W}|\,\mathbf{i} - \tfrac{\sqrt{3}}{2}|\mathbf{W}|\,\mathbf{j}.$$

Resolving (S.6) in the **i**-direction gives

$$-|\mathbf{F}| - |\mathbf{T}| + 0 + \tfrac{1}{2}|\mathbf{W}| = 0,$$

so

$$|\mathbf{F}| = \tfrac{1}{2}|\mathbf{W}| - |\mathbf{T}|. \tag{S.8}$$

Resolving (S.6) in the **j**-direction gives

$$0 + 0 + |\mathbf{N}| - \tfrac{\sqrt{3}}{2}|\mathbf{W}| = 0,$$

so

$$|\mathbf{N}| = \tfrac{\sqrt{3}}{2}|\mathbf{W}|. \tag{S.9}$$

Substituting from (S.8) and (S.9) into (S.7) gives

$$\tfrac{1}{2}|\mathbf{W}| - |\mathbf{T}| \leq 0.2 \times \tfrac{\sqrt{3}}{2}|\mathbf{W}|,$$

which, on rearrangement and using $|\mathbf{W}| = 60g$, gives

$$|\mathbf{T}| \geq 30g - 6\sqrt{3}g \simeq 192.$$

◄Interpret solution►

Therefore the model predicts that a force of at least 192 N up the slope needs to be applied to the rope to keep the crate from sliding down the ramp.

1.8 Model the pallet as a particle, the cable and the rope as model strings, and consider the (static) final position of the pallet.

◄Draw picture►

The final position of the pallet is shown in the following diagram, where we have marked the final distance moved by the pallet as x and also an angle θ. Note that these are related by trigonometry:

$$x = 10 \sin \theta. \tag{S.10}$$

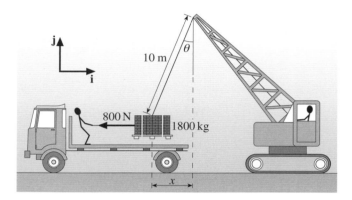

◄Choose axes►

Suitable axes are shown in the diagram.

◄Draw force diagram►

Denoting the tension forces as $\mathbf{T}_1$ and $\mathbf{T}_2$, and the weight as $\mathbf{W}$, the force diagram is as follows.

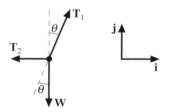

(Note that we have used the fact that opposite angles are equal to find the angle between $\mathbf{T}_1$ and $\mathbf{j}$.)

◄Apply law(s)►

The equilibrium condition for particles gives

$$\mathbf{T}_1 + \mathbf{T}_2 + \mathbf{W} = \mathbf{0}. \tag{S.11}$$

◄Solve equation(s)►

From the diagram,

$$\mathbf{W} = -|\mathbf{W}|\mathbf{j} \quad \text{and} \quad \mathbf{T}_2 = -|\mathbf{T}_2|\mathbf{i}.$$

Using the formula from *Unit 4*:

$$\mathbf{T}_1 = |\mathbf{T}_1| \cos(\tfrac{\pi}{2} - \theta)\,\mathbf{i} + |\mathbf{T}_1| \cos \theta\,\mathbf{j}.$$

This can be slightly simplified by using the fact that $\cos(\tfrac{\pi}{2} - \theta) = \cos \tfrac{\pi}{2} \cos \theta + \sin \tfrac{\pi}{2} \sin \theta = \sin \theta$, to obtain

$$\mathbf{T}_1 = |\mathbf{T}_1| \sin \theta\,\mathbf{i} + |\mathbf{T}_1| \cos \theta\,\mathbf{j}.$$

Resolving (S.11) in the $\mathbf{i}$- and $\mathbf{j}$-directions in turn gives

$$|\mathbf{T}_1| \sin \theta - |\mathbf{T}_2| = 0, \tag{S.12}$$

$$|\mathbf{T}_1| \cos \theta - |\mathbf{W}| = 0. \tag{S.13}$$

Substituting $|\mathbf{T}_2| = 800$ into (S.12) and $|\mathbf{W}| = 1800g$ into (S.13) gives

$$\sin \theta = 800/|\mathbf{T}_1|, \quad \cos \theta = 1800g/|\mathbf{T}_1|,$$

so

$$\tan \theta = 800/1800g \simeq 4/(9 \times 9.81) \simeq 0.045\,305.$$

Hence $\theta \simeq 0.045\,274$, $\sin \theta \simeq 0.045\,259$ and (S.10) gives $x \simeq 0.453$.

◄Interpret solution►

So the model predicts that the pallet can be moved by about 0.45 m horizontally; the crane driver needs to be pretty accurate in positioning the pallet over the lorry in the first place.

1.9 (a)   ◄Draw picture►   ◄Draw force diagram►

The situation is illustrated below.

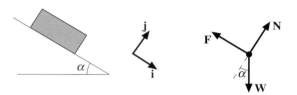

◄Choose axes►

Choose axes so that $\mathbf{i}$ points down the slope and $\mathbf{j}$ is in the direction of the normal reaction.

◄Apply law(s)►

The equilibrium condition for particles gives

$$\mathbf{F} + \mathbf{N} + \mathbf{W} = \mathbf{0}. \tag{S.14}$$

Since the box is on the point of slipping,

$$|\mathbf{F}| = \mu |\mathbf{N}|, \tag{S.15}$$

where μ is the coefficient of static friction.

◄Solve equation(s)►

Two of the forces are aligned with the axes and can be written down immediately:

$$\mathbf{F} = -|\mathbf{F}|\,\mathbf{i} \quad \text{and} \quad \mathbf{N} = |\mathbf{N}|\,\mathbf{j}.$$

The third force is inclined to the axes, so we use the formula from *Unit 4*:

$$\begin{aligned}
\mathbf{W} &= (\mathbf{W} \cdot \mathbf{i})\,\mathbf{i} + (\mathbf{W} \cdot \mathbf{j})\,\mathbf{j} \\
&= |\mathbf{W}| \cos(\tfrac{\pi}{2} - \alpha)\,\mathbf{i} + |\mathbf{W}| \cos(\pi - \alpha)\,\mathbf{j} \\
&= mg(\cos \tfrac{\pi}{2} \cos \alpha + \sin \tfrac{\pi}{2} \sin \alpha)\,\mathbf{i} \\
&\quad + mg(\cos \pi \cos \alpha + \sin \pi \sin \alpha)\,\mathbf{j} \\
&= mg \sin \alpha\,\mathbf{i} - mg \cos \alpha\,\mathbf{j}.
\end{aligned}$$

Resolving (S.14) in the $\mathbf{i}$-direction gives

$$-|\mathbf{F}| + 0 + mg \sin \alpha = 0,$$

so

$$|\mathbf{F}| = mg \sin \alpha.$$

Resolving (S.14) in the $\mathbf{j}$-direction gives

$$0 + |\mathbf{N}| - mg \cos \alpha = 0,$$

so

$$|\mathbf{N}| = mg \cos \alpha.$$

Substituting $|\mathbf{F}|$ and $|\mathbf{N}|$ into (S.15) gives

$$\mu = \frac{|\mathbf{F}|}{|\mathbf{N}|} = \tan\alpha.$$

(This result provides us with a technique for estimating the coefficient of static friction μ for two surfaces. Put the two surfaces in contact, and increase the angle of inclination from the horizontal until slipping begins. The tangent of the angle at which this happens is the required value of μ.)

(b) ◀Interpret solution▶

The result in part (a) tells us that for an object on an inclined plane, the angle at which the object starts to slip depends only on the two surfaces in contact (i.e. on the coefficient of static friction μ). The mass of the object is irrelevant — so the half-full mug will start to slip at the same angle as the empty one.

Section 2

2.1 The force diagrams for the four books (with the topmost book on the left) are as follows.

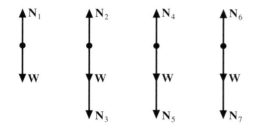

Applying Newton's third law to the system gives

$$\mathbf{N}_1 = -\mathbf{N}_3, \quad \mathbf{N}_2 = -\mathbf{N}_5, \quad \mathbf{N}_4 = -\mathbf{N}_7.$$

The equilibrium condition for particles applied to each book gives

$$\mathbf{N}_1 + \mathbf{W} = \mathbf{0}, \quad \mathbf{N}_2 + \mathbf{N}_3 + \mathbf{W} = \mathbf{0},$$
$$\mathbf{N}_4 + \mathbf{N}_5 + \mathbf{W} = \mathbf{0}, \quad \mathbf{N}_6 + \mathbf{N}_7 + \mathbf{W} = \mathbf{0}.$$

Solving these seven equations for the normal reactions gives

$$\mathbf{N}_1 = -\mathbf{W}, \quad \mathbf{N}_2 = -2\mathbf{W}, \quad \mathbf{N}_3 = \mathbf{W},$$
$$\mathbf{N}_4 = -3\mathbf{W}, \quad \mathbf{N}_5 = 2\mathbf{W}, \quad \mathbf{N}_6 = -4\mathbf{W},$$
$$\mathbf{N}_7 = 3\mathbf{W}.$$

2.2 ◀Draw force diagram▶

The force diagrams for the lamp (plus lampshade) and the toy are as follows.

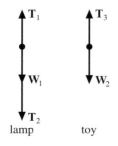

lamp   toy

◀Apply law(s)▶

Applying Newton's third law to the system gives

$$\mathbf{T}_2 = -\mathbf{T}_3.$$

The equilibrium condition for particles applied to each particle gives

$$\mathbf{T}_1 + \mathbf{T}_2 + \mathbf{W}_1 = \mathbf{0}, \quad \mathbf{T}_3 + \mathbf{W}_2 = \mathbf{0}.$$

◀Solve equation(s)▶

Solving these three equations for the tensions gives

$$\mathbf{T}_1 = -\mathbf{W}_1 - \mathbf{W}_2, \quad \mathbf{T}_2 = \mathbf{W}_2, \quad \mathbf{T}_3 = -\mathbf{W}_2.$$

Therefore, since $|\mathbf{W}_1| = 1.5g$ and $|\mathbf{W}_2| = 0.5g$, the magnitude of the tension force due to the cable is

$$|\mathbf{T}_1| = |\mathbf{W}_1 + \mathbf{W}_2| = 1.5g + 0.5g = 2g \simeq 19.6.$$

(An alternative approach is to model the system consisting of lamp, string and toy as a single particle of weight $\mathbf{W}_1 + \mathbf{W}_2$. The equilibrium condition for particles then immediately gives the tension force $\mathbf{T}_1$ due to the cable as $\mathbf{T}_1 = -\mathbf{W}_1 - \mathbf{W}_2$.)

◀Interpret solution▶

The magnitude of the tension force due to the cable is approximately $19.6\,\mathrm{N}$.

2.3 The sack, stone, pulley and rope are modelled as in Example 2.1.

◀Choose axes▶

This time we need two axes, as shown in Figure 2.6.

◀Draw force diagram▶

The force diagrams for the sack and the stone, using the usual notation, are as follows.

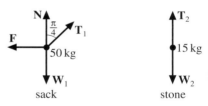

sack   stone

◀Apply law(s)▶

The equilibrium condition for particles gives

$$\mathbf{W}_1 + \mathbf{F} + \mathbf{N} + \mathbf{T}_1 = \mathbf{0}, \tag{S.16}$$
$$\mathbf{W}_2 + \mathbf{T}_2 = \mathbf{0}. \tag{S.17}$$

The fact that we have a model pulley tells us that

$$|\mathbf{T}_1| = |\mathbf{T}_2|.$$

◀Solve equation(s)▶

From the diagram we have

$$\mathbf{N} = |\mathbf{N}|\mathbf{j}, \quad \mathbf{F} = -|\mathbf{F}|\mathbf{i}, \quad \mathbf{W}_1 = -|\mathbf{W}_1|\mathbf{j},$$
$$\mathbf{T}_2 = |\mathbf{T}_2|\mathbf{j}, \quad \mathbf{W}_2 = -|\mathbf{W}_2|\mathbf{j}.$$

Using the formula from *Unit 4*:

$$\mathbf{T}_1 = |\mathbf{T}_1|\cos\tfrac{\pi}{4}\mathbf{i} + |\mathbf{T}_1|\cos\tfrac{\pi}{4}\mathbf{j} = \tfrac{1}{\sqrt{2}}|\mathbf{T}_1|\mathbf{i} + \tfrac{1}{\sqrt{2}}|\mathbf{T}_1|\mathbf{j}.$$

Resolving (S.16) in the $\mathbf{i}$-direction gives

$$0 - |\mathbf{F}| + 0 + \tfrac{1}{\sqrt{2}}|\mathbf{T}_1| = 0,$$

so

$$|\mathbf{F}| = \tfrac{1}{\sqrt{2}}|\mathbf{T}_1|.$$

Resolving (S.16) and (S.17) in the **j**-direction gives

$$-|\mathbf{W}_1| + 0 + |\mathbf{N}| + \tfrac{1}{\sqrt{2}}|\mathbf{T}_1| = 0,$$

$$-|\mathbf{W}_2| + |\mathbf{T}_2| = 0,$$

so

$$|\mathbf{W}_1| = |\mathbf{N}| + \tfrac{1}{\sqrt{2}}|\mathbf{T}_1| \quad \text{and} \quad |\mathbf{W}_2| = |\mathbf{T}_2|.$$

◄Interpret solution►

(a) We have

$$|\mathbf{W}_1| = 50g, \quad |\mathbf{W}_2| = 15g, \quad |\mathbf{T}_1| = |\mathbf{T}_2| = |\mathbf{W}_2|,$$

so

$$|\mathbf{N}| = |\mathbf{W}_1| - \tfrac{1}{\sqrt{2}}|\mathbf{T}_1| = 50g - \tfrac{15}{\sqrt{2}}g \simeq 386.$$

So the model predicts that the magnitude of the normal reaction is about 386 N.

(b) We have

$$|\mathbf{F}| = \tfrac{1}{\sqrt{2}}|\mathbf{T}_1| = \tfrac{1}{\sqrt{2}}|\mathbf{W}_2| = \tfrac{15}{\sqrt{2}}g \simeq 104,$$

so the model predicts that the magnitude of the friction force is about 104 N.

(c) For equilibrium, we must have $|\mathbf{F}| \leq \mu|\mathbf{N}|$, i.e.

$$\mu \geq |\mathbf{F}|/|\mathbf{N}| \simeq 104/386 \simeq 0.27.$$

So the model predicts that the smallest value of μ that allows the system to remain in equilibrium is about 0.27.

2.4 Given that the pulleys can be modelled as model pulleys, we know that the magnitude of the force exerted by the mechanic is the tension in the model string used to model the long rope — and this tension is constant throughout the length of the string. So we need consider only the forces acting on the model pulley attached to the engine.

◄Choose axes►

We use the axes given in Figure 2.7.

◄Draw force diagram►

Using the usual notation, we have the following force diagrams for the engine and the pulley above it.

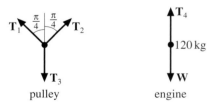

◄Apply law(s)►

The equilibrium condition for particles gives

$$\mathbf{T}_1 + \mathbf{T}_2 + \mathbf{T}_3 = \mathbf{0}, \tag{S.18}$$

$$\mathbf{T}_4 + \mathbf{W} = \mathbf{0}. \tag{S.19}$$

Since the engine is joined to a model pulley by a model string, we have

$$|\mathbf{T}_3| = |\mathbf{T}_4|, \quad |\mathbf{T}_1| = |\mathbf{T}_2|.$$

◄Solve equation(s)►

From the diagram we have

$$\mathbf{T}_3 = -|\mathbf{T}_3|\mathbf{j}, \quad \mathbf{T}_4 = |\mathbf{T}_4|\mathbf{j}, \quad \mathbf{W} = -|\mathbf{W}|\mathbf{j}.$$

Using the formula from *Unit 4*:

$$\mathbf{T}_1 = |\mathbf{T}_1| \cos\tfrac{3\pi}{4}\mathbf{i} + |\mathbf{T}_1| \cos\tfrac{\pi}{4}\mathbf{j}$$

$$= -\tfrac{1}{\sqrt{2}}|\mathbf{T}_1|\mathbf{i} + \tfrac{1}{\sqrt{2}}|\mathbf{T}_1|\mathbf{j},$$

$$\mathbf{T}_2 = |\mathbf{T}_2| \cos\tfrac{\pi}{4}\mathbf{i} + |\mathbf{T}_2| \cos\tfrac{\pi}{4}\mathbf{j}$$

$$= \tfrac{1}{\sqrt{2}}|\mathbf{T}_2|\mathbf{i} + \tfrac{1}{\sqrt{2}}|\mathbf{T}_2|\mathbf{j}.$$

Resolving (S.18) and (S.19) in turn in the **j**-direction:

$$\tfrac{1}{\sqrt{2}}|\mathbf{T}_1| + \tfrac{1}{\sqrt{2}}|\mathbf{T}_2| - |\mathbf{T}_3| = 0,$$

$$|\mathbf{T}_4| - |\mathbf{W}| = 0.$$

Therefore

$$|\mathbf{T}_3| = |\mathbf{T}_4| = |\mathbf{W}|,$$

$$\tfrac{1}{\sqrt{2}}(|\mathbf{T}_1| + |\mathbf{T}_2|) = |\mathbf{T}_3| = |\mathbf{W}|.$$

Since $|\mathbf{T}_1| = |\mathbf{T}_2|$, we have

$$|\mathbf{T}_1| = \tfrac{\sqrt{2}}{2}|\mathbf{W}| = \tfrac{1}{\sqrt{2}} \times 120g \simeq 832.$$

◄Interpret solution►

The model predicts that the force exerted by the mechanic has magnitude about 832 N, which is $\tfrac{1}{\sqrt{2}} \simeq 0.7$ (i.e. 70%) of the weight of the engine.

(Because the engine is joined to the pulley by a model string so that $|\mathbf{T}_3| = |\mathbf{T}_4| = |\mathbf{W}|$ and hence $\mathbf{T}_3 = \mathbf{W}$, an alternative approach is to model the pulley as a particle of mass 120 kg, giving $\mathbf{T}_1 + \mathbf{T}_2 + \mathbf{W} = \mathbf{0}$.)

2.5 ◄Draw picture►

Model the gold medallion and the chain on the shelf as a single particle of mass $0.02 + \tfrac{1}{2} \times 0.03 = 0.035$ kg, and the dangling chain as another particle, of mass $\tfrac{1}{2} \times 0.03 = 0.015$ kg. Model the chain as a model string and the edge of the shelf as a model pulley.

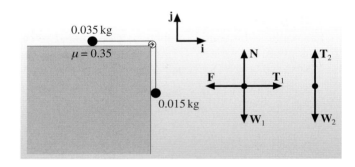

◄Choose axes►   ◄Draw force diagram►

A suitable choice of axes and a force diagram for each particle are shown above.

◄Apply law(s)►

The equilibrium condition for particles gives

$$\mathbf{F} + \mathbf{N} + \mathbf{T}_1 + \mathbf{W}_1 = \mathbf{0}, \tag{S.20}$$

$$\mathbf{T}_2 + \mathbf{W}_2 = \mathbf{0}. \tag{S.21}$$

The assumption of a model pulley gives

$$|\mathbf{T}_1| = |\mathbf{T}_2|.$$

If the medallion and chain are to remain on the shelf, we must have

$$|\mathbf{F}| \leq \mu|\mathbf{N}|, \tag{S.22}$$

where μ is the coefficient of static friction.

◀Solve equation(s)▶

From the diagram
$$\mathbf{T}_1 = |\mathbf{T}_1|\,\mathbf{i}, \quad \mathbf{N} = |\mathbf{N}|\,\mathbf{j}, \quad \mathbf{F} = -|\mathbf{F}|\,\mathbf{i},$$
$$\mathbf{W}_1 = -|\mathbf{W}_1|\,\mathbf{j}, \quad \mathbf{T}_2 = |\mathbf{T}_2|\,\mathbf{j}, \quad \mathbf{W}_2 = -|\mathbf{W}_2|\,\mathbf{j}.$$
Resolving (S.20) in the **i**- and **j**-directions in turn gives
$$-|\mathbf{F}| + |\mathbf{T}_1| = 0,$$
$$|\mathbf{N}| - |\mathbf{W}_1| = 0.$$
Resolving (S.21) in the **j**-direction gives
$$|\mathbf{T}_2| - |\mathbf{W}_2| = 0.$$
Therefore
$$|\mathbf{F}| = |\mathbf{T}_1| = |\mathbf{T}_2| = |\mathbf{W}_2| = 0.015g,$$
$$|\mathbf{N}| = |\mathbf{W}_1| = 0.035g.$$

◀Interpret solution▶

We have
$$|\mathbf{F}| = 0.015g,$$
$$\mu|\mathbf{N}| = 0.35 \times 0.035g = 0.012\,25g.$$
So (S.22) is not satisfied and the model predicts that the medallion will slip off the shelf.

2.6 This is similar to the situation of a pile of books, except that the forces acting on the objects are tension forces not normal reactions. We model the objects as particles and the strings as model strings.

◀Draw picture▶ ◀Choose axes▶
◀Draw force diagram▶

The situation is shown below. Only one axis is needed, a **j**-axis as shown. The force diagrams (topmost mass on the left) are as shown, where the weights are denoted by the $\mathbf{W}_i$ and the tension forces by the $\mathbf{T}_i$.

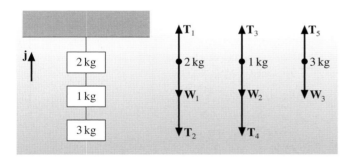

◀Apply law(s)▶

Newton's third law applies to the strings, so
$$\mathbf{T}_2 = -\mathbf{T}_3, \quad \mathbf{T}_4 = -\mathbf{T}_5.$$
The equilibrium condition applied to each particle gives
$$\mathbf{T}_1 + \mathbf{T}_2 + \mathbf{W}_1 = \mathbf{0}, \tag{S.23}$$
$$\mathbf{T}_3 + \mathbf{T}_4 + \mathbf{W}_2 = \mathbf{0}, \tag{S.24}$$
$$\mathbf{T}_5 + \mathbf{W}_3 = \mathbf{0}. \tag{S.25}$$

◀Solve equation(s)▶

Resolving (S.23), (S.24) and (S.25) in turn in the **j**-direction gives
$$|\mathbf{T}_1| - |\mathbf{T}_2| - |\mathbf{W}_1| = 0,$$
$$|\mathbf{T}_3| - |\mathbf{T}_4| - |\mathbf{W}_2| = 0,$$
$$|\mathbf{T}_5| - |\mathbf{W}_3| = 0.$$

Therefore, since
$$|\mathbf{T}_2| = |\mathbf{T}_3|, \quad |\mathbf{T}_4| = |\mathbf{T}_5|,$$
$$|\mathbf{W}_1| = 2g, \quad |\mathbf{W}_2| = g, \quad |\mathbf{W}_3| = 3g,$$
we have
$$|\mathbf{T}_5| = |\mathbf{T}_4| = 3g \simeq 29.4,$$
$$|\mathbf{T}_3| = |\mathbf{T}_2| = 4g \simeq 39.2,$$
$$|\mathbf{T}_1| = 6g \simeq 58.9.$$

◀Interpret solution▶

The model predicts that the tensions in the strings are about 58.9 N, 39.2 N and 29.4 N, in order from top to bottom.

2.7 Model the man in the well as a particle of mass 80 kg, and all the men on the ground as a single particle of mass m.

◀Choose axes▶ ◀Draw force diagram▶

A suitable choice of axes is shown in Figure 2.9. A force diagram for each particle, using the usual notation, is shown below.

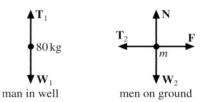

man in well   men on ground

◀Apply law(s)▶

The equilibrium condition for particles gives
$$\mathbf{T}_1 + \mathbf{W}_1 = \mathbf{0}, \tag{S.26}$$
$$\mathbf{T}_2 + \mathbf{N} + \mathbf{F} + \mathbf{W}_2 = \mathbf{0}. \tag{S.27}$$
The assumption of a model pulley gives
$$|\mathbf{T}_1| = |\mathbf{T}_2|.$$
If the men are not to slip, we must have
$$|\mathbf{F}| \le \mu|\mathbf{N}|, \tag{S.28}$$
where μ is the coefficient of static friction.

◀Solve equation(s)▶

Resolving (S.27) in the **i**- and **j**-directions in turn gives
$$-|\mathbf{T}_2| + 0 + |\mathbf{F}| + 0 = 0,$$
$$0 + |\mathbf{N}| + 0 - |\mathbf{W}_2| = 0.$$
Resolving (S.26) in the **j**-direction gives
$$|\mathbf{T}_1| - |\mathbf{W}_1| = 0.$$
Therefore
$$|\mathbf{F}| = |\mathbf{T}_2| = |\mathbf{T}_1| = |\mathbf{W}_1| = 80g,$$
$$|\mathbf{N}| = |\mathbf{W}_2| = mg,$$
hence
$$\mu|\mathbf{N}| = 0.35 \times mg = 0.35mg.$$
So, for (S.28) to be satisfied, we need $0.35mg \ge 80g$, which gives $m \ge 228.57$.

◀Interpret solution▶

The model predicts that three men of mass 80 kg are required to hold the man above the well.

2.8 Equilibrium can be disturbed either by the object of mass m_1 sliding down the board and pulling up the object of mass m_2, or by the object of mass m_2 dropping down and pulling the object of mass m_1 up the board.

◀Draw picture▶

Model the masses as particles joined by a model string hanging over a model pulley representing the edge of the board.

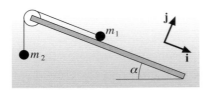

◀Choose axes▶

One choice of axes is shown above.

◀Draw force diagram▶

We need to consider the two cases of possible movement separately, as they lead to different force diagrams and hence to different results.

Consider first the case where m_2 is likely to drop down and pull m_1 up the board. The force diagrams are as follows.

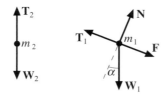

◀Apply law(s)▶

The equilibrium condition for particles gives

$$\mathbf{T}_1 + \mathbf{N} + \mathbf{F} + \mathbf{W}_1 = \mathbf{0}, \tag{S.29}$$
$$\mathbf{T}_2 + \mathbf{W}_2 = \mathbf{0}. \tag{S.30}$$

The use of a model pulley gives

$$|\mathbf{T}_1| = |\mathbf{T}_2|. \tag{S.31}$$

If the system is to remain in equilibrium, we require

$$|\mathbf{F}| \le \mu|\mathbf{N}|, \tag{S.32}$$

where μ is the coefficient of static friction.

◀Solve equation(s)▶

From (S.30) we have $\mathbf{T}_2 = -\mathbf{W}_2$, therefore

$$|\mathbf{T}_2| = |\mathbf{W}_2| = m_2 g.$$

So, by (S.31),

$$|\mathbf{T}_1| = m_2 g.$$

For the particle of mass m_1, the forces acting are

$$\mathbf{F} = |\mathbf{F}|\,\mathbf{i}, \quad \mathbf{N} = |\mathbf{N}|\,\mathbf{j}, \quad \mathbf{T}_1 = -|\mathbf{T}_1|\,\mathbf{i} = -m_2 g\,\mathbf{i}$$

and $\mathbf{W}_1$, which can be resolved using the formula from *Unit 4*:

$$\mathbf{W}_1 = |\mathbf{W}_1|\cos(\tfrac{\pi}{2} - \alpha)\,\mathbf{i} + |\mathbf{W}_1|\cos(\pi - \alpha)\,\mathbf{j}$$
$$= |\mathbf{W}_1|\sin\alpha\,\mathbf{i} - |\mathbf{W}_1|\cos\alpha\,\mathbf{j}.$$

Resolving (S.29) in the **i**- and **j**-directions in turn gives

$$-|\mathbf{T}_1| + 0 + |\mathbf{F}| + |\mathbf{W}_1|\sin\alpha = 0,$$
$$0 + |\mathbf{N}| + 0 - |\mathbf{W}_1|\cos\alpha = 0.$$

Therefore

$$|\mathbf{F}| = |\mathbf{T}_1| - |\mathbf{W}_1|\sin\alpha = m_2 g - m_1 g\sin\alpha,$$
$$|\mathbf{N}| = |\mathbf{W}_1|\cos\alpha = m_1 g\cos\alpha.$$

◀Interpret solution▶

For (S.32) to be satisfied, the model predicts that

$$\mu \ge \frac{|\mathbf{F}|}{|\mathbf{N}|} = \frac{m_2 g - m_1 g\sin\alpha}{m_1 g\cos\alpha}$$
$$= \frac{m_2 - m_1\sin\alpha}{m_1\cos\alpha}. \tag{S.33}$$

◀Draw force diagram▶

Now consider the other case where equilibrium could be disturbed, i.e. where m_1 may slide down the board and pull m_2 up. The force diagrams are as follows.

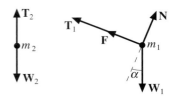

◀Apply law(s)▶

The equilibrium condition and the use of a model pulley lead to the same conditions as before.

◀Solve equation(s)▶

The only difference is that the friction force is in the opposite direction, i.e. $\mathbf{F} = -|\mathbf{F}|\,\mathbf{i}$. This means that when (S.29) is resolved in the **i**-direction, it now gives

$$-|\mathbf{T}_1| + 0 - |\mathbf{F}| + |\mathbf{W}_1|\sin\alpha = 0,$$

leading to

$$|\mathbf{F}| = |\mathbf{W}_1|\sin\alpha - |\mathbf{T}_1|$$
$$= m_1 g\sin\alpha - m_2 g.$$

◀Interpret solution▶

For (S.32) to be satisfied, the model predicts that

$$\mu \ge \frac{|\mathbf{F}|}{|\mathbf{N}|} = \frac{m_1\sin\alpha - m_2}{m_1\cos\alpha}. \tag{S.34}$$

Both (S.33) and (S.34) must hold for the system to be in equilibrium. Since μ is non-negative and the right-hand sides of (S.33) and (S.34) are of opposite signs, we can say

condition (S.33) applies when $m_2 > m_1\sin\alpha$,

condition (S.34) applies when $m_2 < m_1\sin\alpha$.

If there is no friction, then $\mu = 0$, and (S.33) and (S.34) can both be satisfied only if the right-hand side is also zero, i.e. $m_2 = m_1\sin\alpha$.

Section 3

3.1 We can model the see-saw as a model rod. Let Jill's mass be m. Then, assuming that neither Jack's nor Jill's feet are on the ground, we can use Equation (3.1) to obtain

$$mg \times 1.2 = 60g \times 1.$$

Therefore $m = 50$, so Jill's mass is $50\,\text{kg}$.

3.2 The simplest choice of position vector for a point on the line of action of $\mathbf{F}_1$ is $\mathbf{r}_1 = 2\mathbf{i}$, the position vector of the point $(2,0,0)$ relative to O. Similarly, suitably simple choices for $\mathbf{F}_2$ and $\mathbf{F}_3$ are $\mathbf{r}_2 = -2\mathbf{i}$ and $\mathbf{r}_3 = 2\mathbf{k}$. Hence the torques of the three forces relative to O are

$$\mathbf{r}_1 \times \mathbf{F}_1 = 2\mathbf{i} \times 3\mathbf{j} = 6\mathbf{k},$$
$$\mathbf{r}_2 \times \mathbf{F}_2 = -2\mathbf{i} \times 3\mathbf{j} = -6\mathbf{k},$$
$$\mathbf{r}_3 \times \mathbf{F}_3 = 2\mathbf{k} \times 3\mathbf{j} = -6\mathbf{i}.$$

3.3 (a) If O is on the line of action of $\mathbf{F}$, and $\mathbf{r}$ is the position vector relative to O of another point on that line of action, then $\mathbf{r}$ is parallel to $\mathbf{F}$, so $\mathbf{r} \times \mathbf{F} = \mathbf{0}$.

Thus, when O is on the line of action of a force $\mathbf{F}$, the formula $\boldsymbol{\Gamma} = \mathbf{r} \times \mathbf{F}$ gives $\mathbf{0}$ whatever the choice of $\mathbf{r}$.

(b) If $\mathbf{r}_1$ and $\mathbf{r}_2$ are position vectors relative to O of two points, R_1 and R_2, on the line of action of $\mathbf{F}$ (where O is not on this line of action), the triangle rule for the addition of vectors shows that $\mathbf{r}_1 - \mathbf{r}_2$ is parallel to $\mathbf{F}$ (as shown in the diagram below).

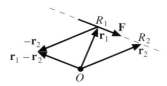

Therefore $(\mathbf{r}_1 - \mathbf{r}_2) \times \mathbf{F} = \mathbf{0}$ and, since

$$(\mathbf{r}_1 - \mathbf{r}_2) \times \mathbf{F} = \mathbf{r}_1 \times \mathbf{F} - \mathbf{r}_2 \times \mathbf{F},$$

we have

$$\mathbf{r}_1 \times \mathbf{F} = \mathbf{r}_2 \times \mathbf{F}.$$

Thus the formula $\boldsymbol{\Gamma} = \mathbf{r} \times \mathbf{F}$ gives the same vector, whatever the choice of $\mathbf{r}$.

3.4 ◀Draw force diagram▶ ◀Choose axes▶

Since a picture of the situation is included in the question, the first step is to draw a force diagram and choose axes. These are shown below, along with the origin O.

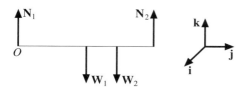

◀Apply law(s)▶

The equilibrium condition for rigid bodies gives

$$\mathbf{N}_1 + \mathbf{N}_2 + \mathbf{W}_1 + \mathbf{W}_2 = \mathbf{0}, \tag{S.35}$$
$$\boldsymbol{\Gamma}_{\text{N}_1} + \boldsymbol{\Gamma}_{\text{N}_2} + \boldsymbol{\Gamma}_{\text{W}_1} + \boldsymbol{\Gamma}_{\text{W}_2} = \mathbf{0}. \tag{S.36}$$

◀Solve equation(s)▶

To be able to use these equations, we need to resolve the vectors into components. The forces involved are all aligned vertically, so by inspection

$$\mathbf{N}_1 = |\mathbf{N}_1|\,\mathbf{k},$$
$$\mathbf{N}_2 = |\mathbf{N}_2|\,\mathbf{k},$$
$$\mathbf{W}_1 = -|\mathbf{W}_1|\,\mathbf{k} = -Mg\,\mathbf{k},$$
$$\mathbf{W}_2 = -|\mathbf{W}_2|\,\mathbf{k} = -mg\mathbf{k}.$$

Resolving (S.35) in the $\mathbf{k}$-direction gives

$$|\mathbf{N}_1| + |\mathbf{N}_2| - Mg - mg = 0. \tag{S.37}$$

This does not give enough information to determine the unknown normal reactions, so we look at (S.36). The position vectors of the points of application relative to the origin O are

$$\mathbf{r}_{\text{N}_1} = \mathbf{0}, \quad \mathbf{r}_{\text{N}_2} = l\mathbf{j},$$
$$\mathbf{r}_{\text{W}_1} = \tfrac{1}{2}l\mathbf{j}, \quad \mathbf{r}_{\text{W}_2} = x\mathbf{j}.$$

The torques can now be evaluated:

$$\boldsymbol{\Gamma}_{\text{N}_1} = \mathbf{r}_{\text{N}_1} \times \mathbf{N}_1 = \mathbf{0} \times (|\mathbf{N}_1|\,\mathbf{k}) = \mathbf{0},$$
$$\boldsymbol{\Gamma}_{\text{N}_2} = \mathbf{r}_{\text{N}_2} \times \mathbf{N}_2 = (l\mathbf{j}) \times (|\mathbf{N}_2|\,\mathbf{k}) = l|\mathbf{N}_2|\,\mathbf{i},$$
$$\boldsymbol{\Gamma}_{\text{W}_1} = \mathbf{r}_{\text{W}_1} \times \mathbf{W}_1 = (\tfrac{1}{2}l\mathbf{j}) \times (-Mg\mathbf{k}) = -\tfrac{1}{2}lMg\mathbf{i},$$
$$\boldsymbol{\Gamma}_{\text{W}_2} = \mathbf{r}_{\text{W}_2} \times \mathbf{W}_2 = (x\mathbf{j}) \times (-mg\mathbf{k}) = -xmg\mathbf{i}.$$

Substituting these torques into (S.36) and resolving in the $\mathbf{i}$-direction gives

$$0 + l|\mathbf{N}_2| - \tfrac{1}{2}lMg - xmg = 0.$$

Solving this for the unknown normal reaction gives

$$|\mathbf{N}_2| = \tfrac{1}{2}Mg + \frac{x}{l}mg.$$

To obtain the normal reaction due to the other bench leg, substitute this into (S.37):

$$|\mathbf{N}_1| + \tfrac{1}{2}Mg + \frac{x}{l}mg - Mg - mg = 0.$$

Rearranging this gives

$$|\mathbf{N}_1| = \tfrac{1}{2}Mg + \left(1 - \frac{x}{l}\right)mg.$$

◀Interpret solution▶

The normal reaction forces of the left and right bench legs are directed upwards and are of magnitudes

$$\tfrac{1}{2}Mg + (l - x)mg/l$$

and

$$\tfrac{1}{2}Mg + xmg/l,$$

respectively. The solution is reasonable since (a) the weight of the bench seat is evenly distributed between the two legs (i.e. $\tfrac{1}{2}Mg$ on each), and (b) if $x = 0$, then the person's weight is entirely supported by the normal reaction of the bench leg directly underneath.

Section 4

4.1
◄Draw force diagram►

There are three forces acting on the rod: the weight $\mathbf{W}$ (at the centre of the rod), the tension force $\mathbf{T}$ due to the string, and the reaction force $\mathbf{R}$ at the hinge. The direction of $\mathbf{R}$ is not known, except that it is in the plane of $\mathbf{W}$ and $\mathbf{T}$. The force diagram is shown below.

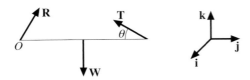

◄Choose axes►

Choose the origin to be at O and axes as shown above.

◄Apply law(s)►

The equilibrium condition for rigid bodies gives

$$\mathbf{R} + \mathbf{T} + \mathbf{W} = \mathbf{0}, \tag{S.38}$$
$$\mathbf{\Gamma}_\mathbf{R} + \mathbf{\Gamma}_\mathbf{T} + \mathbf{\Gamma}_\mathbf{W} = \mathbf{0}. \tag{S.39}$$

◄Solve equation(s)►

Position vectors of the points of application are

$$\mathbf{r}_\mathbf{R} = \mathbf{0}, \quad \mathbf{r}_\mathbf{T} = l\mathbf{j}, \quad \mathbf{r}_\mathbf{W} = \tfrac{1}{2}l\mathbf{j}.$$

From the force diagram,

$$\mathbf{W} = -mg\mathbf{k}.$$

The force $\mathbf{R}$ is unknown except that it is in the plane of $\mathbf{W}$ and $\mathbf{T}$, i.e. the plane defined by $\mathbf{j}$ and $\mathbf{k}$. So in component form

$$\mathbf{R} = R_j\mathbf{j} + R_k\mathbf{k},$$

where R_j and R_k are the $\mathbf{j}$- and $\mathbf{k}$-components of $\mathbf{R}$.

The remaining force can be resolved using the formula from *Unit 4*:

$$\mathbf{T} = |\mathbf{T}| \cos(\pi - \theta)\,\mathbf{j} + |\mathbf{T}| \cos(\tfrac{\pi}{2} - \theta)\,\mathbf{k}$$
$$= -|\mathbf{T}| \cos\theta\,\mathbf{j} + |\mathbf{T}| \sin\theta\,\mathbf{k}.$$

The torques are given by

$$\mathbf{\Gamma}_\mathbf{R} = \mathbf{0}, \quad \mathbf{\Gamma}_\mathbf{T} = l|\mathbf{T}|\sin\theta\,\mathbf{i}, \quad \mathbf{\Gamma}_\mathbf{W} = -\tfrac{1}{2}lmg\mathbf{i}.$$

Resolving (S.39) in the $\mathbf{i}$-direction gives

$$l|\mathbf{T}|\sin\theta - \tfrac{1}{2}lmg = 0,$$

so

$$|\mathbf{T}| = \tfrac{1}{2}mg\,\mathrm{cosec}\,\theta.$$

Resolving (S.38) in the $\mathbf{j}$- and $\mathbf{k}$-directions in turn gives

$$R_j - |\mathbf{T}|\cos\theta = 0,$$
$$R_k + |\mathbf{T}|\sin\theta - mg = 0,$$

so

$$R_j = |\mathbf{T}|\cos\theta = \tfrac{1}{2}mg\cot\theta,$$
$$R_k = mg - |\mathbf{T}|\sin\theta = mg - \tfrac{1}{2}mg = \tfrac{1}{2}mg.$$

So the model predicts that the reaction force at the hinge is

$$\mathbf{R} = \tfrac{1}{2}mg\cot\theta\,\mathbf{j} + \tfrac{1}{2}mg\mathbf{k}.$$

From (S.38), the tension force due to the string is

$$\mathbf{T} = -\mathbf{R} - \mathbf{W} = -\tfrac{1}{2}mg\cot\theta\,\mathbf{j} + \tfrac{1}{2}mg\mathbf{k}.$$

◄Interpret solution►

The $\mathbf{k}$-components of $\mathbf{R}$ and $\mathbf{T}$ are the same. The $\mathbf{j}$-components are of equal magnitude, but with opposite signs. Thus $\mathbf{R}$ and $\mathbf{T}$ have equal magnitude and make the same angle θ with the horizontal, where θ is measured anticlockwise for $\mathbf{R}$ and clockwise for $\mathbf{T}$.

4.2
◄Draw force diagram►

Since the mass of the ladder may be neglected, the forces acting on the ladder are the weights $\mathbf{W}_1$ and $\mathbf{W}_2$ of the two people, the normal reaction forces $\mathbf{N}_1$ and $\mathbf{N}_2$ at the wall and at the floor, and the friction force $\mathbf{F}$ at the floor. (There is no friction force at the wall, as it is smooth.) The force diagram is shown below.

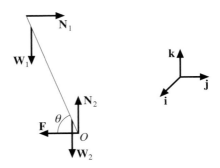

◄Choose axes►

The origin O is best chosen to be at the foot of the ladder. The axes are shown above.

◄Apply law(s)►

The equilibrium condition for rigid bodies gives

$$\mathbf{N}_1 + \mathbf{N}_2 + \mathbf{W}_1 + \mathbf{W}_2 + \mathbf{F} = \mathbf{0}, \tag{S.40}$$
$$\mathbf{\Gamma}_{\mathbf{N}_1} + \mathbf{\Gamma}_{\mathbf{N}_2} + \mathbf{\Gamma}_{\mathbf{W}_1} + \mathbf{\Gamma}_{\mathbf{W}_2} + \mathbf{\Gamma}_\mathbf{F} = \mathbf{0}. \tag{S.41}$$

At the point of slipping,

$$|\mathbf{F}| = \mu|\mathbf{N}_2|, \tag{S.42}$$

where $\mu = 0.25$ is the coefficient of static friction.

◄Solve equation(s)►

Let l denote the length of the ladder (i.e. 3.9 m), and let d denote the distance of the end rungs from the ends of the ladder (i.e. 0.3 m). Relative to the origin O at the bottom of the ladder, two position vectors are zero, namely $\mathbf{r}_{\mathbf{N}_2}$ and $\mathbf{r}_\mathbf{F}$. The remaining position vectors are

$$\mathbf{r}_{\mathbf{N}_1} = -l\cos\theta\,\mathbf{j} + l\sin\theta\,\mathbf{k},$$
$$\mathbf{r}_{\mathbf{W}_1} = -(l - d)\cos\theta\,\mathbf{j} + (l - d)\sin\theta\,\mathbf{k},$$
$$\mathbf{r}_{\mathbf{W}_2} = -d\cos\theta\,\mathbf{j} + d\sin\theta\,\mathbf{k}.$$

The forces are aligned with the axes, and can be put into component form by inspection:

$$\mathbf{N}_1 = |\mathbf{N}_1|\mathbf{j}, \quad \mathbf{N}_2 = |\mathbf{N}_2|\mathbf{k},$$
$$\mathbf{W}_1 = -Mg\mathbf{k}, \quad \mathbf{W}_2 = -mg\mathbf{k}, \quad \mathbf{F} = -|\mathbf{F}|\mathbf{j},$$

where m is the mass of the person on the lower rung and M is the mass of the person on the upper rung.

Two of the torques are zero by choice of origin. The remaining three torques can be calculated as

$$\boldsymbol{\Gamma}_{N_1} = (-l\cos\theta\,\mathbf{j} + l\sin\theta\,\mathbf{k}) \times (|\mathbf{N}_1|\,\mathbf{j})$$
$$= -l|\mathbf{N}_1|\sin\theta\,\mathbf{i},$$

$$\boldsymbol{\Gamma}_{W_1} = (-(l-d)\cos\theta\,\mathbf{j} + (l-d)\sin\theta\,\mathbf{k}) \times (-Mg\mathbf{k})$$
$$= M(l-d)g\cos\theta\,\mathbf{i},$$

$$\boldsymbol{\Gamma}_{W_2} = (-d\cos\theta\,\mathbf{j} + d\sin\theta\,\mathbf{k}) \times (-mg\mathbf{k})$$
$$= mdg\cos\theta\,\mathbf{i}.$$

Substituting these into (S.41) and resolving in the **i**-direction gives

$$-l|\mathbf{N}_1|\sin\theta + M(l-d)g\cos\theta$$
$$+ mdg\cos\theta = 0. \qquad (S.43)$$

Now we need to find the magnitude of the normal reaction $|\mathbf{N}_1|$, which we do by resolving (S.40) in the **j**- and **k**-directions in turn, to obtain

$$|\mathbf{N}_1| - |\mathbf{F}| = 0, \qquad (S.44)$$
$$|\mathbf{N}_2| - Mg - mg = 0. \qquad (S.45)$$

From (S.42), (S.44) and (S.45), we have

$$|\mathbf{N}_1| = |\mathbf{F}| = \mu|\mathbf{N}_2| = \mu(Mg + mg).$$

Substituting for $|\mathbf{N}_1|$ in (S.43) and simplifying gives

$$-l\mu(Mg + mg)\sin\theta + M(l-d)g\cos\theta$$
$$+ mdg\cos\theta = 0,$$

thus

$$-Ml\mu\tan\theta - ml\mu\tan\theta + M(l-d) + md = 0,$$

so

$$m = M\frac{l\mu\tan\theta - l + d}{d - l\mu\tan\theta}.$$

◀Interpret solution▶

To use this formula we need the value of $\tan\theta$, which by trigonometry is equal to $\sqrt{3.9^2 - 1.5^2}/1.5 = 2.4$. Now we substitute in the known values, i.e. $\mu = 0.25$, $d = 0.3\,\mathrm{m}$, $l = 3.9\,\mathrm{m}$ and $M = 100\,\mathrm{kg}$, to find

$$m = 100 \times \frac{3.9 \times 0.25 \times 2.4 - 3.9 + 0.3}{0.3 - 3.9 \times 0.25 \times 2.4} \simeq 61.8.$$

So to prevent the ladder from slipping, the model predicts that the person on the bottom rung must have a mass of at least $61.8\,\mathrm{kg}$.

4.3 ◀Choose axes▶ ◀Draw force diagram▶

Take the origin at the base of the plank, and axes as shown below. The force diagram, using the usual notation, is also shown below.

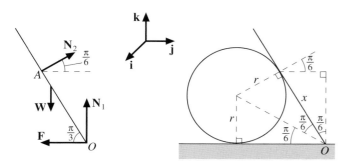

To calculate the torque of the force $\mathbf{N}_2$ about O, we need the angle between $\mathbf{N}_2$ and $\mathbf{j}$, which from the diagram is equal to $\frac{\pi}{6}$. We also need the distance OA along the plank of the point of contact of the pipe and the plank: call this distance x. From the diagram, we have $\tan\frac{\pi}{6} = r/x$, which gives $x = \sqrt{3}r$. Now that we know the distances and angles involved, we can continue with the procedure for solving statics problems.

◀Apply law(s)▶

The equilibrium condition for rigid bodies gives

$$\mathbf{N}_1 + \mathbf{N}_2 + \mathbf{F} + \mathbf{W} = \mathbf{0}, \qquad (S.46)$$
$$\boldsymbol{\Gamma}_{N_1} + \boldsymbol{\Gamma}_{N_2} + \boldsymbol{\Gamma}_F + \boldsymbol{\Gamma}_W = \mathbf{0}. \qquad (S.47)$$

In equilibrium,

$$|\mathbf{F}| \le \mu|\mathbf{N}_1|, \qquad (S.48)$$

where μ is the coefficient of static friction.

◀Solve equation(s)▶

By the choice of origin, two of the position vectors are zero. The other position vectors are

$$\mathbf{r}_W = -l\cos\frac{\pi}{3}\,\mathbf{j} + l\sin\frac{\pi}{3}\,\mathbf{k} = -\frac{1}{2}l\mathbf{j} + \frac{\sqrt{3}}{2}l\mathbf{k},$$
$$\mathbf{r}_{N_2} = -\sqrt{3}r\cos\frac{\pi}{3}\,\mathbf{j} + \sqrt{3}r\sin\frac{\pi}{3}\,\mathbf{k} = -\frac{\sqrt{3}}{2}r\mathbf{j} + \frac{3}{2}r\mathbf{k}.$$

The forces are given by

$$\mathbf{N}_1 = |\mathbf{N}_1|\,\mathbf{k},$$
$$\mathbf{N}_2 = |\mathbf{N}_2|\cos\frac{\pi}{6}\,\mathbf{j} + |\mathbf{N}_2|\cos(\frac{\pi}{2} - \frac{\pi}{6})\,\mathbf{k}$$
$$= \frac{\sqrt{3}}{2}|\mathbf{N}_2|\,\mathbf{j} + \frac{1}{2}|\mathbf{N}_2|\,\mathbf{k},$$
$$\mathbf{F} = -|\mathbf{F}|\,\mathbf{j},$$
$$\mathbf{W} = -mg\mathbf{k}.$$

So the non-zero torques are

$$\boldsymbol{\Gamma}_W = (-\tfrac{1}{2}l\mathbf{j} + \tfrac{\sqrt{3}}{2}l\mathbf{k}) \times (-mg\mathbf{k}) = \tfrac{1}{2}mgl\,\mathbf{i},$$

$$\boldsymbol{\Gamma}_{N_2} = (-\tfrac{\sqrt{3}}{2}r\mathbf{j} + \tfrac{3}{2}r\mathbf{k}) \times (\tfrac{\sqrt{3}}{2}|\mathbf{N}_2|\,\mathbf{j} + \tfrac{1}{2}|\mathbf{N}_2|\,\mathbf{k})$$
$$= -\tfrac{\sqrt{3}}{4}r|\mathbf{N}_2|\,\mathbf{j} \times \mathbf{k} + \tfrac{3\sqrt{3}}{4}r|\mathbf{N}_2|\,\mathbf{k} \times \mathbf{j}$$
$$= -\sqrt{3}r|\mathbf{N}_2|\,\mathbf{i}.$$

Substituting into (S.47) and resolving in the **i**-direction gives

$$\tfrac{1}{2}mgl - \sqrt{3}r|\mathbf{N}_2| = 0.$$

Therefore

$$|\mathbf{N}_2| = \frac{\frac{1}{2}mgl}{\sqrt{3}r} = \frac{mgl}{2\sqrt{3}r}.$$

Resolving (S.46) in the **j**-direction gives

$$\frac{\sqrt{3}}{2}|\mathbf{N}_2| - |\mathbf{F}| = 0.$$

Therefore

$$|\mathbf{F}| = \frac{\sqrt{3}}{2} \times \frac{mgl}{2\sqrt{3}r} = \frac{mgl}{4r}.$$

Resolving (S.46) in the **k**-direction gives

$$|\mathbf{N}_1| + \tfrac{1}{2}|\mathbf{N}_2| - mg = 0.$$

Solving this for $|\mathbf{N}_1|$ gives

$$|\mathbf{N}_1| = mg - \frac{1}{2} \times \frac{mgl}{2\sqrt{3}r}$$
$$= mg\left(1 - \frac{l}{4\sqrt{3}r}\right).$$

Hence, in equilibrium, from (S.48) we have

$$|\mathbf{F}| = \frac{mgl}{4r} \leq \mu|\mathbf{N}_1| = \mu mg\left(1 - \frac{l}{4\sqrt{3}r}\right),$$

so

$$\frac{l}{4r} \leq \mu\left(1 - \frac{l}{4\sqrt{3}r}\right) = \mu\left(\frac{4\sqrt{3}r - l}{4\sqrt{3}r}\right). \qquad (S.49)$$

Now we are given that the distance OA is greater than l and, as we saw above, the distance OA is $x = \sqrt{3}r$. So we have $\sqrt{3}r > l$. Therefore we certainly have $4\sqrt{3}r - l > 0$, and hence we can rearrange (S.49) as

$$\mu \geq \frac{\sqrt{3}l}{4\sqrt{3}r - l}.$$

◀Interpret solution▶

The model predicts that the least coefficient of static friction that ensures equilibrium is $\sqrt{3}l/(4\sqrt{3}r - l)$.

4.4 ◀Draw force diagram▶

If we model the pulley as a model pulley, then the magnitude of the tension force at either side of it is the same. So, to obtain the tension in the rope at the quayside, we need to know only the tension in the rope fixed to the gangplank. We therefore need to consider only the forces on the gangplank.

Modelling the gangplank as a model rod and the rope as a model string, we obtain the force diagram shown below, where the forces are denoted in the usual way. When the gangplank is about to rise, which is the situation that interests us, the normal reaction force from the quay will be at the end of the gangplank. There is no normal reaction force from the ship, because when the gangplank is about to rise, the only force at that end of the gangplank is the tension due to the rope.

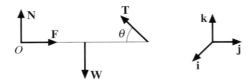

◀Choose axes▶

A suitable origin and axes are shown above.

◀Apply law(s)▶

The equilibrium condition for rigid bodies gives

$$\mathbf{N} + \mathbf{T} + \mathbf{F} + \mathbf{W} = \mathbf{0}, \qquad (S.50)$$
$$\mathbf{\Gamma}_N + \mathbf{\Gamma}_T + \mathbf{\Gamma}_F + \mathbf{\Gamma}_W = \mathbf{0}. \qquad (S.51)$$

If slipping is to be avoided, we must have

$$|\mathbf{F}| \leq \mu|\mathbf{N}|, \qquad (S.52)$$

where μ is the coefficient of static friction.

◀Solve equation(s)▶

With the origin shown, the position vectors are

$$\mathbf{r}_N = \mathbf{0}, \quad \mathbf{r}_T = 5\mathbf{j}, \quad \mathbf{r}_F = \mathbf{0}, \quad \mathbf{r}_W = 2.5\mathbf{j}.$$

From the force diagram,

$$\mathbf{N} = |\mathbf{N}|\,\mathbf{k},$$
$$\mathbf{F} = |\mathbf{F}|\,\mathbf{j},$$
$$\mathbf{W} = -120g\mathbf{k}.$$

Using the formula from *Unit 4*, we obtain

$$\mathbf{T} = |\mathbf{T}|\cos(\pi - \theta)\,\mathbf{j} + |\mathbf{T}|\cos(\tfrac{\pi}{2} - \theta)\,\mathbf{k}$$
$$= -|\mathbf{T}|\cos\theta\,\mathbf{j} + |\mathbf{T}|\sin\theta\,\mathbf{k}.$$

The torques are

$$\mathbf{\Gamma}_N = \mathbf{0},$$
$$\mathbf{\Gamma}_T = 5|\mathbf{T}|\sin\theta\,\mathbf{i},$$
$$\mathbf{\Gamma}_F = \mathbf{0},$$
$$\mathbf{\Gamma}_W = -300g\mathbf{i}.$$

Resolving (S.51) in the **i**-direction gives

$$5|\mathbf{T}|\sin\theta - 300g = 0,$$

so

$$|\mathbf{T}|\sin\theta = 60g. \qquad (S.53)$$

Resolving (S.50) in the **j**- and **k**-directions in turn gives

$$-|\mathbf{T}|\cos\theta + |\mathbf{F}| = 0,$$
$$|\mathbf{N}| + |\mathbf{T}|\sin\theta - 120g = 0,$$

so

$$|\mathbf{F}| = |\mathbf{T}|\cos\theta,$$
$$|\mathbf{N}| = 120g - |\mathbf{T}|\sin\theta = 60g.$$

Hence, for no slipping, using $\mu = 0.4$ in (S.52) gives

$$|\mathbf{T}|\cos\theta \leq 0.4 \times 60g. \qquad (S.54)$$

Substituting $|\mathbf{T}| = 60g/\sin\theta$ from (S.53) into (S.54) gives $\cot\theta \leq 0.4$ or, equivalently, $\tan\theta \geq 2.5$.

◀Interpret solution▶

Let h denote the height of the pulley above the quay, as shown in Figure 4.7. Since $\tan\theta = h/5$, we have, for no slipping, $h/5 \geq 2.5$ and therefore $h \geq 12.5$. So the model predicts that the pulley needs to be at least $12.5\,\mathrm{m}$ above the quay to avoid slipping.

When $\tan\theta \geq 2.5$, $\sin\theta \geq \frac{5}{\sqrt{29}}$ for $0 \leq \theta \leq \frac{\pi}{2}$. Hence

$$|\mathbf{T}| = 60g/\sin\theta \leq 60g\sqrt{29}/5 = 12g\sqrt{29} \simeq 634.$$

So the model predicts that one man should be sufficient to raise the gangplank.

4.5   ◀Draw force diagram▶

Let $\mathbf{R}_1$ and $\mathbf{R}_2$ be the forces exerted by the top and bottom hinges, respectively, and let $\mathbf{W}$ be the weight of the door. Then, modelling the door as a rectangular rigid body, the force diagram is as follows. (The lines of action of $\mathbf{R}_1$ and $\mathbf{R}_2$ are unknown.)

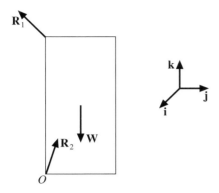

◀Choose axes▶

A suitable choice for the origin is at the lower hinge; this origin and the axes are shown above.

◀Apply law(s)▶

The equilibrium condition for rigid bodies gives

$$\mathbf{R}_1 + \mathbf{R}_2 + \mathbf{W} = \mathbf{0}, \tag{S.55}$$

$$\boldsymbol{\Gamma}_{\mathrm{R}_1} + \boldsymbol{\Gamma}_{\mathrm{R}_2} + \boldsymbol{\Gamma}_{\mathrm{W}} = \mathbf{0}. \tag{S.56}$$

◀Solve equation(s)▶

The position vectors of the points of application of the forces are

$$\mathbf{r}_{\mathrm{R}_1} = 2\mathbf{k}, \quad \mathbf{r}_{\mathrm{R}_2} = \mathbf{0}, \quad \mathbf{r}_{\mathrm{W}} = 0.5\mathbf{j} + \mathbf{k}.$$

The weight of the door is $\mathbf{W} = -20g\mathbf{k}$. Using this information in (S.56) gives

$$2\mathbf{k} \times \mathbf{R}_1 + \mathbf{0} + (0.5\mathbf{j} + \mathbf{k}) \times (-20g\mathbf{k}) = \mathbf{0}. \tag{S.57}$$

Since $\mathbf{R}_1$ is a force in the plane of the door, it is of the form $a\mathbf{j} + b\mathbf{k}$ for some numbers a and b, so (S.57) can be written as

$$-2a\mathbf{i} - 10g\mathbf{i} = \mathbf{0},$$

giving $a = -5g$. Therefore $\mathbf{R}_1 = -5g\mathbf{j} + b\mathbf{k}$, for some number b.

Substituting $\mathbf{R}_1$ and $\mathbf{W}$ into (S.55), we have

$$\mathbf{R}_2 = 5g\mathbf{j} - b\mathbf{k} + 20g\mathbf{k} = 5g\mathbf{j} + (20g - b)\mathbf{k}.$$

Since the forces $\mathbf{R}_1$ and $\mathbf{R}_2$ have the same magnitude, we must have $b = 20g - b$, i.e. $b = 10g$.

◀Interpret solution▶

So the model predicts that the forces are

$$\mathbf{R}_1 = -5g\mathbf{j} + 10g\mathbf{k}, \quad \mathbf{R}_2 = 5g\mathbf{j} + 10g\mathbf{k}.$$

UNIT 6   Dynamics

Study guide for Unit 6

This unit continues the work of *Unit 5* in laying the foundations of New-tonian mechanics that will be needed in the later mechanics units. From the point of view of these later units, the procedure for solving dynamics problems outlined in Section 3 is the most important.

Some of the ideas in this unit may be familiar to you from a prerequisite course.

The prerequisite skills needed for this unit are the ability to solve first- and second-order differential equations (*Units 2* and *3*), a knowledge of vectors (*Unit 4*), and an understanding of the concept of a force (*Unit 5*).

Section 2 contains a video sequence.

The recommended study pattern is to study one section per study session, in the order in which they appear. The media guide describes a multimedia package which supports this unit, which you could study as a fifth study session.

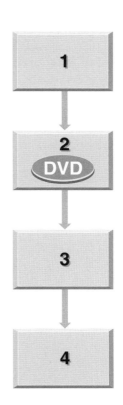

Introduction

Think of an object that is moving in some way. It might be a car accelerating on a motorway, a tennis ball flying through the air, a comet hurtling through space, or a pendulum swinging to and fro. Why does the object move as it does? How will it move in the future? To what extent can you influence its motion? Questions like these are very important from a practical point of view. The control that the human race exerts over the environment depends, to a large extent, on our ability to find the right answers. For example, in Figure 0.1 can we predict whether the comet will collide with the Earth in time for something to be done about it?

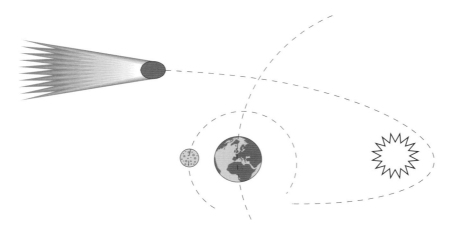

Figure 0.1   Collision course?

Fortunately, the systematic, organized body of knowledge called *mechanics*, which you began to study in *Unit 5*, provides answers to many questions about motion and the forces that cause it.

Unit 5 concentrated on whether objects will stay put; this unit looks at moving objects, i.e. **dynamics**. The starting point for all of Newtonian mechanics is Newton's laws of motion. Newton's laws were stated in words in the Introduction of *Unit 5*. To apply these laws we need to be able to translate them into useful mathematical equations — which is one of the aims of this unit.

You should bear in mind that this unit and *Unit 5* provide only an introduction to the ideas of mechanics. However, the framework of mechanics presented in these units is of great significance as it provides the foundations from which, in later units, more complex ideas are developed.

Section 1 of this unit is concerned with concepts like position, velocity and acceleration, which describe the way an object moves. Section 2 discusses Newton's laws of motion, which predict the motion of an object when the forces acting on the object are known. Section 3 shows how Newton's second law of motion can be used to predict the motion of objects. Section 4 is concerned with modelling some of the forces that occur in nature, which enables more realistic situations to be analysed.

1 Describing motion

This section is devoted to describing the motion of objects modelled as particles. In Subsection 1.1 the motion is described by giving a position vector at each instant in time. The ideas in Subsection 1.1 apply whether the particle moves along a straight line or along a curve of some sort; in Subsection 1.2, however, and for the rest of the unit, only motion along a straight line is considered.

The subject matter of this section, the description of motion, is often referred to by the technical term *kinematics*.

1.1 The motion of a particle

The motion of a real object, say a leaf that is falling to the ground, is very difficult to describe exactly. The leaf may rotate, bend or vibrate while moving along a complicated path in three-dimensional space. And its motion may be affected by the presence of other moving objects, such as other falling leaves. It would be foolhardy to try to meet all of these difficulties head-on, so we shall make a number of simplifications in this unit, some of which will be relaxed later in the course.

Simplification 1 Objects will be modelled as particles.

Simplification 2 Only the motion of *single* particles is considered.

Simplification 3 The motion is along a straight line (i.e. one-dimensional motion).

The motion of rigid bodies is discussed in *Unit 27*, many-particle systems are discussed in *Unit 19*, and three-dimensional motion is discussed in *Unit 14*.

Modelling objects as particles means that we neglect an object's size and internal structure. Neglecting an object's size means that its location at any given time may be described by a single point in space, and that its motion may be described by a single curve. Neglecting the internal structure of an object, and hence also any internal motion, amounts to saying that the curve described in time by the particle gives the only information of interest about the way in which the object moves. In mathematical terms, this means that a particle's motion is completely described by its *position vector* $\mathbf{r}$, relative to some fixed origin O, at those times t in the time interval of interest.

The representation of the motion of a particle by a position vector that changes with time leads naturally to the representation of such motion by a *vector function*.

Definition

A **vector function** $\mathbf{r}(t)$ of some variable t is a vector whose components are functions of t.

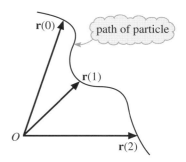

Unlike the components of a vector, which are constant, the components of a vector function vary as the independent variable varies. In the case of the motion of a particle, a vector function $\mathbf{r}(t)$, whose components at each time t represent the position vector $\mathbf{r}$ of the particle at that time, completely describes the particle's motion. The idea is illustrated in Figure 1.1 and in the following example of two-dimensional motion.

Figure 1.1 The path of a particle described by the vector function $\mathbf{r}(t)$

Example 1.1

A juggler throws a ball from one hand to the other, in a vertical plane, as shown in Figure 1.2. The ball is modelled as a particle, and its motion, with respect to the horizontal and vertical axes shown in Figure 1.2, is described by the two-dimensional vector function

$$\mathbf{r}(t) = 1.5t\mathbf{i} + t(4 - 5t)\mathbf{j} \quad (0 \le t \le 1),$$

where distances are measured in metres, and time t is measured in seconds after the ball was thrown. The origin is the juggler's right hand just as he throws the ball, which occurs at time $t = 0$. Let $x(t)$ be the component of $\mathbf{r}(t)$ in the $\mathbf{i}$-direction, i.e. $x(t) = \mathbf{r}(t) \cdot \mathbf{i} = 1.5t$. Similarly, let $y(t)$ be the component of $\mathbf{r}(t)$ in the $\mathbf{j}$-direction, i.e. $y(t) = \mathbf{r}(t) \cdot \mathbf{j} = t(4 - 5t)$. These give the horizontal distance travelled and the height of the ball, respectively, at time t.

Figure 1.2

(a) Calculate $x(t)$ and $y(t)$ at times $t = 0, 0.2, 0.4, 0.6, 0.8, 1$, and sketch the graphs of $y(t)$ against t and against $x(t)$. Comment on what the graphs represent.

(b) Using your graphs, or otherwise, answer the following questions.

   (i) How high does the ball go, and what is its position at its highest point?

   (ii) Does the juggler catch the ball?

Solution

(a) The values are tabulated in Table 1.1, and the graphs are shown in Figure 1.3.

Table 1.1

t	0	0.2	0.4	0.6	0.8	1
$x(t)$	0	0.3	0.6	0.9	1.2	1.5
$y(t)$	0	0.6	0.8	0.6	0	−1

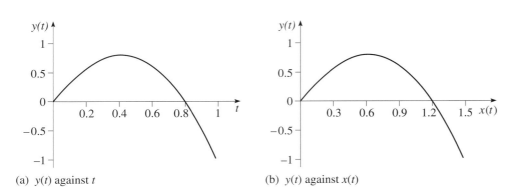

(a) $y(t)$ against t

(b) $y(t)$ against $x(t)$

Figure 1.3

Figure 1.3(a) is a distance–time graph, representing the *height* $y(t)$ of the ball as the time t varies over the interval $[0, 1]$. Figure 1.3(b) represents the *position* of the ball in the (x, y)-plane as t varies; the coordinates $(x(t), y(t))$ of points on this curve are the components of the vector function $\mathbf{r}(t)$ describing the motion of the ball. In this case, since $x(t) = 1.5t$ is just a multiple of t, the two curves appear identical — the only difference is in the scales on the horizontal axes. However, the curves *represent* different things.

You may recognize $(x(t), y(t))$ as a *parametrization* of the path of the ball, in which the Cartesian coordinates of the ball are expressed in terms of another variable (in this case time t).

(b) (i) The quadratic function $y(t) = t(4 - 5t)$ represents a parabola with maximum value in the interval $[0, 0.8]$ (see Figure 1.3(a)). From the symmetry of the parabola, this maximum must occur at $t = 0.4$, at which time $y(t) = 0.8$ (see Table 1.1). So the ball reaches a maximum height of 0.8 m above the juggler's hand after 0.4 s. At this maximum height, $x(t) = 0.6$ (see Table 1.1).

So the ball's position at its maximum height is given by the coordinates $(0.6, 0.8)$ (see Figure 1.3(b)), or equivalently by the position vector $\mathbf{r}(0.4) = 0.6\mathbf{i} + 0.8\mathbf{j}$.

(ii) The juggler probably does not catch the ball, because the ball continues to travel downwards until it is one metre below the juggler's left hand (see Table 1.1 and Figure 1.3). ∎

In general, motion in three-dimensional space is represented by a three-dimensional vector function. However, because the motion in Example 1.1 was in a plane, it was possible by careful choice of axes to represent that motion in three-dimensional space by a two-dimensional vector function. A similarly careful choice of axes can enable certain types of motion in three-dimensional space to be represented by a *one*-dimensional vector function, as the following exercise illustrates.

Exercise 1.1 ————————————————————————

An ice hockey player aims to hit the puck towards the goal, as shown in Figure 1.4, but misses. The puck hits the back wall and bounces straight back, and is then hit by a second player who (incredibly) hits it along the same path as the first player. Let the origin be the point of impact of the puck by the first player, which occurs at time $t = 0$. The motion of the puck, with respect to the axis shown in Figure 1.4, is described by the one-dimensional vector function $\mathbf{r}(t) = x(t)\mathbf{i}$, where the function $x(t)$ is defined by

$$x(t) = \begin{cases} 5t, & 0 \le t < 0.4, \\ 4 - 5t, & 0.4 \le t < 1, \\ 6t - 7, & 1 \le t \le 1.5, \end{cases}$$

where x is measured in metres and t in seconds.

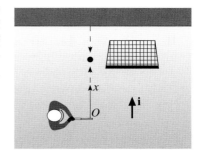

Figure 1.4

(a) Sketch the graph of the function $x(t)$.

(b) Using your graph, or otherwise, answer the following questions.

(i) How far is the first player from the back wall?

(ii) Does the second player hit the puck from a position closer to or further from the back wall than the first player?

(iii) Does the second player give the puck more speed than the first player?

————————————————————————

In Example 1.1 and Exercise 1.1, objects were modelled as particles. The question arises as to when this is appropriate. It seems obvious that small objects can be modelled as particles, but what about large objects such as the Earth? The answer is that it depends on the context. For example, to calculate the Earth's orbit around the Sun, it is permissible to model the Earth as a particle. Newton realized that it was appropriate to model the Earth as a particle in this context, and it was one of his great achievements.

You saw in *Unit 5* that some large static objects can be modelled as particles.

The Earth's diameter (about 13 000 km) is small compared with the Earth–Sun distance (about 1.5×10^8 km).

Whether a particle model will be satisfactory is not just a question of size. For example, if a ball is placed on a rough sloping table, then it will roll down the slope. A particle model could be used to describe the trajectory of the ball's centre, but it would not be adequate to keep track of the rolling motion that takes place about the centre. Note that this inadequacy of the particle model occurs regardless of the ball's size, since the same consideration would apply to a football, a tennis ball, a marble or a ball-bearing.

You might think from this last example that the particle model is of very limited use for moving objects, but in fact the example hints at how this model can be extended. You will see in *Unit 19* that the motion of an object can be described well by specifying:

(a) the motion of the *centre of mass* of an object;

(b) the motion of the whole object relative to its centre of mass.

As you will see in *Unit 19*, the motion of the centre of mass may be predicted by considering a particle of the same mass as the object, placed at the point defined by the centre of mass, and subjected to all of the forces that act upon the object. So, even in this more complicated situation, the concept of a particle is important. Alternatively, it may be appropriate to think of an object as being composed of a number of elements, each of which can be modelled individually as a particle.

You met the idea of centre of mass in *Unit 5*. For the symmetric objects considered in that unit, the centre of mass is the geometric centre.

Position, velocity and acceleration

We have seen how a particle's motion can be completely described by a vector function $\mathbf{r}(t)$, the position vector of the particle at any given time t. For this reason, we shall often refer to particles as having **position $\mathbf{r}(t)$**.

As in *Units 2* and *3*, we may sometimes wish to consider position as a variable rather than as a function, and write $\mathbf{r}$ rather than $\mathbf{r}(t)$.

However, other quantities, such as the speed and acceleration of a particle, are often of more interest than its position. For example, an aggressive motorist might be proud of his acceleration away from traffic lights, whereas a police officer would probably be more interested in the motorist's speed. These quantities can be calculated directly from a particle's position $\mathbf{r}(t)$ by differentiating. But before we can do that, we need to define the derivative of a vector function.

Definition

The **derivative** of a vector function $\mathbf{r}(t)$, whose components are smooth functions of t, is the vector function

$$\frac{d\mathbf{r}(t)}{dt} = \lim_{h \to 0} \left(\frac{\mathbf{r}(t+h) - \mathbf{r}(t)}{h} \right).$$

The derivative $d\mathbf{r}(t)/dt$ is often written as $\mathbf{r}'(t)$ or, where t represents time, as $\dot{\mathbf{r}}(t)$. Sometimes it is written more succinctly as $d\mathbf{r}/dt$, $\mathbf{r}'$ or $\dot{\mathbf{r}}$.

Compare this with the definition of the derivative of a function given in *Unit 1*.

Newton's notation $\dot{\mathbf{r}}(t)$ is commonly used in mechanics.

This definition makes use of the concept of the **limit** of a vector function. As you might expect, the limit of a vector function $\mathbf{f}(h)$ as $h \to 0$ is the vector function whose components are the limits, as $h \to 0$, of the components of $\mathbf{f}(h)$.

Now, as you will recall, velocity is defined to be rate of change of position, so the definition of the derivative of a vector function can be used to define the **velocity** of a particle with position $\mathbf{r}(t)$ as

$$\mathbf{v}(t) = \frac{d\mathbf{r}(t)}{dt}.$$

We sometimes consider velocity as a variable rather than as a function, and write $\mathbf{v}$ rather than $\mathbf{v}(t)$.

The **speed** of the particle, which as you will recall is defined to be the magnitude of the velocity, is therefore given by $|\mathbf{v}(t)|$.

To find the derivative of a vector function, we make use of the following theorem.

Theorem 1.1

If a vector function $\mathbf{r}(t)$ has the component form

$\mathbf{r}(t) = x(t)\mathbf{i} + y(t)\mathbf{j} + z(t)\mathbf{k},$

where $\mathbf{i}, \mathbf{j}, \mathbf{k}$ are the (constant) Cartesian unit vectors, then its derivative is given by

$\dfrac{d\mathbf{r}}{dt} = \dfrac{dx}{dt}\mathbf{i} + \dfrac{dy}{dt}\mathbf{j} + \dfrac{dz}{dt}\mathbf{k}.$

Exercise 1.2

For each of the particles whose positions are given, calculate the velocity and speed of the particle at $t = 1$.

(a) $\mathbf{r}(t) = t^2\mathbf{i} + 10t\mathbf{j}$

(b) $\mathbf{r}(t) = (\sin t)\mathbf{i} + (\cos t)\mathbf{j} + t\mathbf{k}$

In many situations, velocity is less important than *changes* in velocity. For example, if you are on board a train travelling at a steady speed, you may not even notice that you are moving. You will have no difficulty in, say, drinking a cup of tea. However, this operation becomes more hazardous if the driver changes the velocity of the train by putting on the brakes! Similarly, if the train goes round a bend at constant speed, you will notice the change in velocity (hot tea in your lap again!). In both cases, the rate of change of velocity is an important factor.

Now, you will recall that, just as velocity is defined to be rate of change of position, so acceleration is defined to be rate of change of velocity. Therefore, along similar lines to the definition of the velocity of a particle, the **acceleration** of a particle with velocity $\mathbf{v}(t)$ is defined as

$$\mathbf{a}(t) = \frac{d\mathbf{v}(t)}{dt}.$$

As with position and velocity, we sometimes write $\mathbf{a}$ rather than $\mathbf{a}(t)$.

Notice that the definition of acceleration as the rate of change of *velocity* differs from its common everyday meaning as the rate of increase of *speed*. For example, consider the train moving at constant speed around a bend mentioned above. Its speed is constant, so it is not accelerating in the everyday sense. However, it is accelerating in a mathematical sense, because its velocity is changing direction. Similarly, in the everyday sense, the braking train is not accelerating but decelerating, in that its speed is decreasing. However, in a mathematical sense it is accelerating since its velocity is changing.

It is important to understand the difference between the mathematical and everyday meanings of acceleration, and also to be able to interpret the meaning of the components of the vectors defining the position, velocity and acceleration of a particle. The following exercise should help you to do this.

Exercise 1.3

Three particles, A, B and C, are moving along three different straight lines. In each case, the straight line is chosen as the x-axis, so the vectors defining the position, velocity and acceleration of the three particles have only x-components. The graphs of the x-components $x(t)$ of the position of particle A, $\dot{x}(t)$ of the velocity of particle B, and $\ddot{x}(t)$ of the acceleration of particle C are shown in Figure 1.5. Use the graphs to answer the following questions.

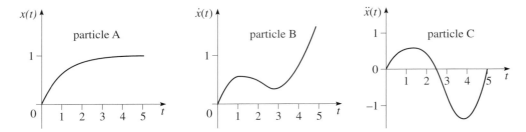

Figure 1.5

(a) When is particle A travelling fastest?

(b) Does particle B change its direction of motion in the time interval shown?

(c) Particle C starts from rest at time $t = 0$. Is particle C momentarily stationary at any later time in the time interval shown?

(*Hint*: Think about the meaning of the area beneath a curve.)

1.2 One-dimensional motion

The ideas in Subsection 1.1 apply to motion in three-dimensional space generally. For the rest of this unit (and also in *Unit 7*) we make the simplification that the motion will be in one dimension, so that the fundamental theory is not obscured.

Restriction to one-dimensional motion still allows a wide range of situations to be covered. One such situation, which is analysed fully in Section 3, is the following.

> If a marble is dropped from the Clifton Suspension Bridge, how long does it take to fall into the River Avon below? And what is its velocity just before it hits the water?

You met this situation in *Unit 3.*

To answer these questions, we need expressions for the position and velocity of the falling marble. It is reasonable to assume that the path of the marble is a straight line; so, under this assumption, although the marble is moving in three-dimensional space, this is a one-dimensional problem.

With badly chosen axes, all three components of the position vector of the marble could be changing. (Imagine fixing your axes on a car as it crossed the bridge at constant speed, or simply axes inclined to the vertical.) What makes this a one-dimensional problem is that if we choose the axes well, then only one component of the position vector is changing. Normally this axis is labelled as the x-axis, with the result that the vector has only an **i**-component. Furthermore, if the situation being considered has an obvious direction of positive motion, then it is usual to choose this direction as the direction of the positive x-axis. So, in the case of the Clifton Suspension Bridge problem (see Figure 1.6), it is sensible to choose the x-axis Ox pointing vertically downwards, so that the marble moves in the positive x-direction.

For one-dimensional problems in which the x-axis corresponds to the direction of motion, the position, velocity and acceleration of the particle can be expressed as

$$\mathbf{r}(t) = x(t)\mathbf{i}, \quad \mathbf{v}(t) = \frac{dx(t)}{dt}\mathbf{i}, \quad \mathbf{a}(t) = \frac{d^2x(t)}{dt^2}\mathbf{i},$$

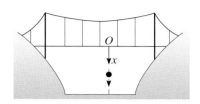

Figure 1.6

respectively. So, for such problems, the position of the particle can be described by the function $x(t)$, the velocity by the function $v(t) = dx(t)/dt$, and the acceleration by the function $a(t) = dv(t)/dt = d^2x(t)/dt^2$. In fact, for one-dimensional motion *along a given x-axis*, the vector quantities position, velocity and acceleration are completely described by the corresponding (scalar) functions $x(t)$, $v(t)$ and $a(t)$, respectively. For example, the magnitude of the velocity is given by $|v(t)|$, its orientation by the given x-axis, and its sense by the sign of $v(t)$. (Remember, from *Unit 4*, that the direction of a vector comprises its orientation and its sense.) Therefore, for the one-dimensional motion of an object along a given x-axis, we can — and frequently shall — refer to $x(t)$ (or x), $v(t)$ (or v) and $a(t)$ (or a) as the position, velocity and acceleration of the object.

As with $\mathbf{r}$, $\mathbf{v}$, and $\mathbf{a}$, we shall sometimes find it convenient to write x, v and a instead of $x(t)$, $v(t)$ and $a(t)$.

In this course v is taken to mean the x-component of the vector $\mathbf{v}$, and the magnitude of $\mathbf{v}$ is written $|\mathbf{v}|$. In some books you may see a different convention, where v is the magnitude of $\mathbf{v}$.

In most of the examples and exercises in this unit so far, the position of the object was known. It is more usual for the forces acting to be known. As you will see in Section 2, this gives information about the acceleration of the object. So in the following examples and exercises we practise finding the position and velocity of a particle, given its acceleration.

Example 1.2

A particle is moving in a straight line along the x-axis. The acceleration $\mathbf{a}$ of the particle at time t is given by

$$\mathbf{a}(t) = (12t^2 + 2)\mathbf{i}.$$

At the instant $t = 1\,\text{s}$, the particle is at $x = 3\,\text{m}$ and has velocity $v = 2\,\text{m s}^{-1}$.

(a) Find the velocity $\mathbf{v}(t)$ and the position $\mathbf{r}(t)$ of the particle.

(b) Find the velocity and position of the particle at time $t = 2\,\text{s}$.

Note that the 'initial' condition for a problem does not have to be at $t = 0$.

Solution

(a) The acceleration is known and is a one-dimensional vector function. Using the notation above, we have

$$a(t) = \mathbf{a}(t) \cdot \mathbf{i} = 12t^2 + 2.$$

Since $a(t) = dv(t)/dt$, we have the first-order differential equation

$$\frac{dv}{dt} = 12t^2 + 2.$$

This equation can be solved by direct integration, giving

$$v = \int (12t^2 + 2)\, dt = 4t^3 + 2t + A.$$

To find the value of the constant A, we use the fact that $v = 2$ when $t = 1$, so that $2 = 4 + 2 + A$, giving $A = -4$. This gives

$$v(t) = 4t^3 + 2t - 4.$$

In general, when trying to find the position of a particle given its acceleration, it is often easier to first find its velocity and then find its position, and thus solve two first-order differential equations, rather than to find its position directly by solving a second-order differential equation.

59

Since $v(t) = dx(t)/dt$, we have the first-order differential equation

$$\frac{dx}{dt} = 4t^3 + 2t - 4.$$

Solving this equation by direct integration gives

$$x = \int (4t^3 + 2t - 4)\,dt = t^4 + t^2 - 4t + B.$$

The initial condition $x = 3$ when $t = 1$ can be used to find the constant B, giving $3 = 1 + 1 - 4 + B$, so that $B = 5$. This gives

$$x(t) = t^4 + t^2 - 4t + 5.$$

So the velocity and position of the particle are

$$\mathbf{v}(t) = (4t^3 + 2t - 4)\mathbf{i}, \quad \mathbf{r}(t) = (t^4 + t^2 - 4t + 5)\mathbf{i}.$$

(b) When $t = 2$, the velocity and position have values

$$\mathbf{v}(2) = (4 \times 2^3 + 2 \times 2 - 4)\mathbf{i} = 32\mathbf{i},$$
$$\mathbf{r}(2) = (2^4 + 2^2 - 4 \times 2 + 5)\mathbf{i} = 17\mathbf{i}.$$

Hence at time 2 seconds the particle has position 17 metres along the positive x-axis and velocity 32 metres per second in the direction of the positive x-axis. ■

Exercise 1.4

A particle is moving in a straight line along the x-axis. At time t the particle has an acceleration given by

$$\mathbf{a}(t) = (18t - 20)\mathbf{i} \quad (t \geq 0).$$

Initially, at $t = 0$, the particle has position $\mathbf{r}(0) = 7\mathbf{i}$ and velocity $\mathbf{v}(0) = 3\mathbf{i}$. Find the position of the particle at time $t = 10$.

Exercise 1.5

A particle is moving in a straight line along the x-axis. At time t the particle has an acceleration given by

$$\mathbf{a}(t) = ge^{-kt}\mathbf{i} \quad (t \geq 0),$$

where g and k are positive constants. Initially, at $t = 0$, the particle is at the origin ($\mathbf{r}(0) = \mathbf{0}$) and is at rest ($\mathbf{v}(0) = \mathbf{0}$). Find the velocity and position of the particle as vector functions.

In general, an **equation of motion** is any equation relating two or more of acceleration, velocity, position and time. The rest of this subsection is devoted to problems involving the solution of equations of motion. We begin with the case of constant acceleration, which occurs frequently.

Example 1.3

A particle moves in a straight line along the x-axis with constant acceleration $\mathbf{a}(t) = a_0\mathbf{i}$ ($a_0 \neq 0$). The particle starts from the origin at time $t = 0$ with initial velocity $\mathbf{v}(0) = v_0\mathbf{i}$.

(a) Show that the velocity and position of the particle are given by

$$v(t) = v = v_0 + a_0 t \quad \text{and} \quad x(t) = x = v_0 t + \tfrac{1}{2}a_0 t^2.$$

(b) By eliminating t between these two equations, show that

$$v^2 = v_0^2 + 2a_0 x.$$

The subscript 0 is used to distinguish the constants a_0 and v_0 from the variables a and v.

As you will see in *Unit 8*, this equation has considerable physical significance.

Solution

(a) We have

$$a(t) = \frac{dv}{dt} = a_0,$$

which on integration yields

$$v = \int a_0 \, dt = a_0 t + A.$$

The initial condition $v(0) = v_0$ gives $A = v_0$, so the velocity is given by

$$v(t) = v = v_0 + a_0 t. \tag{1.1}$$

Note that Equations (1.1) and (1.2) are sometimes quoted using the symbol s instead of x.

Hence

$$\frac{dx}{dt} = v_0 + a_0 t,$$

from which

$$x = \int (v_0 + a_0 t) \, dt = v_0 t + \tfrac{1}{2} a_0 t^2 + B.$$

Since the particle starts at the origin, we have the initial condition $x(0) = 0$, which gives $B = 0$, so the position is given by

$$x(t) = x = v_0 t + \tfrac{1}{2} a_0 t^2. \tag{1.2}$$

(b) Rearranging Equation (1.1) gives, since $a_0 \neq 0$,

$$t = \frac{v - v_0}{a_0}.$$

Substituting this into Equation (1.2) yields

$$x = v_0 \left(\frac{v - v_0}{a_0} \right) + \tfrac{1}{2} a_0 \left(\frac{v - v_0}{a_0} \right)^2.$$

Multiplying through by $2a_0$ and expanding the brackets gives

$$2a_0 x = (2v_0 v - 2v_0^2) + (v^2 - 2v_0 v + v_0^2) = v^2 - v_0^2,$$

which can be rearranged to give

$$v^2 = v_0^2 + 2a_0 x, \tag{1.3}$$

as required. ∎

The results of Example 1.3 can be summarized as follows.

Constant acceleration

If a particle is moving in a straight line along the x-axis with constant acceleration $\mathbf{a}(t) = a_0 \mathbf{i}$, and at time $t = 0$ it is at the origin with initial velocity $\mathbf{v}(0) = v_0 \mathbf{i}$, then its acceleration, velocity and position are given, respectively, by

$$a = a_0,$$
$$v = v_0 + a_0 t,$$
$$x = v_0 t + \tfrac{1}{2} a_0 t^2.$$

Furthermore,

$$v^2 = v_0^2 + 2a_0 x. \tag{1.3}$$

It is always possible to specify that the origin coincides with the particle's position at time $t = 0$, so these results are completely general. However, it is sometimes convenient to take $x = x_0$ when $t = 0$, in which case the position is given by $x = x_0 + v_0 t + \tfrac{1}{2} a_0 t^2$, and Equation (1.3) becomes $v^2 = v_0^2 + 2a_0(x - x_0)$.

We know that, by definition, $a = dv/dt = d^2x/dt^2$. There is a useful alternative expression for a that can be derived using the Chain Rule:

$$a = \frac{dv}{dt} = \frac{dv}{dx}\frac{dx}{dt} = \frac{dv}{dx}v.$$

The Chain Rule, or Composite Rule, was revised in *Unit 1*.

Alternative expressions for $a(t)$

$$a = \frac{dv}{dt} = \frac{d^2x}{dt^2} = v\frac{dv}{dx}$$

The formula $a = v\,dv/dx$ can be used to obtain Equation (1.3) directly, without having to find v and x first, as the following exercise asks you to demonstrate.

Exercise 1.6

A particle moves in a straight line along the x-axis with constant acceleration $\mathbf{a}(t) = a_0\mathbf{i}$. Initially, at time $t = 0$, the particle is at the origin and has velocity $\mathbf{v}(0) = v_0\mathbf{i}$. Use the relationship $a = v\,dv/dx$ to show that

$$v^2 = v_0^2 + 2a_0x.$$

In general, given an equation of motion relating acceleration to one or more of velocity, position and time, we want to obtain an equation relating velocity to position and/or time, or an equation relating position to time. In the case of one-dimensional motion, we can do this by using one of

$$a = \frac{dv}{dt}, \quad a = \frac{d^2x}{dt^2}, \quad a = v\frac{dv}{dx}$$

to substitute for a and then solving the resulting differential equation. The following exercise asks you to decide which formula for a provides the most appropriate substitution in a variety of typical cases.

Exercise 1.7

How would you use the above formulae to substitute for a in the following equations of motion, in order to obtain the specified information? (You are not expected to solve the resulting equations.)

(a) The equation of motion is $a = \cos t$; it is required to find velocity and position in terms of time.

(b) The equation of motion is $a = -x$; it is required to find a relationship between velocity and position.

(c) The equation of motion is $a = -x - v + \cos t$; it is required to find position in terms of time.

End-of-section Exercise

Exercise 1.8

The data in Table 1.2, taken from the United Kingdom *Highway Code*, show the shortest stopping distances of cars travelling along a straight road.

The thinking distance is defined to be the distance travelled by a car in the maximum time it takes for an alert driver to react to a hazardous situation.

Table 1.2

Speed (mph)	Thinking distance (feet)	Braking distance (feet)	Overall stopping distance (feet)
20	20	20	40
30	30	45	75
40	40	80	120
50	50	125	175
60	60	180	240
70	70	245	315

The foot is a unit of length in the British Imperial system, and 1 foot $= 0.3048$ m. The British Imperial unit for speed is miles per hour (mph), and 1 mph $= 0.447\,\mathrm{m\,s^{-1}}$.

(a) The data in Table 1.2 are not from an experiment; they are the predictions of models. Your task is to discover what models were used.

(i) What model (using SI units) was used to obtain the thinking distance data?

(*Hint*: Think about the speed of the car before and after the thinking phase, and use the constant acceleration formula $x = v_0 t + \frac{1}{2}a_0 t^2$.)

(ii) What model (using SI units) was used to obtain the braking distance data?

(*Hint*: Think about the speed of the car before and after the braking phase, and use the constant acceleration formula $v^2 = v_0^2 + 2a_0 x$.)

(b) Use your models from part (a) to predict the overall stopping distance (in metres) for a speed of 45 mph.

2 A theory of motion

Section 1 introduced the basic concepts of position, velocity and acceleration that are needed to *describe* motion. In this section, two concepts introduced in *Unit 5*, *force* and *mass*, enable us to go beyond the mere description of motion and formulate laws *predicting* what motions take place.

At first sight it might seem that a different set of rules of motion would be required for each type of object — one set for tennis balls, another set for planets, and so on. Fortunately, there is a simple underlying pattern. Newton was able to see beyond individual cases, and his three laws of motion form a framework, or theory, for predicting the motion of all objects.

Newton's three laws of motion were stated in the Introduction of *Unit 5*.

Our instinctive ideas of motion are shaped by the presence of friction in almost all things in our everyday lives. Aristotle (384–322 BC) constructed a theory out of this experience that turned out to be completely wrong. This theory and the subsequent development of ideas of motion, leading eventually to Newton's laws, is the subject of the video for this unit. But before viewing the video, consider the following thought experiment to imagine motion without friction.

You met the idea of friction in *Unit 5*. It is discussed further in Subsection 4.1 of this unit.

Consider a toboggan on a horizontal icy surface such as a frozen lake. Left undisturbed, the toboggan remains static; it must be pushed or pulled in some way if it is to be set in motion, i.e. a force must act on the toboggan. However, if you give the toboggan a push and then release it, the toboggan will move across the ice at almost constant speed in the direction that it has been pushed.

Once the toboggan has been released, the force of the push ceases to act on it.

This suggests that under ideal (i.e. frictionless) conditions, the following applies:

in the absence of a force, the toboggan remains at rest or moves with constant speed in a straight line.

In real life, the toboggan does eventually slow down, partly due to air resistance and partly due to friction between the toboggan runners and the ice. In competitive tobogganing, the tobogganers go to great lengths to reduce these resistive forces (i.e. forces resisting motion) by streamlining the toboggan and waxing the runners.

Air resistance is discussed in Subsection 4.2.

*Exercise 2.1

A car on a flat, straight road requires a motive force (supplied by its engine) in order to maintain a constant speed of 70 miles per hour; if the engine is switched off, then the car slows down. It might be thought from the above example that if an object is moving with constant velocity, then there is no force acting on it. Try to explain this apparent contradiction.

Returning to the example above, suppose that you apply a force by pushing the toboggan continuously. You cannot quantify this force, but the sensations in your muscles and nerves will reveal whether you are pushing gently or firmly. From experience, you know that:

the harder you continue to push, the further and faster the toboggan moves in a given time.

This suggests that there is a link between the force that is applied and the way in which the toboggan moves.

*Exercise 2.2

A toboggan on an icy slope may accelerate even when it is not being pushed. Try to identify the force that causes this acceleration.

Next, imagine pushing two identical toboggans, one of which is empty while the other carries a heavy person. If you apply the same force to the two toboggans, then the laden toboggan will move more sluggishly. To achieve the same motion in each case, it is necessary to apply a greater force to the laden toboggan. In other words:

if you apply the same force to the two toboggans, the laden toboggan does not travel as far or as fast in a given time as the empty toboggan;

in order for the two toboggans to move in the same way, a greater force must be applied to the laden toboggan than to the empty toboggan.

In general, it seems that three concepts are linked together:

(a) the *force* that is applied to an object;

(b) the *mass* of the object;

(c) the *motion* of the object.

Newton proposed in his book *Principia* that this link takes the form

$$\text{force} = \text{mass} \times \text{acceleration.} \tag{2.1}$$

The validity of this equation is shown by its success at predicting motion — nearly the whole of nineteenth-century science rested on it! It also provides a more formal definition of **force** than was given in *Unit 5*.

The history of the development of the ideas discussed here and experiments to confirm Equation (2.1) form the subject of the video for this unit.

Watch the video for this unit now.

In the video you saw that Equation (2.1) can be written in the vector form

$$\mathbf{F} = m\mathbf{a},$$

where $\mathbf{F}$ is the vector quantity force, m is the scalar quantity mass, and $\mathbf{a}$ is the vector quantity acceleration. This equation is the bedrock of Newtonian mechanics, and it is usually referred to as **Newton's second law**.

Strictly speaking, the argument concerning the toboggan justifies only the statement that force is *proportional* to mass times acceleration, i.e. $\mathbf{F} = km\mathbf{a}$ with k some constant of proportionality. However, in the SI system of units, k is *chosen* to be 1 by an appropriate definition of the unit of force, the *newton*, which makes use of Newton's second law.

> You met the newton, though not a formal definition of it, in *Unit 5*.

Definition

A force of magnitude one **newton** (1 N) is the force required to accelerate a mass of one kilogram at one metre per second per second (i.e. $1\,\mathrm{N} = 1\,\mathrm{kg\,m\,s^{-2}}$). The direction of the force is the direction in which the mass accelerates.

This is a good point at which to summarize the discussion so far in this section into precise laws comprising the foundations of Newtonian mechanics.

> You met one of these laws, the law of addition of forces, in *Unit 5*.

Fundamental laws of Newtonian mechanics

These laws concern a **particle**, which is a mathematical model for any material object whose size and internal structure may be neglected.

The **mass** of the particle is expressed by a single positive number m. This number is an inherent property of the particle and does not depend on time, position, force or any other variable.

Law of addition of mass

If an object modelled as a particle is composed of a number of parts, then the mass m of the particle is the sum of the masses of the parts.

Law of addition of forces

If several forces act simultaneously on a particle, then the resultant force is the vector sum of the individual forces.

> It is very important to take into account the directions of the individual forces as well as their magnitudes.

Newton's second law

If a particle has a constant mass m and experiences a total force $\mathbf{F}$, then its acceleration $\mathbf{a}$ is given by

$$\mathbf{F} = m\mathbf{a}.$$

> This statement of Newton's second law applies to particles of constant mass, which are the only particles studied in this course.

Newton's first law

When $\mathbf{F}$ is zero, $\mathbf{a}$ is zero: in the absence of a force, a particle either stays permanently at rest or moves at constant velocity, i.e. at a constant speed in a straight line.

> Newton's first law is a special case of Newton's second law. It forms the basis of the equilibrium conditions in *Unit 5*.

---

*Exercise 2.3 _____

If a mass of 200 grams is subjected to a force of magnitude 10 newtons, what is the magnitude of the acceleration produced?

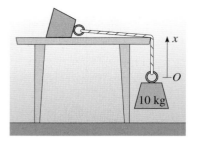

*Exercise 2.4

An object of mass 10 kilograms is attached to a string hanging over the edge of a table, as shown in Figure 2.1. The other end of the string is attached to another object, on top of the table. The object hanging over the edge of the table is observed to be accelerating at $1\,\mathrm{m\,s^{-2}}$ downwards.

(a) What is the resultant force on the hanging object?

(b) Apply Newton's second law to the hanging object, and hence calculate the tension force due to the string acting on the hanging object.

Figure 2.1

End-of-section Exercise

Exercise 2.5

A fighter pilot can experience an acceleration of magnitude approximately six times the magnitude of the acceleration due to gravity before being rendered unconscious. If a fighter of mass 4000 kilograms is subjected to a force of $50\,000\,\mathbf{i} + 60\,000\,\mathbf{j} + 100\,000\,\mathbf{k}$ newtons during an aerobatic manoeuvre, will the pilot remain conscious?

3 Predicting motion

Newton's second law of motion can be used to help solve a huge variety of mechanics problems. The first example considers the motion of an object falling under gravity alone.

The steps involved in the solution are similar to those in Procedure 1.1 of *Unit 5*. As in *Unit 5*, the steps are highlighted by labels in the margin.

Example 3.1

A marble, initially at rest, is dropped from the Clifton Suspension Bridge and falls into the River Avon, 77 metres below. Assuming that the only force acting on the marble is gravity, find:

In Section 4 this example will be remodelled to include air resistance.

(a) the time taken before the marble hits the water;

(b) the speed of the marble just before it hits the water.

Solution

The first step is always to draw a diagram that includes all the relevant information given in the problem, as in Figure 3.1.

◄Draw picture►

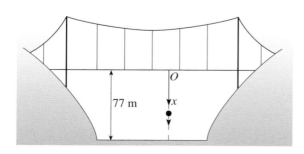

Figure 3.1

Choose an x-axis pointing vertically downwards, with its origin at the point where the object is released, as shown in Figure 3.1. (This makes the algebra simpler as all quantities are positive.) ◄Choose axes►

The marble is modelled as a particle with gravity the only force acting on it. This is represented by the following force diagram, in which m denotes the mass of the marble and $\mathbf{W}$ denotes its weight. ◄Draw force diagram►

The resultant force acting on the marble is $\mathbf{W} = mg\mathbf{i}$ (where, as usual, $\mathbf{i}$ is a unit vector pointing in the direction of the positive x-axis, in this case vertically downwards).

In *Unit 5* the downwards vertical was usually in the $-\mathbf{k}$ direction.

The acceleration, $\mathbf{a}$, is obtained by applying Newton's second law: ◄Apply Newton's 2nd law►

$$ma = mg\mathbf{i}.$$

From this equation we see that only the $\mathbf{i}$-component of $\mathbf{a}$ could be varying, so we have $\mathbf{a} = a(t)\,\mathbf{i}$. So the equation becomes $ma = mg$, and dividing through by m gives

$$a = g.$$

(Notice that since m cancels out, the results apply to a marble of any mass.)

There are several approaches to obtaining the equations needed to solve the problem. One approach requires that we first replace a by dv/dt to obtain ◄Solve differential equation►

$$\frac{dv}{dt} = g.$$

This is integrated to give

$$v = gt + A.$$

The constant acceleration formulae from Subsection 1.2 could be used since $a = g$ is constant, but we choose a more general method that applies even when a is not constant.

The initial condition that the marble is initially at rest (i.e. $v = 0$ when $t = 0$) gives $A = 0$, so

$$v = gt. \tag{3.1}$$

Now, replacing v by dx/dt gives

$$\frac{dx}{dt} = gt.$$

This is integrated to obtain

$$x = \tfrac{1}{2}gt^2 + B.$$

The origin was chosen so that $x = 0$ when $t = 0$, so $B = 0$, which gives

$$x = \tfrac{1}{2}gt^2. \tag{3.2}$$

(a) When the marble hits the water, $x = 77$ and Equation (3.2) gives $77 = \tfrac{1}{2}gt^2$, which on putting $g = 9.81$ gives ◄Interpret solution►

$$t = \sqrt{\frac{2 \times 77}{9.81}} \simeq 3.962.$$

So the model predicts that the marble hits the water approximately 3.96 seconds after being released.

(b) Putting $t = 3.962$ into Equation (3.1) gives

$$v = 9.81 \times 3.962 \simeq 38.87.$$

So the model predicts that the marble has a speed of approximately 38.9 metres per second just before it hits the water. ∎

Try the following exercise following the same steps as given in the margin in the above example.

*Exercise 3.1 ───────────────────────────────

A stone, dropped from rest, takes 3 seconds to reach the bottom of a well. Assuming that the only force acting on the stone is gravity, estimate:

(a) the depth of the well;

(b) the speed of the stone when it reaches the bottom.

Use the more general approach of Example 3.1 rather than the constant acceleration formulae of Subsection 1.2.

The steps highlighted in Example 3.1 and in the solution to Exercise 3.1 are re-stated in the following procedure for solving mechanics problems involving one-dimensional motion using Newton's second law. Remember that it is intended to be a guide rather than a rigid set of rules.

Procedure 3.1   Applying Newton's second law

Given a mechanics problem involving one-dimensional motion in which a question regarding the motion is to be answered, proceed as follows.

(a) Draw a sketch of the physical situation, and annotate it with any relevant information.

◄Draw picture►

(b) Choose the x-axis to lie along the direction of motion, and select an origin. Mark the x-axis, its direction and the origin on your sketch.

◄Choose axes►

(c) Draw a force diagram.

◄Draw force diagram►

(d) Apply Newton's second law to obtain a vector equation. Resolve each force along the chosen axes in order to resolve the vector equation into scalar equations. For one-dimensional motion, this gives a single differential equation if the axes are chosen correctly.

◄Apply Newton's 2nd law►

(e) Substitute $v\,dv/dx$, dv/dt or d^2x/dt^2 for the acceleration a in the equation of motion, and solve the resulting differential equation(s) to obtain the velocity v in terms of the position x or time t, or the position x in terms of the time t, as appropriate.

◄Solve differential equation►

(f) Interpret the solution in terms of the original problem.

◄Interpret solution►

Notes on the procedure

- This procedure assumes that the question to be answered is given. When modelling real-world situations, deriving a suitable question is half the work. This part of the modelling process is looked at in detail in *Unit 16*.

- The importance of drawing a picture cannot be stressed too strongly. Include in the picture all relevant information from the problem, e.g. distances, masses and initial velocities.

- The choices of the origin and of the direction of the x-axis are arbitrary, and will have no effect on the final outcome of your calculations. However, try to make these choices so that the position x and/or the velocity v are positive for the particle's motion, as this will simplify the algebra. If there is a clear starting point for the motion, then this is often a suitable choice for the origin.

- For some problems it may be necessary to choose a y-axis and even a z-axis as well as an x-axis.

See Subsection 4.1.

- Steps (b) and (c) are interchangeable: the force diagram does not change with a different choice of axes. If you have difficulty choosing an x-axis, then draw the force diagram first.

You experienced the interchangeability of these steps in *Unit 5*.

- Your choice of substitution for a will depend on what question you want to answer (for example, you may want an equation linking velocity to time, or velocity to position). (See Exercise 1.7 for examples of this.)

- When the acceleration is constant, you can use the general constant acceleration formulae from Subsection 1.2 to solve the differential equation.

- Perform any readily available checks on your working, and consider whether your answers are physically reasonable. For example, you could check that the units of your answer are correct, or use common sense to tell you whether your answer is in the correct range.

- When you have finished interpreting the solution, write out your conclusion in words, and remember to include the physical units for any quantities given (as in Example 3.1). Also look back at the problem and check that you have fully answered the question asked.

Try using the procedure in the following exercise.

*Exercise 3.2

A ball is thrown vertically upwards from ground level with an initial speed of 10 metres per second. Assuming that gravity is the only force acting on the ball, find:

(a) the time taken for the ball to reach its maximum height;

(b) the maximum height attained;

(c) the time taken for the ball to return to the ground;

(d) the speed of the ball as it reaches the ground on its return.

In Example 3.1, which considered the motion of a marble falling from the Clifton Suspension Bridge, first the velocity and then the position were found as functions of time (by using the substitutions dv/dt for a and dx/dt for v). However, as was indicated in the solution to that example, there are other approaches to solving the problem. You are asked to adopt one of these other approaches in the following exercise.

*Exercise 3.3

A marble, initially at rest, is dropped from the Clifton Suspension Bridge and falls into the River Avon, 77 metres below. Assume that the only force acting on the marble is gravity.

(a) By putting $a = v\,dv/dx$ in Newton's second law and solving the resulting differential equation, find the marble's velocity v as a function of the distance x through which it has fallen.

(b) By putting $v = dx/dt$ in your answer to part (a), find the time t that the object takes to fall a distance x.

(c) Hence find the time taken before the marble hits the water, and the speed of the marble just before it hits the water.

In the previous examples and exercises, all of the forces acting on an object were in the same direction; but this does not have to be so for the motion to be in one dimension. This is illustrated in the following example.

Example 3.2

A crate of empty bottles of total mass 30 kilograms is being hauled by rope up a smooth ramp from the cellar of a pub. The ramp makes an angle of $\pi/6$ radians with the horizontal. When the crate has been hauled 2 metres up the ramp (i.e. 2 metres along the slope of the ramp), the rope suddenly breaks. It is estimated that if the crate hits the bottom of the ramp at a speed of 5 metres per second or greater, then the bottles in the crate will break. Assuming that there is no friction between the crate and the ramp, and assuming that air resistance can be neglected, will the bottles break?

A similar problem was considered in *Unit 5*. The problem is reconsidered in the presence of friction between the crate and the ramp in Section 4.

Solution

The situation is sketched in Figure 3.2. ◀Draw picture▶

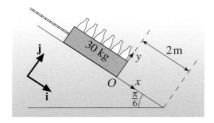

Figure 3.2

The crate moves down the slope, so we choose the x-axis to point down the slope, with the origin at the crate's position when the rope breaks. (We model the crate as a particle, so its position is at a point.) Choose a y-axis perpendicular to this, as shown in Figure 3.2. Also shown in the picture are the unit vectors $\mathbf{i}$ and $\mathbf{j}$ implied by this choice of axes. Note the difference between drawing the axes (which have a fixed origin) and drawing the unit vectors (which are not fixed and only convey directions).

◀Choose axes▶

The only forces on the crate are the weight $\mathbf{W}$ and the normal reaction $\mathbf{N}$ of the ramp (since we are neglecting friction and air resistance in this example). So, modelling the crate as a particle of mass m, the force diagram (showing also how the relevant angles are calculated) is as follows.

◀Draw force diagram▶

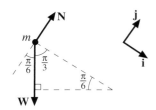

Now, Newton's second law for this system gives ◀Apply Newton's 2nd law▶

$$m\mathbf{a} = \mathbf{W} + \mathbf{N}. \tag{3.3}$$

From the force diagram, $\mathbf{N} = |\mathbf{N}|\,\mathbf{j}$. The weight can be resolved into components using the formula from *Unit 4*:

$$
\begin{aligned}
\mathbf{W} &= (\mathbf{W} \cdot \mathbf{i})\,\mathbf{i} + (\mathbf{W} \cdot \mathbf{j})\,\mathbf{j} \\
&= |\mathbf{W}| \cos \tfrac{\pi}{3}\,\mathbf{i} + |\mathbf{W}| \cos(\tfrac{\pi}{2} + \tfrac{\pi}{3})\,\mathbf{j} \\
&= \tfrac{1}{2}|\mathbf{W}|\,\mathbf{i} - \tfrac{\sqrt{3}}{2}|\mathbf{W}|\,\mathbf{j}.
\end{aligned}
$$

We use the letter m rather than the value 30 kg for the mass since, as is discussed in *Unit 16*, inserting actual data values too early in the modelling process can obscure features of the resulting model.

The motion is along the slope, so $\mathbf{a} = a\mathbf{i}$. (All we are saying here is that there is no resultant force in the $\mathbf{j}$-direction.) Now that we have all the vectors in component form, we can immediately resolve Equation (3.3) in the $\mathbf{i}$-direction:

$$ma = \tfrac{1}{2}|\mathbf{W}| + 0.$$

Substituting $|\mathbf{W}| = mg$ gives $ma = \tfrac{1}{2}mg$, so

$$a = \tfrac{1}{2}g.$$

Again m cancels out, so the results apply to a crate of any mass.

We want an equation for the velocity v in terms of the distance travelled x. Since the acceleration is constant, we can use Equation (1.3), i.e.

$$v^2 = v_0^2 + 2ax.$$

◄Solve differential equation►

This gives the final velocity in terms of known quantities: the initial velocity $v_0 = 0\,\mathrm{m\,s^{-1}}$, the distance travelled $x = 2\,\mathrm{m}$, and the constant acceleration $a = \tfrac{1}{2}g$.

Putting the data into the equation gives

$$v^2 = 0^2 + 2 \times \tfrac{1}{2}g \times 2 \simeq 19.6.$$

◄Interpret solution►

So $v \simeq 4.4$, which means that the crate is travelling at about 4.4 metres per second when it hits the bottom of the ramp. This speed is just below the estimated speed at which the bottles will break, so — provided that the estimate of the speed at which the bottles will break is a good one — this model predicts that the bottles will not break. ■

Exercise 3.4 —————————————————————————

A skier of mass 65 kilograms starts from rest at the top of a 120-metre ski slope (i.e. 120 metres is the vertical distance from top to bottom), as shown in Figure 3.3. The skier is to ski down the slope before taking off and then landing some distance further down the hill. Use the x-axis shown, which points down the slope with the origin at the top of the slope. Let θ be the angle that the slope makes with the horizontal. Assuming that friction and air resistance can be neglected, answer the following questions.

This problem is reconsidered in the presence of friction in Section 4.

(a) If $\theta = \frac{\pi}{4}$, what is the speed of the skier at the bottom of the slope?

(b) If $\theta = \frac{\pi}{3}$, what is the speed of the skier at the bottom of the slope?

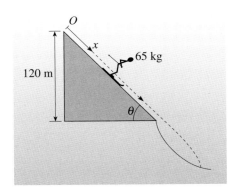

Figure 3.3

End-of-section Exercise

Exercise 3.5 _____

A man leaning from a window throws a ball vertically upwards from a point 4.4 metres above the ground. The initial speed of the ball is 7.6 metres per second. It travels up and then down in a straight vertical line, and eventually reaches the ground. Assuming that gravity is the only force acting on the ball, estimate:

(a) the time that elapses before the ball reaches the ground

(b) the speed of the ball when it strikes the ground.

4 Some more force models

In Section 3 a procedure for predicting the motion of a particle using Newton's second law was described. To use the procedure, every force acting on the particle must first be modelled. In this section, models of forces due to friction, air resistance and water resistance are described. This greatly extends the range of problems that can be solved using the procedure.

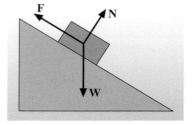

4.1 Friction

In *Unit 5* you encountered a model for the friction force that acts on an object at rest in contact with a surface. This force $\mathbf{F}$ has magnitude less than or equal to $\mu|\mathbf{N}|$, i.e. $|\mathbf{F}| \leq \mu|\mathbf{N}|$, where $\mathbf{N}$ is the normal reaction force and μ is the coefficient of static friction between the object and the surface. The direction of the friction force opposes any possible motion (e.g. is up the slope in Figure 4.1).

Figure 4.1 The forces acting on a block at rest on a slope

The coefficient μ is called the coefficient of *static* friction to distinguish it from the **coefficient of sliding friction**, denoted by μ', which is used when an object is moving along a surface. In this situation, experiments show that the magnitude of the friction force $\mathbf{F}$ is equal to $\mu'|\mathbf{N}|$, i.e. $|\mathbf{F}| = \mu'|\mathbf{N}|$, where $\mathbf{N}$ is the normal reaction force and μ' is the coefficient of sliding friction; the direction of the friction force is opposite to the direction of motion.

The names *coefficient of dynamical friction* or *coefficient of kinetic friction* are sometimes used instead of the name *coefficient of sliding friction*.

Modelling sliding friction

(a) The friction force $\mathbf{F}$ acts in a direction perpendicular to the normal reaction $\mathbf{N}$ and opposite to the motion.

(b) $|\mathbf{F}| = \mu'|\mathbf{N}|$, where μ' is the coefficient of sliding friction for the two surfaces involved.

The numerical value of the coefficient of sliding friction μ' is always smaller than the numerical value of the coefficient of static friction μ. (It is harder to get objects moving than to keep them moving.) A generalization that is often useful is

$$\mu' \simeq \tfrac{3}{4}\mu.$$

The use of the sliding friction model is best explained by an example.

Example 4.1

Consider again the problem of Example 3.2 concerning the crate of empty bottles sliding down a cellar ramp, but this time assume that there is friction between the crate and the ramp, with coefficient of sliding friction $\mu' = 0.15$.

(a) Estimate the speed of the crate when it reaches the bottom of the ramp. Will the bottles break?

(b) Compare the answer to part (a) with the answer to Example 3.2, and comment.

Solution

The situation is sketched in Figure 4.2.   ◀Draw picture▶

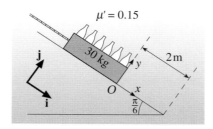

Figure 4.2

Choose the x-axis parallel to the ramp and the y-axis perpendicular to it,   ◀Choose axes▶
as shown in Figure 4.2. Choose the origin to be the crate's position when
the rope breaks.

The forces acting on the crate are its weight, the normal reaction of the   ◀Draw force diagram▶
ramp, and friction.

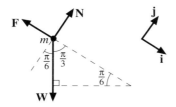

Using m for the mass of the crate (as in Example 3.2), applying Newton's   ◀Apply Newton's 2nd law▶
second law to this system gives

$$m\mathbf{a} = \mathbf{W} + \mathbf{N} + \mathbf{F}. \tag{4.1}$$

From the force diagram, $\mathbf{N} = |\mathbf{N}|\,\mathbf{j}$ and $\mathbf{F} = -|\mathbf{F}|\,\mathbf{i}$. It is also apparent that
the motion is one-dimensional parallel to the x-axis, i.e. $\mathbf{a} = a\mathbf{i}$. The weight
is resolved into components using the formula from *Unit 4*:

$$\mathbf{W} = |\mathbf{W}|\cos\tfrac{\pi}{3}\,\mathbf{i} + |\mathbf{W}|\cos(\tfrac{\pi}{2} + \tfrac{\pi}{3})\,\mathbf{j}$$
$$= \tfrac{1}{2}mg\,\mathbf{i} - \tfrac{\sqrt{3}}{2}mg\,\mathbf{j}.$$

Now we can immediately resolve Equation (4.1) in the $\mathbf{i}$-direction to obtain

$$ma = \tfrac{1}{2}mg + 0 - |\mathbf{F}|.$$

Using the friction model $|\mathbf{F}| = \mu'|\mathbf{N}|$ gives

$$ma = \tfrac{1}{2}mg - \mu'|\mathbf{N}|. \tag{4.2}$$

So, to find a, we need to find $|\mathbf{N}|$. To do this, we resolve Equation (4.1) in
the $\mathbf{j}$-direction to obtain

$$0 = -\tfrac{\sqrt{3}}{2}mg + |\mathbf{N}| + 0,$$

which gives $|\mathbf{N}| = \frac{\sqrt{3}}{2}mg$. Substituting this into Equation (4.2) gives

$$ma = \tfrac{1}{2}mg - \tfrac{\sqrt{3}}{2}\mu' mg,$$

so

$$a = \tfrac{1}{2}g - \tfrac{\sqrt{3}}{2}\mu' g.$$

As in Example 3.2, the acceleration is constant, so we can use   ◄Solve differential equation►

$$v^2 = v_0^2 + 2ax.$$

This gives the final speed in terms of known quantities: the initial velocity
$v_0 = 0\,\mathrm{m\,s^{-1}}$, the distance travelled $x = 2\,\mathrm{m}$, and the constant acceleration
$a = \tfrac{1}{2}g - \tfrac{\sqrt{3}}{2}\mu' g$ where $\mu' = 0.15$.

(a) Putting the data into the equation gives   ◄Interpret solution►

$$v^2 = 0^2 + 2 \times (\tfrac{1}{2}g - \tfrac{\sqrt{3}}{2} \times 0.15 \times g) \times 2 \simeq 14.5.$$

So $v \simeq 3.8$, which means that the crate is travelling at about 3.8 metres
per second when it hits the bottom of the ramp. This speed is well
below the estimated speed at which the bottles will break, so this model
predicts that the bottles will not break.

(b) The model that neglected friction (Example 3.2) predicted a speed of
$4.4\,\mathrm{m\,s^{-1}}$. The new prediction of $3.8\,\mathrm{m\,s^{-1}}$ is slower, as should be expected after the incorporation of friction into the model (this is a good
quick check of the solution), and is significantly slower than the breaking threshold of $5\,\mathrm{m\,s^{-1}}$. So in this case, even if the estimated breaking
threshold is not terribly accurate, we can be reasonably confident that
our prediction that the bottles will not break is correct. ∎

Table 4.1 shows some values of the coefficient of sliding friction that may be
useful in problems involving sliding objects.

Table 4.1   Coefficients of sliding friction

Object	Surface	μ'
waxed ski	dry snow	0.03
brass	ice	0.02
vulcanized rubber	dry tarmac	1.07
vulcanized rubber	wet tarmac	0.95

Exercise 4.1 ———————————————————————————

A tip-up truck is delivering a concrete block to a building site. The driver
increases the angle of tip of the carrier until the concrete block begins to
slide, then keeps the carrier at this constant angle. The coefficient of static
friction between a concrete block and metal is approximately 0.4, and the
coefficient of sliding friction is approximately 0.3.

(a) Calculate the angle at which the concrete block begins to slide.

(b) If the concrete block has 3 metres to travel before leaving the carrier,
how long will it take to unload it?

Exercise 4.2 ———————————————————————————

Repeat Exercise 3.4 (page 71) under the new modelling assumption that friction cannot be neglected; the coefficient of sliding friction between (waxed)
skis and snow is 0.03. Compare your answers here with those to Exercise 3.4,
and comment.

———————————————————————————————————

4.2 Air resistance

In many situations it is adequate to treat a falling object taking into account only the force of gravity. For example, we predicted a time of fall of a marble from the Clifton Suspension Bridge of 3.96 seconds, which is close to an experimental value of 4.1 seconds. Most of the time difference can be attributed to air resistance, which is modelled in this subsection.

Unit 14 looks more closely at the problem of which model to apply.

The idea of air resistance is quite familiar in everyday life. For example, any experienced cyclist knows the following.

- Air resistance tends to slow one down and resists one's attempts to increase speed.

- At low speeds air resistance has little effect, but at higher speeds it becomes more noticeable, making it difficult to cycle faster than about 40 kilometres per hour.

- Air resistance can be reduced by crouching over the handlebars to present a smaller profile to the wind.

From these observations we conclude that air resistance is a force, $\mathbf{R}$, whose direction is opposite to that of the motion of an object and whose magnitude, $|\mathbf{R}|$, depends on the object's speed, shape and size.

To simplify the discussion, we shall restrict our attention to smooth spherical objects. For such an object, we would expect $|\mathbf{R}|$ to increase as the object's speed $|\mathbf{v}|$ and diameter D increase. In fact, experiments show that the force on a sphere depends only on the product $D|\mathbf{v}|$. The results of such experiments are shown as the solid black line in Figure 4.3 (where, because of the wide range of values, a log–log graph has been used). The graph has a complicated shape, so the air resistance force is modelled by a complicated function of $D|\mathbf{v}|$. However, there are two simple models that fit the experimental data for wide ranges of situations, namely the following linear and quadratic models:

$$|\mathbf{R}| = c_1 D|\mathbf{v}| \quad \text{and} \quad |\mathbf{R}| = c_2 D^2 |\mathbf{v}|^2,$$

where c_1 and c_2 are positive constants. The best fit of these models to the experimental data (when using SI units) is given by $c_1 = 1.7 \times 10^{-4}$ and $c_2 = 0.20$ over certain ranges:

$$|\mathbf{R}| \simeq 1.7 \times 10^{-4} D|\mathbf{v}| \quad \text{for } D|\mathbf{v}| \lesssim 10^{-5};$$
$$|\mathbf{R}| \simeq 0.2 D^2 |\mathbf{v}|^2 \qquad \text{for } 10^{-2} \lesssim D|\mathbf{v}| \lesssim 1.$$

The symbol $\lesssim$ means 'less than about'.

These approximations for air resistance are shown as broken lines in Figure 4.3, together with their ranges of validity (shaded).

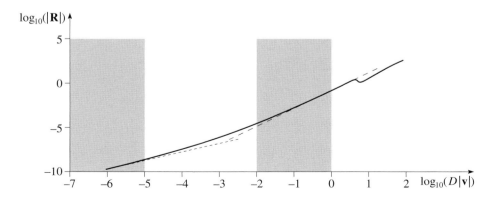

Notice the 'kink' when $\log_{10}(D|\mathbf{v}|)$ is approximately zero: in this region there is less air resistance as the sphere travels faster! The physical reason for this is that a highly chaotic layer of air develops around the sphere.

Figure 4.3 The experimental data for air resistance together with broken lines showing the two simplest models and their ranges of validity (shaded)

Consider a sphere of given diameter D. From Figure 4.3 it can be seen that the linear model applies for low velocities and the quadratic model applies for an intermediate range of velocities. Notice also that there are large ranges of velocities where neither of these simple models applies.

The air resistance force $\mathbf{R}$ always opposes the motion, i.e. it is in the direction of $-\mathbf{v}$. So the vector equations for the air resistance models given above are

$$\mathbf{R} = -c_1 D\mathbf{v} \quad \text{and} \quad \mathbf{R} = -c_2 D^2 |\mathbf{v}|\mathbf{v}.$$

Note that the vector and scalar statements of the quadratic air resistance model agree since
$$\left|(-c_2 D^2 |\mathbf{v}|\mathbf{v})\right| = c_2 D^2 |\mathbf{v}||\mathbf{v}|$$
$$= c_2 D^2 |\mathbf{v}|^2.$$

Air resistance

The **air resistance** force $\mathbf{R}$ on a smooth spherical object of diameter D travelling with velocity $\mathbf{v}$ can be modelled by

$$\mathbf{R} = \begin{cases} -c_1 D\mathbf{v} & \text{for } D|\mathbf{v}| \lesssim 10^{-5} & \text{(linear model)}, \\ -c_2 D^2 |\mathbf{v}|\mathbf{v} & \text{for } 10^{-2} \lesssim D|\mathbf{v}| \lesssim 1 & \text{(quadratic model)}, \end{cases}$$

where $c_1 \simeq 1.7 \times 10^{-4}$ and $c_2 \simeq 0.20$.

The use of these models is illustrated by examples, the first of which adds air resistance to Example 3.1.

Example 4.2

In Example 3.1 (page 66), the falling time for a marble dropped from the Clifton Suspension Bridge into the River Avon was calculated to be 3.96 seconds. The experimental value is 4.1 seconds. Can the discrepancy be accounted for by a linear air resistance model?

The investigation is subdivided into the following steps.

(a) Find how, under a linear air resistance model, the distance from the point of release varies with time for an arbitrary spherical object of mass m and diameter D.

(b) Calculate the time, under a linear air resistance model, that a marble of diameter 2 centimetres and mass 13 grams takes to fall the 77 metres from the Clifton Suspension Bridge into the River Avon below.

(c) Comment on the validity of the linear air resistance model for this problem.

Solution

(a) The picture is the same as in Example 3.1 — see Figure 3.1 on page 66. ◄Draw picture►

The x-axis, shown in Figure 3.1, points vertically downwards with its origin at the point where the marble is released. ◄Choose axes►

There are two forces acting on the marble, gravity downwards and air resistance upwards, as shown in the force diagram below. ◄Draw force diagram►

Apply Newton's second law to the marble to obtain ◄Apply Newton's 2nd law►

$$m\mathbf{a} = \mathbf{W} + \mathbf{R}. \tag{4.3}$$

From the force diagram, $\mathbf{W} = |\mathbf{W}|\mathbf{i} = mg\mathbf{i}$. Using the linear air resistance model, we have $\mathbf{R} = -c_1 D\mathbf{v} = -c_1 Dv\mathbf{i}$, since the motion is downwards. The acceleration is also downwards, so $\mathbf{a} = a\mathbf{i}$. Now we can resolve Equation (4.3) in the **i**-direction to obtain

$$ma = mg - c_1 Dv.$$

We want the distance x in terms of the time t. One way of obtaining this is to first use the substitution $a = dv/dt$, and then substitute dx/dt for v later. So we have

$$m\frac{dv}{dt} = mg - c_1 Dv.$$

◀Solve differential equation▶

Notice that the acceleration is not constant here, so we cannot use the constant acceleration formulae.

We now make the assumption that $mg - c_1 Dv > 0$ (i.e. the air resistance never becomes so strong as to overcome the marble's weight). Under this assumption, the differential equation can be solved by the separation of variables method, to obtain

$$\int \frac{m}{mg - c_1 Dv} \, dv = \int 1 \, dt,$$

which is equivalent to

$$\int \frac{1}{g - kv} \, dv = \int 1 \, dt,$$

This assumption is checked later. Notice that it is certainly true initially as the marble is dropped from rest.

where $k = c_1 D/m$. Integrating, using the assumption that $g - kv > 0$, gives

$$-\frac{1}{k}\ln(g - kv) = t + A, \tag{4.4}$$

Note that $g - kv > 0$ if $mg - c_1 Dv > 0$.

where A is an arbitrary constant. Rearranging gives

$$g - kv = e^{(-kt - kA)} = Be^{-kt},$$

where $B = e^{-kA}$ is another constant. The initial condition that the marble is initially at rest (i.e. $v = 0$ when $t = 0$) gives $B = g$, so

$$v = \frac{g}{k}\left(1 - e^{-kt}\right). \tag{4.5}$$

Writing dx/dt for v gives

$$\frac{dx}{dt} = \frac{g}{k}\left(1 - e^{-kt}\right).$$

Integrating gives

$$x = \frac{g}{k}t + \frac{g}{k^2}e^{-kt} + C.$$

Since c_1, D, t and m are all greater than or equal to zero, so that $kt > 0$, this equation predicts that $v < g/k = mg/c_1 D$ for all t, which is consistent with the assumption made in obtaining Equation (4.4).

The initial condition $x = 0$ when $t = 0$ gives $C = -g/k^2$, so

$$x = \frac{g}{k}t - \frac{g}{k^2}\left(1 - e^{-kt}\right), \tag{4.6}$$

where $k = c_1 D/m$.

(b) We want to find t given $x = 77$. To do this, we could try to rearrange Equation (4.6) to give t in terms of x; however, no such rearrangement is possible. We can use a numerical method, however. First we use the given data to interpret Equation (4.6) in the context of the current problem. We have

◀Interpret solution▶

$$k = \frac{c_1 D}{m} = \frac{1.7 \times 10^{-4} \times 0.02}{0.013} \simeq 2.6 \times 10^{-4},$$

so

$$x \simeq \frac{9.81}{2.6 \times 10^{-4}}t - \frac{9.81}{(2.6 \times 10^{-4})^2}\left(1 - e^{-2.6 \times 10^{-4} \times t}\right). \tag{4.7}$$

Now we already have two values for the time taken for the marble to fall 77 metres: 3.96 seconds estimated in Example 3.1, and 4.1 seconds given by experiment. Substituting these values for t into Equation (4.7), we obtain

$$x(3.96) \simeq 76.89 \quad \text{and} \quad x(4.1) \simeq 82.42.$$

So it looks like $t = 3.96$ is close to the solution of Equation (4.7) for $x = 77$. Trying $t = 3.97$ gives

$$x(3.97) \simeq 77.28.$$

Bisecting the interval $[3.96, 3.97]$, we try $t = 3.965$, which gives

$$x(3.965) \simeq 77.09.$$

So $t = 3.96$ (to two decimal places) when $x = 77$, i.e. the marble takes about 3.96 seconds to reach the River Avon under the linear air resistance model. This is exactly the same value, to two decimal places, as for the model without air resistance (Example 3.1).

More detailed calculation shows that the linear air resistance model predicts that the marble will hit the water approximately one thousandth of a second later than it will in the case of the model without air resistance.

(c) A condition for the linear air resistance model to be valid is that the product of the diameter of the marble and its speed is less than about 10^{-5}. Using Equation (4.5) gives $|\mathbf{v}(3.96)| \simeq 38.8\,\mathrm{m\,s^{-1}}$, so $D|\mathbf{v}| \simeq 0.78$, which is much greater than 10^{-5}. So the linear air resistance model is not appropriate. ∎

In fact, $D|\mathbf{v}(t)| \lesssim 10^{-5}$ for $t \lesssim 5.1 \times 10^{-5}$, so the linear model applies for only about the first 51 microseconds of the motion of the marble.

From Example 4.2 it seems that the linear air resistance model may apply only to objects moving very slowly — not to the speeds experienced in everyday life. So our attention turns to the quadratic air resistance model. In general, the differential equations that arise from this model are harder to solve than the ones that arise from the linear model. However, some of the differential equations are easily soluble, as the following example shows.

Example 4.3

Revisit the Clifton Suspension Bridge problem in Example 4.2 using the quadratic air resistance model.

(a) Derive an expression for the marble's velocity in terms of its position.

(b) Use the expression derived in part (a) to estimate the speed of the marble just before it hits the water.

(c) Is the quadratic air resistance model valid for this problem?

Solution

(a) Everything is the same as in Example 4.2 up to the point where we apply Newton's second law to the marble, to obtain

◀Apply Newton's 2nd law▶

$$m\mathbf{a} = \mathbf{W} + \mathbf{R}. \tag{4.8}$$

As before, $\mathbf{W} = mg\mathbf{i}$, but now we use the quadratic air resistance model $\mathbf{R} = -c_2 D^2 |\mathbf{v}|\mathbf{v}$. Since the motion is downwards, we have $\mathbf{v} = v\mathbf{i}$, so $\mathbf{R} = -c_2 D^2 v^2 \mathbf{i}$. Resolving Equation (4.8) in the $\mathbf{i}$-direction gives

$$ma = mg - c_2 D^2 v^2.$$

The question asks for v in terms of x, so we use the substitution $a = v\,dv/dx$ to obtain

◄Solve differential equation►

$$mv\frac{dv}{dx} = mg - c_2 D^2 v^2.$$

We now make the assumption that $mg - c_2 D^2 v^2 > 0$ (i.e. the air resistance never becomes so strong as to overcome the marble's weight). Under this assumption, the differential equation can be solved by separation of variables,

This assumption is checked later.

$$\int \frac{mv}{mg - c_2 D^2 v^2}\, dv = \int 1\, dx,$$

which is equivalent to

$$\int \frac{v}{g - kv^2}\, dv = \int 1\, dx,$$

where $k = c_2 D^2/m$. Integrating, using the assumption that $g - kv^2 > 0$, gives

Note that $g - kv^2 > 0$ if $mg - c_2 D^2 v^2 > 0$, as assumed.

$$-\frac{1}{2k} \ln(g - kv^2) = x + A,$$

where A is an arbitrary constant, so

$$g - kv^2 = e^{(-2kx - 2kA)} = Be^{-2kx},$$

where $B = e^{-2kA}$ is another constant. The initial condition that the marble is initially at rest at the origin (i.e. $v = 0$ when $x = 0$) gives $B = g$, so

$$g - kv^2 = ge^{-2kx}, \quad \text{or, equivalently,} \quad v^2 = \frac{g}{k}\left(1 - e^{-2kx}\right).$$

Therefore

$$v = \sqrt{\frac{g}{k}}\sqrt{1 - e^{-2kx}}, \tag{4.9}$$

where $k = c_2 D^2/m$ and we take the positive square root since we must have $v \geq 0$ from the description of the problem.

Note that c_2, D, x and m are all greater than or equal to zero, so $0 < \exp(-2kx) \leq 1$, and Equation (4.9) predicts that $v < \sqrt{g/k} = \sqrt{mg/c_2 D^2}$ for all t, which is consistent with the assumption made earlier.

(b) Substituting the values for the marble (see page 76) gives

◄Interpret solution►

$$k = \frac{c_2 D^2}{m} = \frac{0.2 \times (0.02)^2}{0.013} \simeq 6.2 \times 10^{-3},$$

so, from Equation (4.9),

$$v = \sqrt{\frac{9.81}{6.2 \times 10^{-3}}}\sqrt{1 - e^{-2 \times 6.2 \times 10^{-3} \times 77}} \simeq 31.2.$$

So the model predicts that the speed of the marble is about 31 metres per second just before it hits the water.

(c) To test whether the quadratic air resistance model applies to the motion, we must calculate $D|\mathbf{v}|$ and check that it is in the range 0.01 to 1. At the end of the motion, $D|\mathbf{v}(77)| \simeq 0.62$, which is within the limits of applicability of the model. The motion starts from rest, and $D|\mathbf{v}(0)| = 0$ is obviously outside the limits of the model. However, $D|\mathbf{v}(0.01)| \simeq 0.01$, so after the marble has dropped approximately one centimetre, the quadratic model applies. So the quadratic model applies for almost all of the motion. ∎

The given air resistance models apply only to smooth spherical objects. To apply these models to other objects, we have to model the objects as smooth spheres. The diameter of the sphere used to model an object is referred to as the **effective diameter** of the object. The following exercise makes use of this idea.

The determination of an effective diameter for an object is beyond the scope of this course.

Exercise 4.3

In the discussion leading up to the statement of Newton's second law in Section 2, the motion of an empty toboggan sliding on ice was considered. In this exercise, the effect of air resistance on the motion is examined.

Assume that the quadratic air resistance model applies, and that the effective diameter of the toboggan is 5 centimetres. If the toboggan has mass 2 kilograms and an initial speed of 2 metres per second, by what percentage has its speed diminished after travelling 100 metres?

Terminal velocity

The general equation for the velocity of an object falling from rest under gravity, ignoring the effects of air resistance, was derived in Example 3.1 as

$$v = gt.$$

This predicts that v increases indefinitely as t increases.

The general equation for the velocity of an object falling from rest under gravity with linear air resistance was derived in Example 4.2 to be

$$v = \frac{g}{k}\left(1 - e^{-kt}\right),$$

where $k = c_1 D/m$. The exponential term decreases to zero as time increases, so

$$v \to \frac{g}{k} = \frac{mg}{c_1 D} \quad \text{as } t \to \infty.$$

This behaviour, which is quite different from the case of the model that neglects air resistance, is illustrated in Figure 4.4. The limiting value is called the **terminal velocity** of the object and is denoted by v_T. So, in the case of the linear air resistance model, the terminal velocity (in SI units) is

$$v_T = \frac{g}{k} = \frac{mg}{c_1 D}. \tag{4.10}$$

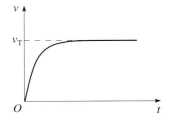

Figure 4.4

The quadratic air resistance model predicts results which are qualitatively similar to the linear case. The general equation for the velocity of an object falling from rest under gravity with quadratic air resistance was derived in Example 4.3 to be

$$v = \sqrt{\frac{g}{k}}\sqrt{1 - e^{-2kx}},$$

where $k = c_2 D^2/m$. The exponential term decreases to zero as x increases, so the quadratic model predicts a terminal velocity (in SI units) given by

$$v_T = \sqrt{\frac{g}{k}} = \sqrt{\frac{mg}{c_2 D^2}}. \tag{4.11}$$

There is another way of looking at the concept of terminal velocity. The equation of motion of an object falling from rest under gravity with linear air resistance is $ma = mg - c_1 Dv$; thus $v_T = mg/c_1 D$ is exactly that value of v for which $a = 0$. The equation of motion of an object falling from rest under gravity with quadratic air resistance is $ma = mg - c_2 D^2 v^2$; again $v_T = \sqrt{mg/c_2 D^2}$ is such that $a = 0$. Thus in each case the terminal velocity is the velocity at which the object can fall without accelerating, or in other

See Example 4.2.

See Example 4.3.

words at which the air resistance just balances the object's weight. This way of looking at terminal velocity enables us to derive equations for the terminal velocity for any falling object, irrespective of whether or not the object is falling from rest, as the following example illustrates.

Example 4.4

A small spider is blown by the wind into the high atmosphere and, once the wind has died away, falls back to Earth. The spider may be modelled as a sphere of effective diameter 2 millimetres.

If the spider has mass 0.004 grams, calculate the speed at which it will land, assuming that the fall is long enough for the spider effectively to reach terminal velocity.

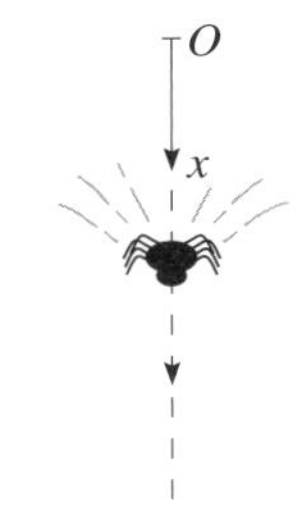

Solution

The first step is to draw a picture and mark the x-axis on it (Figure 4.5). Next draw the force diagram.

Figure 4.5

When the spider is travelling at its terminal velocity, it is not accelerating. Therefore by Newton's second law the resultant force on the spider must be zero, i.e.

$$\mathbf{W} + \mathbf{R} = \mathbf{0}. \tag{4.12}$$

Suppose that the linear air resistance model is valid.

The force models are $\mathbf{W} = mg\mathbf{i}$ and $\mathbf{R} = -c_1 D\mathbf{v_T}$. The motion is downwards, so $\mathbf{v_T} = v_T\mathbf{i}$. Resolving Equation (4.12) in the $\mathbf{i}$-direction gives

$$mg - c_1 Dv_T = 0,$$

so

$$v_T = \frac{mg}{c_1 D} = \frac{4 \times 10^{-6} \times 9.81}{1.7 \times 10^{-4} \times 0.002} \simeq 115.$$

So the terminal velocity of the spider under the linear air resistance model is about 115 metres per second. This gives $D|\mathbf{v_T}| \simeq 0.2$, which is much greater than 10^{-5}, so the linear air resistance model is not valid.

Now suppose that the quadratic air resistance model holds.

The weight is $\mathbf{W} = mg\mathbf{i}$, as before. The air resistance force is now given by the equation $\mathbf{R} = -c_2 D^2|\mathbf{v_T}|\mathbf{v_T}$. As before, the motion is downwards, so $\mathbf{v_T} = v_T\mathbf{i}$ and so $\mathbf{R} = -c_2 D^2 v_T^2 \mathbf{i}$. Resolving Equation (4.12) in the $\mathbf{i}$-direction gives

$$mg - c_2 D^2 v_T^2 = 0,$$

which can be rearranged to obtain

$$v_T = \sqrt{\frac{mg}{c_2 D^2}} = \sqrt{\frac{4 \times 10^{-6} \times 9.81}{0.2 \times (0.002)^2}} \simeq 7.$$

So the terminal velocity of the spider under the quadratic air resistance model is about 7 metres per second. This gives $D|\mathbf{v_T}| \simeq 0.014$, which is in the range of validity for the quadratic model. So the quadratic air resistance model is valid and gives a terminal velocity of about 7 metres per second. ∎

The results about the terminal velocity of objects falling under the influence of gravity and air resistance alone are summarized in the following box.

Terminal velocity under air resistance

The **terminal velocity** of an object falling under gravity and air resistance is the constant velocity that the object will acquire as time tends to infinity, and is the velocity at which air resistance just balances the object's weight. For an object of mass m and effective diameter D it is given (using SI units) by

$$v_T = \begin{cases} \dfrac{mg}{c_1 D} & \text{under the linear air resistance model,} \\[2ex] \sqrt{\dfrac{mg}{c_2 D^2}} & \text{under the quadratic air resistance model,} \end{cases}$$

where g is the magnitude of the acceleration due to gravity, $c_1 \simeq 1.7 \times 10^{-4}$ and $c_2 \simeq 0.20$.

The terminal velocity of an object is an important concept that is often the only quantity of interest in a problem including air resistance. For example, it is often assumed that the landing speed of a parachute is essentially its terminal velocity, so considering terminal velocity is a crucial aspect of the design of parachutes.

Exercise 4.4

A parachutist of mass 65 kilograms has a parachute of effective diameter 10 metres when fully opened. Estimate the landing speed of the parachutist, assuming that the parachute jump is long enough for the terminal velocity effectively to be reached.

4.3 Water resistance

The above models for the air resistance force can be equally well applied to motion through other gases and also liquids, with suitable changes in the constants appearing in the models. For example, the appropriate models for objects moving through water are as follows.

Water resistance

The **water resistance** force $\mathbf{R}$ on a smooth spherical object of diameter D travelling with velocity $\mathbf{v}$ can be modelled by

$$\mathbf{R} = \begin{cases} -d_1 D \mathbf{v} & \text{for } D|\mathbf{v}| \lesssim 10^{-6} & \text{(linear model),} \\ -d_2 D^2 |\mathbf{v}|\mathbf{v} & \text{for } 10^{-3} \lesssim D|\mathbf{v}| \lesssim 10^{-1} & \text{(quadratic model),} \end{cases}$$

where $d_1 \simeq 9.4 \times 10^{-3}$ and $d_2 \simeq 156$.

These models are used in exactly the same manner as the air resistance models, as the following example illustrates.

Example 4.5

Suppose that a water company decides to use water from a lake as a water source for a city. The lake water is contaminated with sand particles, so the water company decides to put the water into tanks which are 2 metres deep, to allow the sand to settle. The sand particles can be modelled as smooth spheres of diameter 5×10^{-5} m and mass 1.7×10^{-10} kg. How long does it take for the sand to settle?

Solution

A picture of one of the tanks and a sand particle is shown in Figure 4.6.   ◀Draw picture▶

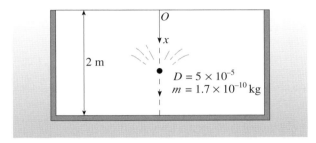

Figure 4.6

Choose the origin to be at the top of the tank, with the x-axis pointing downwards, as shown in Figure 4.6.   ◀Choose axes▶

The force diagram for a sand particle is as follows.   ◀Draw force diagram▶

Applying Newton's second law to the sand particle gives   ◀Apply Newton's 2nd law▶

$$m\mathbf{a} = \mathbf{W} + \mathbf{R}. \tag{4.13}$$

From the force diagram, $\mathbf{W} = |\mathbf{W}|\,\mathbf{i} = mg\mathbf{i}$. As a first model, we assume that the linear water resistance model is appropriate, i.e. $\mathbf{R} = -d_1 D\mathbf{v} = -d_1 Dv\mathbf{i}$, as the motion is downwards. Resolving Equation (4.13) in the $\mathbf{i}$-direction gives

$$ma = mg - d_1 Dv.$$

Using the substitution $a = dv/dt$ and rearranging, we obtain   ◀Solve differential equation▶

$$\frac{dv}{dt} = g - \frac{d_1 D}{m}v = g - kv,$$

where $k = d_1 D/m$ is a constant. Solving this differential equation by separation of variables,

$$\int \frac{1}{g - kv}\,dv = \int 1\,dt,$$

so

$$-\frac{1}{k}\ln(g - kv) = t + A.$$

Hence

$$g - kv = Be^{-kt},$$

As in Example 4.2, we assume that $g - kv > 0$ (i.e. the water resistance force never becomes so strong as to overcome the sand particle's weight).

where $B = e^{-kA}$ is a constant. The value of B can be determined using an initial condition. The sand particle that will take longest to settle out of the tank starts at the top of the tank from rest. So, in terms of the question to be answered, the initial condition to use is $v = 0$ when $t = 0$, which gives $B = g$. Therefore

$$v = \frac{g}{k}(1 - e^{-kt}).$$

The value of k can be evaluated as

$$k = \frac{d_1 D}{m} = \frac{9.4 \times 10^{-3} \times 5 \times 10^{-5}}{1.7 \times 10^{-10}} \simeq 2765.$$

Hence

$$v \simeq \frac{g}{2765}\left(1 - e^{-2765t}\right).$$

The exponential term in this equation becomes very small extremely quickly (e.g. after 10 milliseconds the exponential term is approximately 10^{-13}). So the sand particle quickly reaches a velocity of about $9.81/2765 \simeq 0.004\,\mathrm{m\,s^{-1}}$.

The validity of the linear model can now be checked: $D|\mathbf{v}| \simeq 10^{-7}$, so it is appropriate.

◀Interpret solution▶

This velocity is effectively the *terminal velocity* of the sand particle falling under gravity and water resistance.

The time for a particle to fall the 2-metre depth of the tank can now be estimated as $2/0.004 = 500\,\mathrm{s}$. So the model predicts that it will take approximately 500 seconds (or about 8 minutes) for the sand to settle in the tank. ■

As with the air resistance models, the water resistance models can be applied to objects other than smooth spheres by modelling the objects as smooth spheres. As before, the diameter of the sphere is referred to as the *effective diameter* of the object.

Exercise 4.5

A submarine is travelling horizontally through sea water. The actual diameter of the submarine is 10 metres, but due to streamlining it has an effective diameter of 1 metre for resistance force models. The maximum force that the engines can produce has magnitude 30 000 newtons. Assuming that the vertical forces are in equilibrium, so that the only forces that need to be modelled are the horizontal ones, what is a reasonable estimate for the maximum horizontal speed that the submarine can achieve?

End-of-section Exercises

Exercise 4.6

The maximum speed at which a parachutist can land safely is about 13 metres per second. Assuming that the parachute jump is long enough for the terminal velocity effectively to be reached, calculate the effective diameter of a parachute that will enable a parachutist of mass 70 kilograms to land safely.

Exercise 4.7

Revisit the Clifton Suspension Bridge problem described in Example 4.3, with different initial conditions. Assume now that instead of it being dropped from rest, the marble is catapulted downwards with an initial velocity of $50\,\mathrm{m\,s^{-1}}$. The initial stages of the solution will be exactly the same as in the example, since the initial conditions are not used until the solving the differential equation step. So the equation of motion of the marble is still

$$v\frac{dv}{dx} = g - kv^2,$$

where $k = c_2 D^2/m$ is a positive constant.

(a) Derive an expression for the marble's velocity in terms of its position.

(b) Describe the motion of the marble.

Outcomes

After studying this unit you should be able to:

- understand and use the basic terms for the description of the motion of particles: position, velocity and acceleration;
- understand, use and differentiate vector functions;
- understand the fundamental laws of Newtonian mechanics;
- solve mechanics problems in one dimension by drawing a sketch, choosing a suitable x-axis and origin, drawing a force diagram, applying Newton's second law, taking the x-component, and making suitable substitutions;
- solve mechanics problems in one dimension that involve one or more of the forces of gravity, friction, air resistance and water resistance;
- understand the concept of terminal velocity and use it in solving mechanics problems in one dimension.

Solutions to the exercises

Section 1

1.1 (a)

(b) (i) The distance between the first player and the back wall is the distance between where the puck starts and where it first changes direction. This can be read off the graph as 2 m.

(ii) The second player must be further away than the first player since the x-coordinate is negative when the puck changes direction for a second time.

(iii) The speed at which the puck is travelling is given by the slope of the distance–time graph. The slope after the second player hits the puck is greater than the slope after the first player hits the puck, so the second player gives the puck more speed.

1.2 (a) $\dfrac{d}{dt}\mathbf{r}(t) = \left(\dfrac{d}{dt}t^2\right)\mathbf{i} + \left(\dfrac{d}{dt}10t\right)\mathbf{j} = 2t\mathbf{i} + 10\mathbf{j}.$

So the velocity of the particle at $t = 1$ is
$$\mathbf{v} = 2\mathbf{i} + 10\mathbf{j},$$
and the speed is
$$|\mathbf{v}| = \sqrt{4 + 100} = \sqrt{104} \simeq 10.20.$$

(b) $\dfrac{d}{dt}\mathbf{r}(t) = (\cos t)\mathbf{i} - (\sin t)\mathbf{j} + \mathbf{k}.$

So the velocity of the particle at $t = 1$ is
$$\mathbf{v} = (\cos 1)\mathbf{i} - (\sin 1)\mathbf{j} + \mathbf{k},$$
and the speed is
$$|\mathbf{v}| = \sqrt{\cos^2 1 + \sin^2 1 + 1} = \sqrt{2} \simeq 1.41.$$

1.3 (a) The graph for particle A is its position–time graph. The velocity of the particle along the x-axis is given by the slope of this graph: it can be seen that the slope starts at a high value and decreases as time increases. So particle A is travelling fastest when $t = 0$.

(b) The graph for particle B shows the variation with time of the particle's velocity along the x-axis. For the particle to change direction, this velocity must change from positive to negative or from negative to positive (i.e. the graph must cross the t-axis). The graph shown does not do this, so particle B does not change its direction.

(c) The graph for particle C shows the variation with time of the particle's acceleration along the x-axis. To discover whether the particle is ever stationary for $t > 0$, we need to know whether its velocity along the x-axis is ever zero for $t > 0$. Now, since acceleration is obtained by differentiating velocity, we can obtain velocity by integrating acceleration. We also know that the definite integral of a function over a given interval gives the 'area' under the graph of the function, where 'areas' below the t-axis are negative. So the 'area' under the graph gives us the velocity.

Now, on the interval $[0, 2.5]$, the 'area' under the curve is positive, and, since the particle started from rest, the velocity after 2.5 seconds is positive. However, on the interval $[2.5, 5]$, the 'area' under the curve is negative, and furthermore the magnitude of this 'area' is greater than the magnitude of the 'area' for the interval $[0, 2.5]$; therefore the velocity after 5 seconds is negative. Hence, since the particle has both positive and negative velocity in the given time interval, it must be momentarily stationary at some point towards the end of the time interval.

1.4 Since
$$a(t) = \frac{dv}{dt} = 18t - 20,$$
we have
$$v = \int (18t - 20)\,dt = 9t^2 - 20t + A.$$

Using the initial condition $v(0) = 3$, we obtain $A = 3$. Hence the velocity of the particle is given by
$$v(t) = 9t^2 - 20t + 3.$$
Now $v(t) = dx/dt$, so
$$x = \int (9t^2 - 20t + 3)\,dt = 3t^3 - 10t^2 + 3t + B.$$

The initial condition $x(0) = 7$ gives $B = 7$. Hence the position of the particle is given by
$$x(t) = 3t^3 - 10t^2 + 3t + 7.$$
Substituting $t = 10$ into this expression gives
$$x(10) = 3000 - 1000 + 30 + 7 = 2037,$$
so at time $t = 10$ the particle is 2037 units along the positive x-axis.

1.5 We have
$$a(t) = \frac{dv}{dt} = ge^{-kt}.$$
Integrating this gives
$$v = \int ge^{-kt}\,dt = A - \frac{g}{k}e^{-kt}.$$

The initial condition $v(0) = 0$ gives $A = g/k$, so the velocity is given by
$$v(t) = \frac{g}{k} - \frac{g}{k}e^{-kt} = \frac{g}{k}(1 - e^{-kt}).$$
Then from $v(t) = dx/dt$ we have
$$x = \int \left(\frac{g}{k} - \frac{g}{k}e^{-kt}\right)dt = \frac{g}{k}t + \frac{g}{k^2}e^{-kt} + B.$$

The initial condition $x(0) = 0$ gives $B = -g/k^2$, so the position is given by

$$x(t) = \frac{g}{k}t + \frac{g}{k^2}e^{-kt} - \frac{g}{k^2} = \frac{g}{k}t - \frac{g}{k^2}(1 - e^{-kt}).$$

Therefore the velocity and position of the particle are given by the vector functions

$$\mathbf{v}(t) = \frac{g}{k}\left(1 - e^{-kt}\right)\mathbf{i},$$
$$\mathbf{r}(t) = \left(\frac{g}{k}t - \frac{g}{k^2}(1 - e^{-kt})\right)\mathbf{i}.$$

1.6 Given that $a(t) = a_0$, the relationship $a = v\,dv/dx$ gives

$$v\frac{dv}{dx} = a_0.$$

Applying the separation of variables method to this differential equation gives

$$\int v\,dv = \int a_0\,dx,$$

so

$$\tfrac{1}{2}v^2 = a_0 x + C.$$

Using the initial condition, that the velocity is v_0 along the x-axis at the origin (i.e. when $x = 0$), gives $C = \tfrac{1}{2}v_0^2$, so

$$\tfrac{1}{2}v^2 = a_0 x + \tfrac{1}{2}v_0^2.$$

Multiplying through by 2 and rearranging gives

$$v^2 = v_0^2 + 2a_0 x,$$

as required.

1.7 (a) To find v in terms of t, substitute dv/dt for a; then v may be found by direct integration. To find x in terms of t, substitute dx/dt for v and integrate again.

(b) To find a relationship between v and x, substitute $v\,dv/dx$ for a. The result is an equation that can be solved by separation of variables, whose solution will give the required relationship.

(c) To find x in terms of t, substitute d^2x/dt^2 for a, and dx/dt for v. The result is a linear constant-coefficient second-order differential equation for the variable x, namely $\ddot{x} + \dot{x} + x = \cos t$. This can be solved by the methods of *Unit 3*.

1.8 (a) (i) The speed of a car before the thinking phase is the value given in the table. The speed after the thinking phase is exactly the same, because the driver has not yet reacted to the hazard. So the acceleration is zero during this phase, and the formula $x = v_0 t + \tfrac{1}{2}a_0 t^2$ reduces to $x = v_0 t$.

The values of v_0 and the thinking distance x, in SI units, can be calculated from the values given in the table (using the conversion factors given in the margin next to the question); the only unknown is the thinking time t. The value of t for each pair of speeds and distances can be calculated from $t = x/v_0$.

The calculation for the first pair (20 mph, 20 feet), using the given conversion factors, is

$$t = \frac{x}{v_0} = \frac{20 \times 0.3048}{20 \times 0.447} \simeq 0.68\,\text{s}.$$

(Other pairs give the same value for the thinking time.) So the model used for calculating the thinking distance data is

$$x = v_0 t = 0.68 v_0.$$

(ii) The speed of a car at the start of the braking phase is the speed at the end of the thinking phase (i.e. the value given in the table). The speed at the end of the braking phase is zero ($v = 0$). Assuming that the braking is uniform, so that the acceleration is constant, we can use the formula $v^2 = v_0^2 + 2a_0 x$, which for $v = 0$ reduces to $0 = v_0^2 + 2a_0 x$.

The values of v_0 and the braking distance x, in SI units, can be calculated from the values given in the table; the only unknown is the acceleration a_0. The value of a_0 for each pair of speeds and distances can be calculated from $a_0 = -v_0^2/(2x)$. (Note that from this equation the acceleration is negative, which is a good check because the car is stopping!)

The calculation for the last pair of values given in the table is

$$a_0 = -\frac{v_0^2}{2x} = \frac{-(70 \times 0.447)^2}{2(245 \times 0.3048)} \simeq -6.55\,\text{m s}^{-2}.$$

(Other pairs give the same value for the acceleration, which is about two-thirds of the acceleration due to gravity.)

So the model used for calculating the braking distance data is

$$x = -\frac{v_0^2}{2a_0} = \frac{v_0^2}{13.1}.$$

(b) The overall stopping distance is equal to the thinking distance plus the braking distance, which are calculated separately using the models in part (a). The thinking distance at 45 mph is calculated using

$$x = 0.68 v_0 = 0.68 \times (45 \times 0.447) \simeq 13.68\,\text{m}.$$

The stopping distance at 45 mph is calculated using

$$x = \frac{v_0^2}{13.1} = \frac{(45 \times 0.447)^2}{13.1} \simeq 30.89\,\text{m}.$$

This gives an overall stopping distance of

$$13.68 + 30.89 = 44.57\,\text{m}.$$

(Note that the calculated distance is about 146 feet, which is nearly half-way between the tabulated values for 40 mph and 50 mph — it is not *exactly* half-way, because the braking distance is not a linear function of v_0.)

Section 2

2.1 Any moving car is subject to resistive forces, namely air resistance, the internal frictional forces in the car's engine, transmission and wheel bearings, and the external frictional forces between the car's tyres and the road. In order to maintain a constant velocity, it is necessary to apply a motive force that balances these resistive forces.

2.2 The component of the force of gravity in the direction of a unit vector pointing down the slope is non-zero. If the slope is steep enough, then this force down the slope will be greater than the resistive force of friction, causing the toboggan to accelerate.

2.3 Newton's second law, $\mathbf{F} = m\mathbf{a}$, is a vector equation. Taking the magnitude of both sides of the equation (and using the fact that mass is always positive) gives the scalar equation $|\mathbf{F}| = m|\mathbf{a}|$, into which the values given in the question can be substituted (after converting the mass from grams into the SI unit kilograms) to obtain

$$10 = 0.2|\mathbf{a}|.$$

This gives $|\mathbf{a}| = 50$, so the force produces an acceleration of magnitude $50\,\mathrm{m\,s^{-2}}$.

2.4 (a) The only forces on the hanging object are the tension force $\mathbf{T}$ due to the string (an upward force, in the direction of the positive x-axis shown) and the weight $\mathbf{W}$ of the object (a downward force, in the direction of the negative x-axis). The resultant force on the object is the sum $\mathbf{T} + \mathbf{W}$ of these forces. This information is shown in the force diagram below.

(b) Applying Newton's second law to this system gives

$$m\mathbf{a} = \mathbf{W} + \mathbf{T}. \tag{S.1}$$

From the force diagram, we have $\mathbf{W} = -|\mathbf{W}|\,\mathbf{i} = -mg\mathbf{i}$, where g is the magnitude of the acceleration due to gravity. Similarly, the tension force due to the string is $\mathbf{T} = |\mathbf{T}|\,\mathbf{i}$. The given acceleration of the hanging object is $1\,\mathrm{m\,s^{-2}}$ downwards, so $\mathbf{a} = -\mathbf{i}$. With this information we can resolve Equation (S.1) in the $\mathbf{i}$-direction to obtain

$$m \times (-1) = -mg + |\mathbf{T}|.$$

Substituting $m = 10$ and rearranging gives

$$|\mathbf{T}| = 10g - 10 \simeq 88.1 \quad (\text{using } g = 9.81\,\mathrm{m\,s^{-2}}).$$

So $\mathbf{T} = |\mathbf{T}|\,\mathbf{i} = 88.1\mathbf{i}$, i.e. the tension force due to the string is 88.1 newtons in the upward direction.

2.5 Substitute the given force and mass into the equation for Newton's second law to obtain

$$4000\,\mathbf{a} = 50\,000\,\mathbf{i} + 60\,000\,\mathbf{j} + 100\,000\,\mathbf{k}.$$

So $\mathbf{a} = 12.5\mathbf{i} + 15\mathbf{j} + 25\mathbf{k}$, which has a magnitude of approximately $32\,\mathrm{m\,s^{-2}}$. This is well below the threshold of $6g \simeq 59\,\mathrm{m\,s^{-2}}$, so the pilot should remain conscious.

Section 3

3.1 ◀Draw picture▶

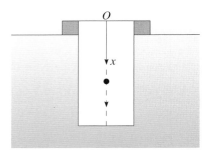

◀Choose axes▶

The x-axis is chosen to point vertically downwards, with the origin at the top of the well, as shown above.

◀Draw force diagram▶

The model assumes that the only force is gravity, so the force diagram is as follows.

◀Apply Newton's 2nd law▶

Applying Newton's second law to the stone gives $\mathbf{W} = m\mathbf{a}$. Since $\mathbf{W} = mg\mathbf{i}$, we have $m\mathbf{a} = mg\mathbf{i}$, and resolving in the $\mathbf{i}$-direction gives

$$a = g.$$

◀Solve differential equation▶

Using $a = dv/dt$, we obtain

$$\frac{dv}{dt} = g.$$

Integrating this gives

$$v = gt + A.$$

The initial condition that the stone is dropped from rest ($v = 0$ when $t = 0$) gives $A = 0$. Hence

$$v = gt. \tag{S.2}$$

Now using $v = dx/dt$, we have

$$\frac{dx}{dt} = gt.$$

Integrating this gives

$$x = \tfrac{1}{2}gt^2 + B.$$

The initial condition $x = 0$ when $t = 0$ gives $B = 0$. So

$$x = \tfrac{1}{2}gt^2. \tag{S.3}$$

◀Interpret solution▶

(a) Using Equation (S.3) with $t = 3$ gives

$$x = \tfrac{1}{2} \times 9.81 \times 3^2 = 44.15.$$

So the well is estimated to be about 44 m deep.

(b) Using Equation (S.2) with $t = 3$ gives

$$v = 9.81 \times 3 = 29.43.$$

So the predicted speed of the stone as it reaches the bottom is about $29\,\mathrm{m\,s^{-1}}$.

3.2

◀Draw picture▶

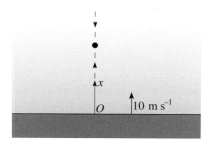

◀Choose axes▶

Choose the x-axis to point vertically upwards, with its origin at the point from which the ball is thrown, as shown above.

◀Draw force diagram▶

The model assumes that gravity is the only force acting on the ball, so the force diagram is as follows.

◀Apply Newton's 2nd law▶

Applying Newton's second law to the ball gives

$$m\mathbf{a} = \mathbf{W}. \tag{S.4}$$

Since the x-axis points upwards, the weight of the ball is given by $\mathbf{W} = -mg\mathbf{i}$. The acceleration is downwards, so $\mathbf{a} = a\mathbf{i}$. Resolving Equation (S.4) in the $\mathbf{i}$-direction gives $ma = -mg$. Dividing by the mass gives

$$a = -g.$$

◀Solve differential equation▶

To answer the question we need an equation relating x to t, and another relating v to t or to x. Since the acceleration $a = -g$ is constant, one approach is to use the constant acceleration formulae of Subsection 1.2. The initial velocity is $10\,\mathrm{m\,s^{-1}}$ upwards from the origin. So, using the notation of Subsection 1.2, we have $v_0 = 10$ and $a_0 = -g$, and hence

$$v = v_0 + a_0 t = 10 - gt, \tag{S.5}$$
$$x = v_0 t + \tfrac{1}{2}a_0 t^2 = 10t - \tfrac{1}{2}gt^2. \tag{S.6}$$

(The approach of Example 3.1, using the substitutions $a = dv/dt$ and $v = dx/dt$ and integrating, leads to the same pair of equations.)

◀Interpret solution▶

(a) The ball reaches its maximum height when $v = 0$, and from Equation (S.5) this occurs at time

$$t = \frac{10}{g} \simeq 1.$$

Since the motion started at $t = 0$, the duration of the upward flight of the ball is about 1 s.

(b) Substituting $t = 10/g$ into Equation (S.6), we have

$$x = \frac{100}{g} - \frac{100}{2g} \simeq 5.1.$$

So the maximum height attained by the ball is about 5.1 m.

(c) The ball reaches the ground when $x = 0$, and from Equation (S.6) this occurs when

$$0 = 10t - \tfrac{1}{2}gt^2 = t(10 - \tfrac{1}{2}gt).$$

Hence $t = 0$ or $t = 20/g$. Now $t = 0$ corresponds to the time when the ball is thrown, so the ball returns to the ground after a time $20/g \simeq 2\,\mathrm{s}$.

(d) Substituting $t = 20/g$ into Equation (S.5) gives

$$v = 10 - 20 = -10.$$

So the ball reaches the ground on its return with a speed of $10\,\mathrm{m\,s^{-1}}$. (The minus sign indicates that the ball is now travelling in the direction of decreasing x, i.e. downwards.)

3.3

(a) Choose the same x-axis and the same origin as in Example 3.1, and proceed in exactly the same way as before until you reach the equation $a = g$. Now write a as $v\,dv/dx$ to obtain

$$v\frac{dv}{dx} = g.$$

Solving this differential equation by the method of separation of variables, we have

$$\int v\,dv = \int g\,dx, \quad \text{so} \quad \tfrac{1}{2}v^2 = gx + A.$$

Now the marble starts from rest, so $v = 0$ when $x = 0$, which leads to $A = 0$. Hence $\tfrac{1}{2}v^2 = gx$, or, equivalently,

$$v = \sqrt{2gx}, \tag{S.7}$$

where we have taken the positive square root because the velocity is positive throughout the motion.

(Equation (S.7) could also have been obtained from the constant acceleration formula (1.3).)

(b) Putting $v = dx/dt$ in Equation (S.7) gives

$$\frac{dx}{dt} = \sqrt{2gx}.$$

Again we use the method of separation of variables to solve this differential equation. So we have

$$\int 1\,dt = \int \frac{1}{\sqrt{2gx}}\,dx = \frac{1}{\sqrt{2g}}\int x^{-1/2}dx,$$

so

$$t = \sqrt{\frac{2x}{g}} + B.$$

The marble starts at the origin, so $x = 0$ when $t = 0$, which gives $B = 0$. Hence

$$t = \sqrt{\frac{2x}{g}}. \tag{S.8}$$

(Equation (S.8) could also have been obtained from the constant acceleration formula (1.2).)

(c) At $x = 77$, Equation (S.8) yields

$$t = \sqrt{\frac{2 \times 77}{9.81}} \simeq 3.962,$$

and Equation (S.7) gives

$$v = \sqrt{2 \times 9.81 \times 77} \simeq 38.87.$$

So the object hits the water after about 3.96 s, with a speed of about $38.9\,\mathrm{m\,s^{-1}}$. (The answers are, of course, the same as those in Example 3.1.)

3.4 As the questions ask for the speed for two different angles of the slope of the jump, it is sensible (as suggested in Figure 3.3) to use θ to be an arbitrary angle of slope and substitute for θ at the end.

◀Draw picture▶

A diagram of the situation is shown next to the exercise as Figure 3.3, and is repeated here.

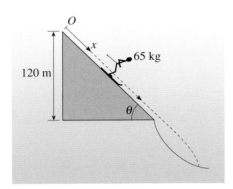

◀Choose axes▶

The x-axis is given as pointing down the slope with origin at the top of the slope, as shown above.

◀Draw force diagram▶

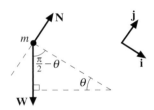

◀Apply Newton's 2nd law▶

Applying Newton's second law to the skier gives

$$ma = \mathbf{W} + \mathbf{N}. \tag{S.9}$$

From the force diagram, $\mathbf{N} = |\mathbf{N}|\mathbf{j}$. We can resolve $\mathbf{W}$ into components using the formula from *Unit 4*:

$$\mathbf{W} = |\mathbf{W}|\cos(\tfrac{\pi}{2} - \theta)\,\mathbf{i} + |\mathbf{W}|\cos(\pi - \theta)\,\mathbf{j}$$
$$= mg\sin\theta\,\mathbf{i} - mg\cos\theta\,\mathbf{j}.$$

Now we can resolve Equation (S.9) in the $\mathbf{i}$-direction to obtain

$$ma = mg\sin\theta,$$

so

$$a = g\sin\theta.$$

◀Solve differential equation▶

Since we want the velocity when the skier has travelled a vertical distance of 120 metres, it is best to find v as a function of x. Since the acceleration is constant, we can use Equation (1.3) to obtain

$$v^2 = v_0^2 + 2ax = 0 + 2(g\sin\theta)x,$$

so

$$v = \sqrt{2gx\sin\theta}. \tag{S.10}$$

◀Interpret solution▶

(a) The task is to find the velocity when the skier has travelled a vertical distance of 120 metres. Now x is the distance travelled down the slope; so, using trigonometry, $x = 120/\sin\theta$. Substituting for x in Equation (S.10) gives

$$v = \sqrt{2g \times \frac{120}{\sin\theta} \times \sin\theta} = \sqrt{240g} \simeq 48.5.$$

So the speed of the skier at the bottom of the slope angled at $\frac{\pi}{4}$ is about $48.5\,\mathrm{m\,s^{-1}}$.

(b) In part (a), all mention of θ cancelled from the final expression. So the answer remains the same: the speed at the bottom of the $\frac{\pi}{3}$ slope is about $48.5\,\mathrm{m\,s^{-1}}$. (In *Unit 8* you will see that this result can be explained by considering the energy of the skier.)

3.5   ◀Draw picture▶

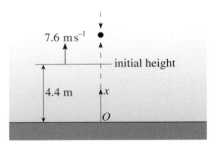

◀Choose axes▶

The x-axis is chosen to point vertically upwards with the origin at ground level, as shown in the diagram. (The other obvious choice for the origin, which you may well have chosen, is at the point where the ball is thrown. Both choices of course lead to the same answers to (a) and (b) below.)

◀Draw force diagram▶

The model assumes that the only force acting on the ball is gravity, so the force diagram is as follows.

◀Apply Newton's 2nd law▶

Applying Newton's second law to the ball gives $m\mathbf{a} = \mathbf{W}$, where $\mathbf{W} = -mg\mathbf{i}$ (as the x-axis points upwards). Resolving in the $\mathbf{i}$-direction gives

$$ma = -mg, \quad \text{so } a = -g.$$

◀Solve differential equation▶

We want equations relating x to t, and v to x or t. One approach is to use the substitution $a = dv/dt$, to obtain

$$\frac{dv}{dt} = -g.$$

Integrating this, we obtain

$$v = -gt + A.$$

The initial velocity of the ball is $7.6\mathbf{i}$, so $v = 7.6$ when $t = 0$, which gives $A = 7.6$. So

$$v = -gt + 7.6. \tag{S.11}$$

Therefore, using the substitution $v = dx/dt$ gives

$$\frac{dx}{dt} = -gt + 7.6.$$

Integrating this gives

$$x = -\tfrac{1}{2}gt^2 + 7.6t + B.$$

The initial condition that $x = 4.4$ when $t = 0$ leads to $B = 4.4$. So

$$x = -\tfrac{1}{2}gt^2 + 7.6t + 4.4. \tag{S.12}$$

(Since the acceleration is constant, another approach is use the constant acceleration formulae to obtain Equations (S.11) and (S.12). Note that, with the choice of origin used here, $x_0 = 4.4$ (i.e. $x \neq 0$ when $t = 0$), so you would have to use the equation $x = x_0 + v_0 t + \tfrac{1}{2}a_0 t^2$ rather than $x = v_0 t + \tfrac{1}{2}a_0 t^2$ to obtain Equation (S.12).)

◄Interpret solution►

(a) The ball reaches the ground when $x = 0$. Substituting this into Equation (S.12) gives a quadratic equation for the time t,

$$4.905t^2 - 7.6t - 4.4 = 0,$$

whose solution is

$$t = \frac{7.6 \pm \sqrt{7.6^2 + 4 \times 4.905 \times 4.4}}{2 \times 4.905},$$

so $t \simeq 1.998$ or -0.4489. The negative time is before the ball is thrown and may therefore be ignored. So the ball lands about 2 seconds after being thrown.

(b) Substituting this time into Equation (S.11) gives

$$v = -9.81 \times 1.998 + 7.6 \simeq -12.00.$$

So the ball lands with a speed of about $12\,\mathrm{m\,s^{-1}}$. (The negative sign for v confirms that the ball is moving downwards.)

Section 4

4.1 (a)　　　　　　　　　　　　◄Draw picture►

Let θ be the angle that the carrier makes with the horizontal, as shown below, and let m be the mass of the block.

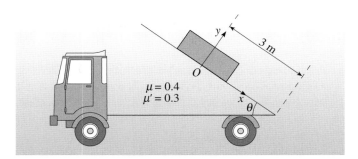

◄Choose axes►

Choose the axes to be parallel and perpendicular to the carrier, with origin at the rest position of the concrete block, as shown above.

◄Draw force diagram►

Modelling the block as a particle then gives the following force diagram.

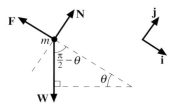

◄Apply law(s)►

The equilibrium condition for the block is

$$\mathbf{F} + \mathbf{N} + \mathbf{W} = \mathbf{0}. \tag{S.13}$$

When the block is on the point of moving, the magnitude of the friction force is given by

$$|\mathbf{F}| = \mu|\mathbf{N}|. \tag{S.14}$$

◄Solve equation(s)►

From the force diagram, $\mathbf{N} = |\mathbf{N}|\mathbf{j}$ and $\mathbf{F} = -|\mathbf{F}|\mathbf{i}$. The weight can be resolved into components using the formula from *Unit 4*:

$$\begin{aligned}\mathbf{W} &= |\mathbf{W}|\cos(\tfrac{\pi}{2} - \theta)\,\mathbf{i} + |\mathbf{W}|\cos(\pi - \theta)\,\mathbf{j} \\ &= mg\sin\theta\,\mathbf{i} - mg\cos\theta\,\mathbf{j}.\end{aligned}$$

Now Equation (S.13) can be resolved in the $\mathbf{i}$-direction, giving $-|\mathbf{F}| + mg\sin\theta = 0$, so

$$|\mathbf{F}| = mg\sin\theta.$$

Resolving Equation (S.13) in the $\mathbf{j}$-direction gives $|\mathbf{N}| - mg\cos\theta = 0$, so

$$|\mathbf{N}| = mg\cos\theta.$$

But when the block is on the point of slipping, Equation (S.14) applies, and substituting the values of $|\mathbf{F}|$ and $|\mathbf{N}|$ gives

$$mg\sin\theta = \mu mg\cos\theta.$$

Rearranging this gives

$$\tan\theta = \mu.$$

◄Interpret solution►

Substituting $\mu = 0.4$ into this equation gives $\theta = \arctan 0.4 \simeq 0.381$.

So the angle at which the concrete block begins to slide is about 0.381 radians.

(b) To solve the dynamics problem when the block is in motion down the carrier, we start in exactly the same way as for the statics problem. So we start the analysis of the motion by applying Newton's second law.

◄Apply Newton's 2nd law►

Applying Newton's second law to the block gives

$$m\mathbf{a} = \mathbf{F} + \mathbf{N} + \mathbf{W}. \tag{S.15}$$

The acceleration is down the carrier, so $\mathbf{a} = a\mathbf{i}$ and all the forces are resolved in exactly the same way as in the statics problem. So we can resolve Equation (S.15) in the $\mathbf{i}$-direction to obtain

$$ma = mg \sin \theta - |\mathbf{F}|. \qquad (S.16)$$

Now, from the moment at which the block begins to slide, $|\mathbf{F}| = \mu'|\mathbf{N}|$, so Equation (S.16) becomes

$$ma = mg \sin \theta - \mu'|\mathbf{N}|. \qquad (S.17)$$

To find $|\mathbf{N}|$, we resolve Equation (S.15) in the $\mathbf{j}$-direction to obtain

$$0 = -mg \cos \theta + |\mathbf{N}|.$$

Therefore $|\mathbf{N}| = mg \cos \theta$ (as before). Substituting this into Equation (S.17) gives

$$ma = mg \sin \theta - \mu' mg \cos \theta,$$

so

$$a = g \sin \theta - \mu' g \cos \theta. \qquad (S.18)$$

◀Solve differential equation▶

For a fixed angle θ, the acceleration is constant, so we can use the constant acceleration formulae from Section 1. Since we want to relate time to distance travelled, the appropriate formula is

$$x = v_0 t + \tfrac{1}{2} a_0 t^2.$$

Initially, the block is at rest, so $v_0 = 0$ and the equation becomes

$$x = \tfrac{1}{2} g (\sin \theta - \mu' \cos \theta) t^2. \qquad (S.19)$$

◀Interpret solution▶

The time before the block slides off the back of the truck is calculated from Equation (S.19) with the value of θ calculated in part (a). Substituting the distance travelled ($x = 3$) and $\mu' = 0.3$, we obtain

$$3 \simeq \tfrac{1}{2} g [\sin(0.381) - 0.3 \cos(0.381)] t^2 \simeq 0.458 t^2,$$

so $t \simeq 2.56$.

So, once the concrete block begins to slide, it takes about 2.6 seconds to slide off the back of the truck.

4.2

◀Draw picture▶

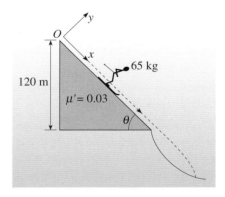

◀Choose axes▶

The x-axis is given to be parallel to the slope with origin at the top of the slope. Choose the y-axis to be perpendicular to the slope, as shown above.

◀Draw force diagram▶

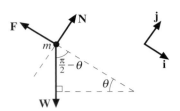

◀Apply Newton's 2nd law▶

Applying Newton's second law to the skier gives

$$m\mathbf{a} = \mathbf{W} + \mathbf{N} + \mathbf{F}. \qquad (S.20)$$

From the force diagram, $\mathbf{N} = |\mathbf{N}|\mathbf{j}$ and $\mathbf{F} = -|\mathbf{F}|\mathbf{i}$. The weight can be resolved using the formula from *Unit 4*:

$$\begin{aligned} \mathbf{W} &= |\mathbf{W}| \cos(\tfrac{\pi}{2} - \theta)\mathbf{i} + |\mathbf{W}| \cos(\pi - \theta)\mathbf{j} \\ &= mg \sin \theta \, \mathbf{i} - mg \cos \theta \, \mathbf{j}. \end{aligned}$$

The acceleration is down the slope, so $\mathbf{a} = a\mathbf{i}$, and we can resolve Equation (S.20) in the $\mathbf{i}$-direction to obtain

$$ma = mg \sin \theta + 0 - |\mathbf{F}|. \qquad (S.21)$$

Using $|\mathbf{F}| = \mu'|\mathbf{N}| = 0.03|\mathbf{N}|$, Equation (S.21) becomes

$$ma = mg \sin \theta - 0.03|\mathbf{N}|. \qquad (S.22)$$

Resolving Equation (S.20) in the $\mathbf{j}$-direction leads to

$$0 = -mg \cos \theta + |\mathbf{N}| + 0,$$

so $|\mathbf{N}| = mg \cos \theta$. Substituting into Equation (S.22) gives

$$ma = mg \sin \theta - 0.03 \times mg \cos \theta,$$

so

$$a = g \sin \theta - 0.03g \cos \theta.$$

◀Solve differential equation▶

Using Equation (1.3), we obtain

$$v^2 = v_0^2 + 2ax = 0 + 2(g \sin \theta - 0.03g \cos \theta)x,$$

so

$$v = \sqrt{2g(\sin \theta - 0.03 \cos \theta)x}. \qquad (S.23)$$

◀Interpret solution▶

(a) As in Exercise 3.4, $x = 120/\sin \theta$, so from Equation (S.23),

$$\begin{aligned} v &= \sqrt{2g(\sin \theta - 0.03 \cos \theta)\frac{120}{\sin \theta}} \\ &= \sqrt{240g - 7.2g \cot \theta}. \end{aligned}$$

Substituting $\theta = \tfrac{\pi}{4}$ into this equation gives $v \simeq 47.8$.

So the speed of the skier at the bottom of the slope angled at $\tfrac{\pi}{4}$ is about $47.8 \, \text{m s}^{-1}$.

(b) Substituting $\theta = \tfrac{\pi}{3}$ into the equation gives $v \simeq 48.1$.

So the speed of the skier at the bottom of the slope angled at $\tfrac{\pi}{3}$ is about $48.1 \, \text{m s}^{-1}$.

From the answers to (a) and (b), it can be seen that the steeper the slope, the faster the final speed of the skier. The final speed is always less than the $48.5 \, \text{m s}^{-1}$ calculated in Exercise 3.4, which omitted friction from the model.

4.3

◀Draw picture▶

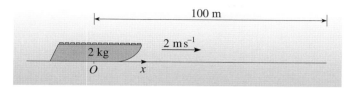

◀Choose axes▶

Choose the x-axis along the direction of motion, with origin at the point where the toboggan has speed $2\,\mathrm{m\,s^{-1}}$, as shown in the diagram.

◀Draw force diagram▶

The vertical forces $\mathbf{W}$ and $\mathbf{N}$ are in equilibrium and do not affect the motion. This leaves only the air resistance force, $\mathbf{R}$, which opposes the motion, as shown in the force diagram below.

$$\mathbf{R} \longleftarrow \bullet\ 2\,\mathrm{kg}$$

◀Apply Newton's 2nd law▶

Applying Newton's second law gives

$$m\mathbf{a} = \mathbf{R}.$$

The exercise states that the quadratic air resistance model should be used, so $\mathbf{R} = -c_2 D^2|\mathbf{v}|\mathbf{v} = -c_2 D^2 v^2\mathbf{i}$. Resolving in the $\mathbf{i}$-direction gives

$$ma = -c_2 D^2 v^2.$$

◀Solve differential equation▶

The question requires the velocity of the toboggan after $100\,\mathrm{m}$, so we use the substitution $a = v\,dv/dx$ to obtain

$$mv\frac{dv}{dx} = -c_2 D^2 v^2.$$

Solving by separation of variables,

$$\int \frac{1}{v}\,dv = -\int k\,dx,$$

where $k = c_2 D^2/m$, so

$$\ln v = -kx + A.$$

Hence

$$v = Be^{-kx},$$

where $B = e^A$. The initial condition that the toboggan is initially moving at $2\,\mathrm{m\,s^{-1}}$ (i.e. $v = 2$ when $x = 0$) gives $B = 2$, so

$$v = 2e^{-kx},$$

where $k = c_2 D^2/m$.

◀Interpret solution▶

Substitute the data given in the question to find the velocity after $100\,\mathrm{m}$:

$$k = \frac{c_2 D^2}{m} = \frac{0.2 \times (0.05)^2}{2} = 2.5 \times 10^{-4},$$

$$v(100) = 2\exp(-2.5 \times 10^{-4} \times 100) \simeq 1.95.$$

So the percentage decrease in velocity is about

$$100\frac{v(0) - v(100)}{v(0)} = 100\frac{2 - 1.95}{2} = 2.5,$$

i.e. after $100\,\mathrm{m}$ the toboggan has lost only about 2.5% of its speed.

4.4

First suppose that the linear air resistance model applies, so that the terminal velocity is

$$v_{\mathrm{T}} = \frac{mg}{c_1 D} = \frac{65 \times 9.81}{1.7 \times 10^{-4} \times 10} \simeq 4 \times 10^5.$$

So $Dv_{\mathrm{T}} \simeq 4 \times 10^6$, which is greater than 10^{-5}, so the linear model does not apply.

Now suppose that the quadratic model applies, so that the terminal velocity is

$$v_{\mathrm{T}} = \sqrt{\frac{mg}{c_2 D^2}} = \sqrt{\frac{65 \times 9.81}{0.2 \times 10^2}} \simeq 5.6.$$

So $Dv_{\mathrm{T}} \simeq 56$, which is greater than 1, so the quadratic model does not apply either.

The condition for the quadratic model is closer to being satisfied than the condition for the linear model, so the quadratic model is likely to produce the better estimate. So the conclusion is that the landing speed of the parachutist is approximately $6\,\mathrm{m\,s^{-1}}$.

(Looking at Figure 4.3 (page 75), it can be seen that $6\,\mathrm{m\,s^{-1}}$ (with $D = 10$, so that $\log_{10}(D|\mathbf{v}|) \simeq 1.8$) falls to the right of the range of validity of the quadratic model. In this region, you can see that the quadratic model lies just above the experimental curve, so that it gives a slight overestimate of the air resistance. So it should be expected that the actual landing speed is slightly greater than $6\,\mathrm{m\,s^{-1}}$.)

4.5

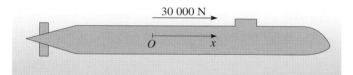

Choose the x-axis to be aligned with the submarine's motion, as shown in the diagram.

The horizontal forces on the submarine are shown in the following force diagram, in which $\mathbf{R}$ is the resistance force and $\mathbf{E}$ is the force of the engines.

$$\mathbf{R} \longleftarrow \overset{m}{\bullet} \longrightarrow \mathbf{E}$$

If the submarine has effectively reached the required maximum velocity, then the acceleration is zero and so, by Newton's second law, the resultant force must be zero, i.e.

$$\mathbf{E} + \mathbf{R} = \mathbf{0}.$$

Resolving in the $\mathbf{i}$-direction gives

$$30\,000 + \mathbf{R} \cdot \mathbf{i} = 0. \tag{S.24}$$

First assume a linear model for the resistance force, so that $\mathbf{R} = -d_1 D\mathbf{v}$. Substituting this into Equation (S.24) gives

$$30\,000 - d_1 Dv = 0,$$

so

$$v = \frac{30\,000}{d_1 D} = \frac{30\,000}{9.4 \times 10^{-3} \times 1} \simeq 3.2 \times 10^6.$$

For this model to be valid, we must have $Dv \lesssim 10^{-6}$. This is not true, so the linear model is not valid.

Now assume a quadratic model for the resistance force, so that $\mathbf{R} = -d_2 D^2 |\mathbf{v}| \mathbf{v}$, and substitute this into Equation (S.24) to obtain

$$30\,000 - d_2 D^2 v^2 = 0.$$

Therefore

$$v = \sqrt{\frac{30\,000}{d_2 D^2}} = \sqrt{\frac{30\,000}{156 \times 1^2}} \simeq 14.$$

For this model to apply we must have $10^{-3} \lesssim Dv \lesssim 10^{-1}$, which is not true. So the quadratic model does not apply either; but it is a much better approximation than the linear one, since Dv is much nearer the range of validity of the model.

So our best estimate of the maximum horizontal speed of the submarine is $14\,\mathrm{m\,s^{-1}}$ (or, in nautical units, 26 knots).

4.6 You saw in Exercise 4.4 that the quadratic air resistance model is better than the linear model for problems of this type. Rearrangement of the quadratic model $v_\mathrm{T} = \sqrt{mg/c_2 D^2}$ gives

$$D = \sqrt{\frac{mg}{c_2 v_\mathrm{T}^2}} = \sqrt{\frac{70 \times 9.81}{0.2 \times 13^2}} \simeq 4.5.$$

So the effective diameter needs to be at least 4.5 metres. As in the solution to Exercise 4.4, we have $\log_{10}(D|\mathbf{v}|) = \log_{10}(4.5 \times 13) \simeq 1.8$, so the quadratic model over-estimates the air resistance in this case. So, to be safe, a parachute with effective diameter of 5 or even 6 metres would probably be needed.

4.7 (a) The equation of motion of the marble is given in the question as

$$v\frac{dv}{dx} = g - kv^2,$$

where $k = c_2 D^2/m$ is a positive constant.

Proceeding as in the example, we solve the differential equation by separation of variables:

$$\int \frac{v}{g - kv^2}\, dv = \int 1\, dx.$$

Now the first difference due to the changing initial conditions occurs, since if $v = 50\,\mathrm{m\,s^{-1}}$, then

$$g - kv^2 = 9.81 - \frac{0.2 \times (0.02)^2 \times (50)^2}{0.013} \simeq -5.6.$$

So the denominator of the first integrand is negative (whereas it was positive before). Re-writing this to make the denominator positive gives

$$-\int \frac{v}{kv^2 - g}\, dv = \int 1\, dx,$$

so

$$-\frac{1}{2k}\ln(kv^2 - g) = x + A.$$

To determine A, use the initial condition that $v = v_0$ when $x = 0$:

$$-\frac{1}{2k}\ln(kv_0^2 - g) = 0 + A.$$

Substituting for A and rearranging gives

$$-2kx = \ln(kv^2 - g) - \ln(kv_0^2 - g),$$

so

$$e^{-2kx} = \frac{kv^2 - g}{kv_0^2 - g}$$

or

$$e^{-2kx}(kv_0^2 - g) = kv^2 - g,$$

thus

$$kv^2 = g + e^{-2kx}(kv_0^2 - g). \qquad \text{(S.25)}$$

So

$$v = \sqrt{\frac{g}{k} + e^{-2kx}\frac{kv_0^2 - g}{k}}.$$

(b) The eventual behaviour of the velocity can be seen from Equation (S.25), since as x becomes larger, the exponential term will become vanishingly small. So as x becomes larger, v satisfies the equation

$$g = kv^2.$$

This means that the velocity will tend to $\sqrt{g/k}$ as x becomes larger.

This is the same eventual behaviour as in Example 4.3, i.e. the marble's speed tends to a terminal velocity. Moreover, the terminal velocity $\sqrt{g/k}$ has the same value as for the marble falling from rest. Now, however, the speed *decreases* exponentially towards the terminal velocity. The behaviour is shown in the following sketch.

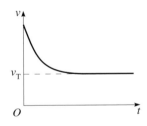

UNIT 7   Oscillations

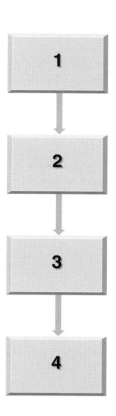

Study guide for Unit 7

This unit continues with the theme of Newtonian mechanics, as introduced and developed in *Units 5* and *6*. It assumes the following background knowledge (in addition to the material in *Unit 1*):

- solving second-order linear constant-coefficient differential equations (*Unit 3*);
- taking the dot product of two vectors (*Unit 4*);
- solving statics problems (*Unit 5*);
- applying Newton's second law to mechanics problems (*Unit 6*).

The sections should be studied in their numerical order, if possible.

The results and methods from Sections 2, 3 and 4 will be required later in the course, particularly in *Units 17* and *18*.

Introduction

All around you there are mechanical systems that vibrate or oscillate (the two words can be used interchangeably). Each day you probably experience oscillations in a wide variety of forms: the buzzing of an alarm clock, the vibrations of an electric hair-drier or razor, the sideways movements of a train or boat, and so on. Vibrations vary in scale from the small motions of atoms within solid objects, to the swaying of bridges and tall buildings; and from the irregular bending of a tree in the wind, to the extremely regular oscillations involved in any device that is designed to measure accurately the passage of time.

A common feature of many of these vibrations or oscillations is *periodicity*, where the vibration exhibits a pattern of movement or displacement that repeats itself over and over again as time progresses. Not all oscillations repeat themselves exactly. They may become more or less pronounced if the system is *forced* or *damped*, or the oscillations may even become chaotic. In this unit, however, attention will be directed towards systems for which the effects of damping or forcing are of secondary importance. We model these systems by assuming that such complicating effects may be ignored completely. As a result, the behaviour predicted by the model is periodic and, in particular, *sinusoidal* (having a pattern of motion in which the displacement can be represented by a sine or cosine function of time).

Sinusoidal oscillations arise in a wide variety of electrical, thermal and mechanical systems, but we concentrate here on the last of these. In this context, the sinusoidal nature of the oscillations can often be seen as a consequence of a further modelling assumption: namely, that the force acting on a moving object in order to bring it back towards its equilibrium position is proportional to its displacement from that position. This 'force law' was first put forward by Robert Hooke, in 1678. As an aid to visualizing this type of force, we introduce the concept of a *model spring* to embody it. The sinusoidal behaviour that arises from a model spring is known as *simple harmonic motion*, and is the simplest effective model for an oscillating system.

A model spring is a hypothetical object that can be either stretched or compressed from its 'natural length', and for which the force exerted depends on its length. This is in contrast to the *model string* introduced in *Unit 5*. A model string is inelastic, and hence has a fixed length, though it is capable of sustaining a range of pulling forces. The model spring, on the other hand, can provide pushing as well as pulling forces.

Figure 0.1 shows, in diagrammatic form, some of the systems that we shall discuss. In each case, part of the system moves up and down, or to and fro, about an average position. We shall attempt to explain these oscillations by applying the laws of Newtonian mechanics.

You saw some examples of oscillations in *Unit 3*.

Forced and damped oscillations are considered in *Unit 17*. You met them briefly in *Unit 3*.

The motion of the pendulum in *Unit 3* was described by a sinusoidal function.

This force is often referred to as a *restoring force*.

Robert Hooke (1635–1703) was a contemporary of Isaac Newton. There was a dispute between the two men as to which had first proposed an inverse square law to describe the effects of gravitation.

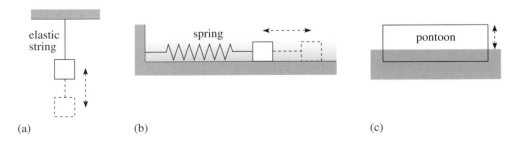

(a)   (b)   (c)

Figure 0.1

The system in Figure 0.1(a) is a weight hanging from an elastic string. This is a simplified representation of the system for which experiments are described in Section 1, and could also be regarded as a model for a 'baby bouncer'. Figure 0.1(b) shows an object connected to a spring, which is attached to a fixed point at its other end. This might be used as a model for a spring-loaded buffer, which reverses the motion of a vehicle making contact with it. Alternatively, it could model the release mechanism in a pinball machine while in contact with the ball. Figure 0.1(c) represents a floating pontoon, bobbing up and down in water.

Section 1 describes a simple experiment involving an oscillating system. Various aspects of this simple experiment are analysed throughout the unit, as the theory develops. Section 2 introduces *Hooke's law* as a model for the force exerted by a spring, and goes on to consider how this law applies in various situations where no movement takes place. Section 3 uses Newton's second law to model the oscillations of the simplest oscillating system, which consists of a single particle attached to a single horizontal spring. In Section 4 more systems are analysed, such as vertical springs and systems with two springs.

Unit 18 takes up this story where more than one particle is involved.

1 A home-made oscillating system

To introduce oscillations, we describe the behaviour of a simple mechanical system set up at home, first in equilibrium (at rest) and then in motion.

1.1 Description of the experiment

The mechanical system to be considered is illustrated in Figure 1.1. It was constructed by tying together several rubber bands, to produce an elastic string, which was then used to suspend a small bag from a door lintel. The bag itself had little mass, but it contained a number of identical coins, each of which had mass 10 grams (0.01 kg).

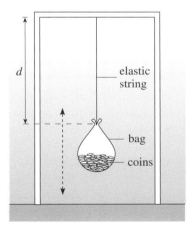

The position of a point at the top of the bag was specified by its depth d below the door lintel, as shown in Figure 1.1. This depth is the same as the length of the elastic string. First, d was measured with the bag static, that is, in equilibrium. Then observations were made of how d varied with time when the bag was set in motion by raising it up and releasing it. Both stages of the experiment were repeated with different numbers of coins in the bag.

Figure 1.1

1.2 Results for a static bag

With 5 coins in the bag, it was found to remain static when the depth of the bag below the lintel was 0.37 metres. We shall call this value of d the static depth of the bag, and denote it by the symbol d_5, where the suffix indicates that the bag contains 5 coins. Similarly, d_n represents the static depth when there are n coins in the bag.

On adding more coins to the bag, the elastic string became increasingly stretched. Table 1.1 and Figure 1.2 show the static depths measured when the bag contained 5, 10, 15, 20 and 25 coins.

Table 1.1

Number of coins, n	5	10	15	20	25
Static depth of bag, d_n/metres	0.37	0.52	0.75	0.99	1.21

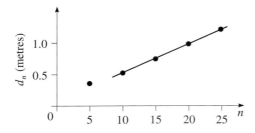

Figure 1.2

Figure 1.2 shows that the number of coins n and the static depth d_n are related in an approximately linear way when the bag is between 0.5 and 1.2 metres below the lintel. A straight line that fits these experimental data points well is given by

$$d_n \simeq 0.06 + 0.046n \quad (0.5 < d_n < 1.2). \tag{1.1}$$

Since each of the coins has mass 0.01 kg, the bag containing n coins has mass $0.01n$ kg and weight $\mathbf{W}_n$ with magnitude $9.81 \times 0.01n$ (in newtons). Hence we have

$$|\mathbf{W}_n| = 0.0981n,$$

and Equation (1.1) can be rewritten as

$$d_n \simeq 0.06 + 0.47|\mathbf{W}_n| \quad (0.5 < d_n < 1.2). \tag{1.2}$$

Later reference will be made to this equation, but it is worth pointing out at once that it can be regarded as a relationship between the length of the elastic string and the tension in the string. Since the bag containing n coins is in equilibrium, its weight $\mathbf{W}_n$ must be exactly counteracted by the upward force provided by the elastic string. The force provided by the string is therefore $-\mathbf{W}_n$, and the tension in the string is the magnitude of this force, which is $|-\mathbf{W}_n| = |\mathbf{W}_n|$. Hence Equation (1.2) tells us that the length of the elastic string is related approximately linearly to the tension in the string. Another way of putting this is that, as coins are added to the bag, the *increase* in the length of the elastic string is approximately proportional to the *increase* in the magnitude of the force that it provides (or vice versa).

The first point, for $n = 5$, does not appear to lie so close to the line specified. We therefore treat this point as an 'outlier' and restrict the range for d_n to exclude it.

As a modelling assumption, the mass of the bag is taken to be zero.

Exercise 1.1

Use either Equation (1.1) or the graph in Figure 1.2 to estimate answers to the following questions.

(a) If the bag contains 22 coins, what is its static depth below the lintel?

(b) If the bag is static at a depth of 0.66 metres below the lintel, how many coins does it contain?

1.3   Results for an oscillating bag

To study oscillations, the bag containing coins was raised above its static position and then released. Care was taken to ensure that the elastic string did not go slack at any stage, and the resulting oscillations were timed. Figure 1.3 gives a rough idea of the motion that was observed: the bag fell and rose many times before eventually settling down at its static position.

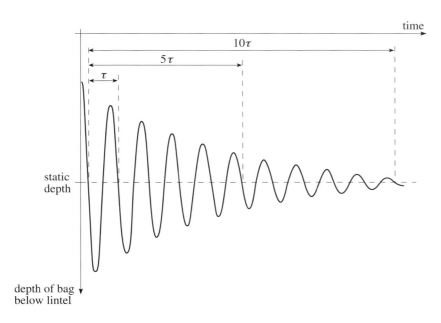

Figure 1.3

Consider the motion that occurs between two successive minima of the depth d, that is, the motion between two successive highest points that the bag reaches. As the bag falls, it picks up speed until it passes through the position of its static depth d_n below the lintel. Then it slows down and comes momentarily to rest at the bottom of its descent. After that it rises once more, picking up speed, until it passes through the static position for a second time. From then on, the bag slows down until it comes momentarily to rest at the next highest point (its minimum depth below the lintel for that cycle). The motion from one static depth position to the next but one is known as a **cycle** of the oscillation. The time that elapses in undergoing a cycle is called the **period** of the cycle and is denoted by the symbol τ, in seconds (see Figure 1.3). In order to describe more features of the general shape of Figure 1.3, we shall look at the functions that describe this motion.

The oscillations in Figure 1.3 are reminiscent of the oscillations of the trigonometric functions sin and cos that you met in *Unit 1*. Generalizing these, we obtain a relationship between position x and time t of the general form

$$x(t) = A\cos(\omega t + \phi), \tag{1.3}$$

where A, ω and ϕ are constants, with $A > 0$ and $\omega > 0$. The function $x(t)$ is called a **sinusoid** or a **sinusoidal function**. A graph of this function is shown in Figure 1.4.

(The name 'sinusoidal' may seem a little odd for a cosine function, but since $\cos t = \sin(t + \frac{\pi}{2})$ we have

$$A\cos(\omega t + \phi) = A\sin(\omega t + \frac{\pi}{2} + \phi) = A\sin(\omega t + \psi),$$

where $\psi = \frac{\pi}{2} + \phi$. Thus the general forms $A\sin(\omega t + \psi)$ and $A\cos(\omega t + \phi)$

cover exactly the same family of functions. We usually take $A\cos(\omega t + \phi)$ as the general form of a sinusoidal function, because this form proves to be more convenient at times.)

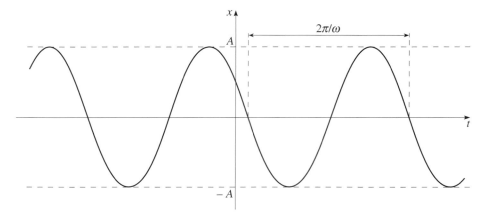

Figure 1.4   The graph of $x = A\cos(\omega t + \phi)$

In Equation (1.3) there are three constants, namely A, ω and ϕ, that we can identify as parameters of the curve; below, we name each parameter and give a description of the effect of varying it on the graph in Figure 1.4.

The parameter A is called the **amplitude** of the sinusoidal function. The variation of x is between fixed bounds, and these bounds are $\pm A$ (rather like sine being bounded by ± 1).

The parameter ω is called the **angular frequency** of the sinusoidal function, and is related to the period of the oscillations. The graph in Figure 1.4 is repetitive, in that moving the graph to the right (or left) by a suitable amount results in exactly the same graph. For cos or sin, a move through 2π gives this repetition. For this general sinusoidal function, the graph repeats when shifted through $2\pi/\omega$, i.e. $x(t + 2\pi/\omega) = x(t)$ for any value of t. So we have the following result.

The relationship between the period τ and the angular frequency ω is

$$\tau = \frac{2\pi}{\omega}.$$

The parameter ϕ reflects the extent to which graph of the function $A\cos(\omega t)$ needs to be moved sideways (left for positive ϕ and right for negative ϕ) to become that of $A\cos(\omega t + \phi)$, and is called the **phase** or **phase angle** of the sinusoidal function.

These definitions are important, and you should remember them. Here are a couple of exercises to test your understanding.

Exercise 1.2 ————————————————————————————

Consider the following function that is closely related to a sinusoid:

$$x = 10 + A\cos 5t, \quad \text{where } A > 0.$$

(a) What is the period of the oscillations?

(b) Suppose you know that x can never take negative values. What can you deduce about the value of A?

*Exercise 1.3 _____

Show that the sinusoidal function $A\cos(\omega t + \phi)$ can be written in the form $B\cos(\omega t) + C\sin(\omega t)$, giving expressions for B and C in terms of A and ϕ.

_____

Now we return to the home-made oscillating system and the behaviour shown in Figure 1.3. By comparing Figures 1.3 and 1.4, we see that the amplitude of the oscillations is decreasing with time. This effect is known as *damping* — for the time being, we shall not model this feature of the motion.

A model for damping will be developed in *Unit 17*.

Looking at Figure 1.3, you can see that the motion starts at a peak of a cycle in exactly the same way that the cosine function does. So the phase, ϕ, is zero. This always happens for particles released from rest, and this is the reason for preferring cos rather than sin in Equation (1.3).

Another feature of the motion became apparent when the number of coins in the bag was changed. Table 1.2 and Figure 1.5 show how the period was affected by these changes. It is clear that the period was greater for a greater number of coins.

Table 1.2

Number of coins, n	5	10	15	20	25
Period of oscillation, τ/seconds	0.7	1.25	1.6	1.8	2.1

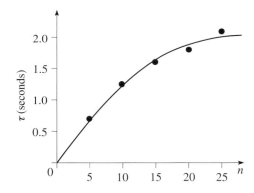

Figure 1.5

Exercise 1.4 _____

Figure 1.5 suggests that the period of oscillation τ may not depend linearly on the number of coins n. By plotting τ^2 against n, but then ignoring the point for $n = 5$ as before, show that a fair approximation to these experimental data is that τ^2 is directly proportional to n.

_____

At this point we shall move away from discussion of the experiment, in order to set up a general mathematical model that can account for some of these experimental findings. This model also provides a link between the experimental situation and the various systems shown in Figure 0.1 of the Introduction. In Subsections 2.2 and 4.1 we shall return for a further look at the experimental results in the light of the general model.

2 The model spring

In this section the important concept of a *model spring* is introduced. Subsection 2.1 shows how the idealized concept of a model spring leads to a simple type of force law. In Subsection 2.2 this model is applied to some statics problems.

2.1 Force law for a model spring

The word 'spring' suggests a helical coil made of metal wire, and in representing a 'model spring' diagrammatically, as in Figure 2.1, it is a stylized form of this physical realization that is portrayed. However, a 'model spring' is in fact, as it says, nothing more than a model for a particular simple variation of force with displacement. While it may be used as an idealized representation of a real coil spring, it can also be made to stand for part of a mechanical system that contains no spring at all, but behaves in the appropriate way. In our idealized model, the 'spring' has zero mass.

The concept of a model spring may be compared with those of a model string and a model pulley, which were introduced in *Unit 5*.

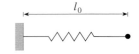

Figure 2.1

Suppose that Figure 2.1 represents a real spring which is in its undisturbed state. One end is attached to a fixed object such as a wall, and the other end is free to move on a frictionless horizontal surface. The weight of the spring and the normal reaction on it from the surface are equal in magnitude and opposite in direction, and cancel each other. So although the free end of the spring is free to move, it does not do so because the resultant force is zero. The length of the spring under these circumstances is its *free length*, which we denote by l_0. If its length is made longer or shorter than l_0, then the spring will always try to return to its free length.

Suppose now that the spring is *extended* (see Figure 2.2), so that its length is greater than its free length; such a spring is said to be *in extension*, or alternatively *in tension*. You probably know from experience that if you hold the free end of an extended spring, then you will be pulled towards the fixed end. The magnitude of this pulling force is called the **tension** in the spring (just as, in *Unit 5*, we referred to the *tension* in a taut string). The more the spring is extended, the more it pulls; in other words, the tension in the spring increases with its extension.

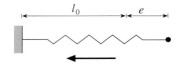

Figure 2.2

Now suppose that the spring can be *compressed* (see Figure 2.3), so that its length is less than its free length; such a spring is said to be *in compression*. In this case, if you hold the free end of the spring, then the spring will push you away from its fixed end. Again, the more the spring is compressed, the more it pushes; the magnitude of the pushing force increases with compression.

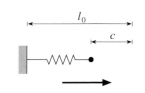

Figure 2.3

A *model spring* is a special model of a real spring. This model is based on the assumption that *the magnitude of the force exerted by the spring is proportional to the amount of its deformation* (extension or compression). The constant of proportionality k, which relates the force magnitude to the deformation for a model spring, is known as the *stiffness* of the spring. Also, we refer to the undisturbed length of a model spring (the length from which deformations are measured) as its *natural length*. While this is also denoted by l_0, it may differ from the free length of a corresponding real spring, since the behaviour of a real spring may not approximate that of a model spring for all deformations. (For example, the experimental elastic string in Section 1 can be approximated closely by a model spring, but only when the deformations from its free length are not too small.)

The SI units for stiffness are newtons per metre ($\mathrm{N\,m^{-1}}$).

Definition

A **model spring** is characterized by two positive constants, its **natural length** l_0 and its **stiffness** k. It has zero mass.

Such a spring exerts a force on any object attached to either of its ends, as follows.

(a) When the length of the spring equals l_0, the force is zero.

(b) When the spring is extended by an amount e (where $e > 0$), so that its length is $l_0 + e$, the force is directed along the axis of the spring towards the centre of the spring and has magnitude ke (stiffness × extension).

(c) When the spring is compressed by an amount c (where $c > 0$), so that its length is $l_0 - c$, the force is directed along the axis of the spring away from the centre of the spring and has magnitude kc (stiffness × compression).

The force law for a model spring is often known as **Hooke's law**, in honour of Robert Hooke. In 1678 Hooke declared, in *De Potentia Restitutiva*:

> It is very evident that the Rule or Law of Nature in every springing body is, that the force or power thereof to restore itself to its natural position is always proportionate to the Distance or space it is removed therefrom.

Actually, this rather overstates the case. The 'model spring' is only a model. Real springs exert forces that have a non-linear dependence on extension or compression and that also depend on other factors such as the velocities of the ends or the mass of the spring. Also, as pointed out earlier, the concept of natural length may not carry over to an actual physical length associated with a real spring. Nevertheless, many real springs conform fairly closely to the idealized behaviour of a model spring for certain ranges of extension and compression. We shall therefore use model springs to represent all the springs discussed in this unit. A bonus of this model is that it leads to a differential equation that can be integrated. But you should remember that this is only an *approximation* when comparing predictions with the real world.

Exercise 2.1 _____

A model spring has natural length $0.3\,\mathrm{m}$ and stiffness $200\,\mathrm{N\,m^{-1}}$. It is attached to a fixed bracket at one end, while the other end is attached to an object (resting on a frictionless horizontal surface) whose distance l from the fixed bracket is variable (see Figure 2.4).

Determine the magnitude and the direction, relative to the centre of the spring, of the force on the object when:

(a) $l = 0.35$ metres;

(b) $l = 0.2$ metres.

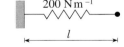

Figure 2.4

So far we have discussed a spring with one end attached to a fixed point and considered the force at the free end of the spring. However, if you take a spring with an end in each hand and extend it, you will be made aware that there are pulling forces exerted by the spring at *both* ends.

For a model spring in tension, these two forces have equal magnitudes and are both directed towards the centre of the spring (see Figure 2.5). The magnitude of each of these forces is given, as before, by stiffness × extension. If we denote the length of the extended spring by l, and its natural length by l_0, then its extension is $e = l - l_0$ and so, by the force law for a model spring, the tension in the spring is equal to $k(l - l_0)$.

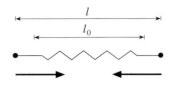

Figure 2.5

If the same spring is compressed by being pushed towards its centre at both ends, then its length l is less than its natural length l_0 by the amount $c = l_0 - l$, and the magnitude of the force provided by the spring is equal to $k(l_0 - l)$.

On the face of it, we need to look at two different cases whenever we consider the force that may be exerted by a model spring, depending on whether the spring is extended or compressed. However, it turns out that this is not necessary, because it is possible to write a single *vector* formula for the force, which will apply correctly whatever the configuration of the spring.

We have said that the force exerted by a model spring of length l, natural length l_0 and stiffness k, on any object attached to one of its ends, is:

(a) directed towards the centre of the spring, with magnitude $k(l - l_0)$, if the spring is extended from its natural length ($l > l_0$);

(b) directed away from the centre of the spring, with magnitude $k(l_0 - l)$, if the spring is compressed ($l < l_0$).

Suppose that we are concerned with the forces on an object attached to one end of a spring, and that $\widehat{\mathbf{s}}$ is a unit vector in the direction from the centre of the spring towards the end where the object is attached (see Figure 2.6). The force $\mathbf{H}$ that the spring exerts on the object can be written in terms of $\widehat{\mathbf{s}}$ as follows.

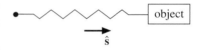

Figure 2.6

(a) If the spring is extended ($l > l_0$), then it provides a force in the opposite direction to $\widehat{\mathbf{s}}$, namely $\mathbf{H} = -k(l - l_0)\widehat{\mathbf{s}}$.

(b) If the spring is compressed ($l < l_0$), then it provides a force in the same direction as $\widehat{\mathbf{s}}$, namely $\mathbf{H} = k(l_0 - l)\widehat{\mathbf{s}}$.

Since $-k(l - l_0) = k(l_0 - l)$, we actually have the same algebraic relationship in each case! It follows that this vector equation provides a complete description of the model spring force law, whether the spring is extended or compressed.

The vector equation also gives the correct outcome of zero force when the spring has its natural length ($l = l_0$).

> ### Theorem 2.1   Vector version of Hooke's law
>
> Suppose that a model spring has natural length l_0 and stiffness k. Then, on an object attached to a particular end, the spring exerts a force
>
> $$\mathbf{H} = -k(l - l_0)\widehat{\mathbf{s}}, \tag{2.1}$$
>
> where l is the length of the spring and $\widehat{\mathbf{s}}$ is a unit vector in the direction from the centre of the spring towards the end where the object is attached.

Exercise 2.2

Use the vector form of Hooke's law to answer once more the questions posed in Exercise 2.1.

2.2 Model springs at rest

The chief purpose behind introducing the concept of a model spring is to provide a simple mathematical model that describes the oscillatory behaviour of certain systems, such as those shown in the Introduction. However, before considering systems in motion, it is instructive to look at some static configurations that feature model springs.

The approach to analysing these situations is similar to that which you studied in *Unit 5*, with the addition of Hooke's law to describe the force provided by a model spring.

See Procedure 1.1 in Unit 5.

Example 2.1

A particle of mass 5 kg is suspended from a model spring that is attached at its top end to a fixed point (see Figure 2.7(a)). The natural length of the spring is 0.3 metres. The length of the spring is 0.5 metres when the particle is suspended from it.

What is the stiffness k of the spring?

Solution

Take the **i**-direction to be vertically downwards, as shown in Figure 2.7(a).   ◄Choose axes►

◄Draw picture►

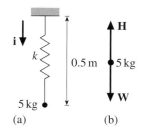

Figure 2.7

The force diagram is shown in Figure 2.7(b). The mass of the particle is 5 kg, so its weight is $\mathbf{W} = 5g\mathbf{i}$.   ◄Draw force diagram►

The unit vector $\widehat{\mathbf{s}}$ in the direction from the centre of the spring towards the particle points downwards, so $\widehat{\mathbf{s}} = \mathbf{i}$.

By Hooke's law (Equation (2.1)), the model spring provides a force   ◄Apply law(s)►

$$\mathbf{H} = -k(l - l_0)\widehat{\mathbf{s}} = -k(0.5 - 0.3)\mathbf{i} = -0.2k\mathbf{i}.$$

Since the particle is in equilibrium, we have   The equilibrium condition for particles was introduced in *Unit 5*.

$$\mathbf{W} + \mathbf{H} = \mathbf{0}.$$

Resolving in the **i**-direction gives   ◄Solve equation(s)►

$$5g - 0.2k = 0,$$

so

$$k = 25g.$$

We conclude that the stiffness of the spring is   ◄Interpret solution►

$$k = 25g \simeq 245\,\text{N}\,\text{m}^{-1}. \quad \blacksquare$$

Exercise 2.3

A 'baby bouncer' (see Figure 2.8) consists of a seat and straps, whose combined mass is 0.5 kg, suspended from two identical springs that are attached to a door lintel. When a baby of mass 7.5 kg is strapped into the seat, the seat descends by 3 cm. What is the stiffness of each of the springs?

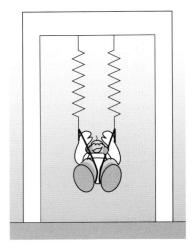

Figure 2.8

Example 2.2

An object of mass m is attached to two model springs, whose other ends are attached to fixed points that are 0.9 metres apart (see Figure 2.9(a)).

The left-hand spring has stiffness $40\,\mathrm{N\,m^{-1}}$ and natural length 0.3 metres, while the right-hand spring has stiffness $60\,\mathrm{N\,m^{-1}}$ and natural length 0.2 metres. The object is supported by a table and is free to move on the table without friction.

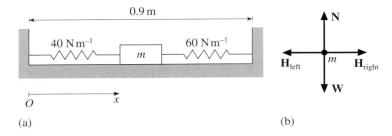

(a)   (b)

Figure 2.9

Determine the equilibrium position of the object, and find the tension in the springs.

Solution

Suppose that the object is modelled as a particle. The forces acting on the particle are shown in Figure 2.9(b), where $\mathbf{W}$ is the weight, $\mathbf{N}$ is the normal reaction, and $\mathbf{H}_{\text{left}}$ and $\mathbf{H}_{\text{right}}$ are the forces exerted by the left-hand and right-hand springs, respectively.

For each spring, the force exerted is given by Hooke's law as

$$\mathbf{H} = -k(l - l_0)\widehat{\mathbf{s}},$$

where $\widehat{\mathbf{s}}$ is a unit vector directed from the centre of the spring towards the particle. Suppose that the x-axis is chosen to point from left to right, with origin at the left-hand fixed point. Then the lengths of the two springs are x (left spring) and $0.9 - x$ (right spring), so that the forces exerted are

$$\mathbf{H}_{\text{left}} = -40(x - 0.3)\mathbf{i},$$
$$\mathbf{H}_{\text{right}} = -60((0.9 - x) - 0.2)(-\mathbf{i}) = 60(0.7 - x)\mathbf{i}.$$

Here we have used $\widehat{\mathbf{s}}_{\text{left}} = \mathbf{i}$ and $\widehat{\mathbf{s}}_{\text{right}} = -\mathbf{i}$.

Since the particle is held in equilibrium, we have

$$\mathbf{W} + \mathbf{N} + \mathbf{H}_{\text{left}} + \mathbf{H}_{\text{right}} = \mathbf{0}.$$

Resolving in the $\mathbf{i}$-direction gives

$$60(0.7 - x) - 40(x - 0.3) = 0.$$

The solution of this equation is $x = 0.54$, so we conclude that the particle is 0.54 metres from the left-hand fixed point (and hence 0.36 metres from the right-hand fixed point).

The magnitudes of the forces can be found by substituting $x = 0.54$ into the above expressions for the forces to obtain

$$\mathbf{H}_{\text{left}} = -40(0.54 - 0.3)\mathbf{i} = -9.6\mathbf{i},$$
$$\mathbf{H}_{\text{right}} = 60(0.7 - 0.54)\mathbf{i} = 9.6\mathbf{i}.$$

So, as expected, the forces exerted by the springs are of equal magnitude and opposite directions (which provides a useful quick check). The tension in the springs is the magnitude of the above forces, that is, 9.6 newtons. ∎

Exercise 2.4

Consider a modified version of the problem stated in Example 2.2, in which the distance between the two fixed ends is reduced to 0.3 metres, but all other aspects of the problem remain unchanged. Solve this modified problem (finding, at the end, the magnitude of the compressive forces exerted by the springs).

Example 2.3

A model spring hangs vertically from a fixed point, with a particle of mass m suspended from its lower end (see Figure 2.10(a)). The particle is in equilibrium. Express the length l of the spring in terms of its stiffness k and natural length l_0, the mass m, and the magnitude of the acceleration due to gravity g.

Solution

Choose the $\mathbf{i}$-direction to be vertically downwards, as shown in Figure 2.10(a). The force diagram is shown in Figure 2.10(b). The weight of the particle is $\mathbf{W} = mg\mathbf{i}$, and the force exerted on it by the spring is

$$\mathbf{H} = -k(l - l_0)\widehat{\mathbf{s}}$$
$$= -k(l - l_0)\mathbf{i}.$$

Since $\mathbf{H} + \mathbf{W} = \mathbf{0}$ (the particle is in equilibrium), we have

$$-k(l - l_0) + mg = 0, \qquad (2.2)$$

that is,

$$l = l_0 + \frac{mg}{k}. \quad ∎$$

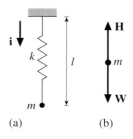

Figure 2.10

Exercise 2.5

An object of mass 1.5 kg is attached to the floor at A by a model spring of stiffness $50\,\mathrm{N\,m^{-1}}$ and natural length 0.5 metres. It is also attached to the ceiling at B, a point 2.1 metres vertically above A, by a model spring of stiffness $20\,\mathrm{N\,m^{-1}}$ and natural length 0.3 metres (see Figure 2.11).

In equilibrium, what is the height of the object above the floor?

To conclude this section, we return to the experimental observations from Subsection 1.2, where a bag of coins was suspended from the end of an elastic string. It will be assumed that the elastic string may be modelled by an extended model spring provided that, as was ensured during the experiment, the string never becomes slack.

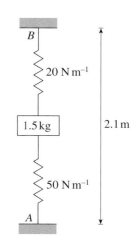

Figure 2.11

Suppose that this model spring has stiffness k and natural length l_0, and that its equilibrium length is l when a particle of mass m is suspended from it. Then, as shown in Example 2.3, we have

$$l = l_0 + \frac{mg}{k} = l_0 + \frac{|\mathbf{W}|}{k},$$

where $\mathbf{W}$ is the weight of the bag of coins. This equation can be compared directly with the experimental relationship

$$d_n \simeq 0.06 + 0.47|\mathbf{W}_n| \quad (0.5 < d_n < 1.2), \tag{1.2}$$

between the static length d_n of the elastic string and the weight magnitude $|\mathbf{W}_n|$ when the bag contains n coins. This comparison shows that if the model is to 'fit' the experimental situation, we must have

$$l_0 \simeq 0.06, \quad k \simeq 1/0.47 \simeq 2.1.$$

The corresponding model spring therefore has natural length 0.06 metres and stiffness $2.1\,\mathrm{N\,m^{-1}}$. We shall refer to these model spring parameter values when we model the oscillations of the bag of coins in Subsection 4.1.

End-of-section Exercises

Exercise 2.6

Figure 2.12 represents a dish dispenser, such as may be found in large catering establishments. Dishes are stacked in a pile on top of a spring that is compressed by their weight, so that the top dish is always at the same height, to be picked up conveniently.

(a) Suppose that the dishes involved each have thickness 7 mm and mass 590 grams. Assuming that the dispenser is to achieve the purpose described above, what stiffness should the spring have?

(b) Would you expect a dispenser with the same spring stiffness to work satisfactorily with dishes of other dimensions?

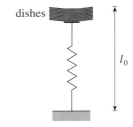

Figure 2.12

Exercise 2.7

Suppose that a model spring of stiffness k and natural length l_0 is cut in half, to produce two identical model springs of natural length $\frac{1}{2}l_0$. In terms of k, what is the stiffness of each of the two shorter springs?

Exercise 2.8

A battery of length 5 cm is put into a battery holder. The holder has an internal length of 5.5 cm, and has a spring at each end to hold the battery in place (see Figure 2.13, which is not to scale). One spring has stiffness $30\,\mathrm{N\,m^{-1}}$ and natural length 0.4 cm, while the other has stiffness $10\,\mathrm{N\,m^{-1}}$ and natural length 0.3 cm.

What is the magnitude of the spring forces acting on the battery, assuming that there are no friction forces?

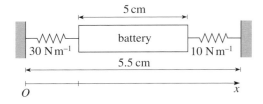

Figure 2.13

3 The simplest oscillating system

You have seen in Section 2 how the concept of a model spring can be applied in circumstances where no motion occurs, by extension of the approach to statics problems from *Unit 5*. We turn in this section to the application of model springs in situations where movement takes place.

In Subsection 3.1 we derive the equation of motion for oscillations of a horizontal model spring. This (differential) equation is solved and the solutions interpreted in Subsection 3.2.

3.1 Setting up an equation of motion

In *Unit 6* you saw how to analyse the one-dimensional motion of a particle under the influence of forces such as gravity and air resistance. Here we are again concerned solely with one-dimensional motion, but now we concentrate on how a particle behaves when connected to the end of a model spring.

As before, the analysis is based on Newton's second law, which states that if a particle has mass m and experiences a resultant force $\mathbf{F}$, then its acceleration $\mathbf{a}$ is given by

See Unit 6.

$$\mathbf{F} = m\mathbf{a}.$$

You saw in *Unit 6* that the acceleration $\mathbf{a}(t)$ of a particle at time t is defined as the derivative of its velocity $\mathbf{v}(t)$, which is in turn defined as the derivative of its position $\mathbf{r}(t)$. Using Newton's 'dot' notation for derivatives with respect to time, we therefore have $\mathbf{a} = \ddot{\mathbf{r}}$, so Newton's second law may also be expressed as

Recall that $\dot{\mathbf{r}}$ means $d\mathbf{r}/dt$ and $\ddot{\mathbf{r}}$ means $d\dot{\mathbf{r}}/dt = d^2\mathbf{r}/dt^2$. Each dot stands for '$d/dt$'.

$$m\ddot{\mathbf{r}} = \mathbf{F}. \tag{3.1}$$

Example 3.1 below illustrates the type of approach that is required where a model spring is involved. As indicated in the margin alongside the solution, it is still appropriate to adopt here the procedural steps for applying Newton's second law that were used in *Unit 6*. The last two stages of this procedure, solving the differential equation and interpreting the solution, will be dealt with in the following subsection.

See Procedure 3.1 of *Unit 6* for the listing of these steps.

Example 3.1

A spring is attached to a wall at one end of a straight frictionless horizontal air track. The other end of the spring is attached to a glider that moves along the track. Model the glider by a particle of mass m and the spring by a model spring of natural length l_0 and stiffness k. Find the equation of motion for the particle when its position x is measured in the direction away from the wall, with the origin at the equilibrium position of the particle, as indicated in Figure 3.1.

The statement of Example 3.1 refers to an air track and glider as shown in the video associated with *Unit 6*.

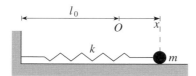

Figure 3.1

(This model system is similar to that of Figure 0.1(b) in the Introduction, and, as mentioned there, it might provide a first model for a spring-loaded buffer.)

109

Solution

Figure 3.1 sketches the physical situation. It shows the x-axis given in the question, directed away from the fixed end of the spring. Since the origin is taken at the equilibrium position of the particle, the right-hand end of the spring is at $x = 0$ when the length of the spring is equal to its natural length l_0. At other positions, the length of the spring is given by $l_0 + x$, with the spring extended for $x > 0$ and compressed for $x < 0$.

◀Draw picture▶

◀Choose axes▶

Apart from its weight $\mathbf{W}$ and the balancing normal reaction $\mathbf{N}$, the only force acting on the particle is that provided by the model spring, but how should this be portrayed on a force diagram? As you saw in Subsection 2.1, this force will pull the particle if the spring is extended and push the particle if the spring is compressed, so we can expect the force exerted by the spring on the particle to act in the direction of $\mathbf{i}$ at some times and in the direction of $-\mathbf{i}$ at others. We are therefore unable to make a single 'correct' choice for the direction of this force $\mathbf{H}$, but *either choice will do* for the purposes of the diagram. (The force diagram shown in Figure 3.2 corresponds to the situation when the spring is extended.)

◀Draw force diagram▶

Figure 3.2

Applying Newton's second law to the particle gives

◀Apply Newton's 2nd law▶

$$m\ddot{\mathbf{r}} = \mathbf{H} + \mathbf{W} + \mathbf{N}. \tag{3.2}$$

To proceed further we need to model all the forces. The force $\mathbf{H}$ exerted by the model spring on the particle is described by Hooke's law, which gives

$$\mathbf{H} = -k(l - l_0)\hat{\mathbf{s}}, \tag{2.1}$$

where l is the length of the spring and $\hat{\mathbf{s}}$ is a unit vector in the direction from the centre of the spring towards the end where the particle is attached.

For the current situation, $l = l_0 + x$ and $\hat{\mathbf{s}} = \mathbf{i}$, so the force exerted is

$$\mathbf{H} = -kx\mathbf{i}.$$

The forces $\mathbf{W}$ and $\mathbf{N}$ act vertically and are in equilibrium, i.e. $\mathbf{W} + \mathbf{N} = \mathbf{0}$. Substituting this and the expression for $\mathbf{H}$ into Equation (3.2) gives

$$m\ddot{\mathbf{r}} = \mathbf{H} = -kx\mathbf{i}. \tag{3.3}$$

For motion in the x-direction, we have $\mathbf{r}(t) = x(t)\mathbf{i}$, so we also have $\dot{\mathbf{r}}(t) = \dot{x}(t)\mathbf{i}$ and $\ddot{\mathbf{r}}(t) = \ddot{x}(t)\mathbf{i}$. Hence, on resolving Equation (3.3) in the $\mathbf{i}$-direction, we obtain $m\ddot{x} = -kx$, that is,

$$m\ddot{x} + kx = 0. \tag{3.4}$$

This differential equation is the required equation of motion. ∎

Equation (3.4) is a second-order homogeneous linear constant-coefficient differential equation. This is exactly the type of differential equation that was studied in *Unit 3* (this is no coincidence), and it can be solved using the methods described in that unit. This will be done in the next subsection, but to conclude this subsection, we ask you to look at the derivation of another equation of motion.

In Example 3.1 the position x of the particle was measured from its equilibrium position, where the length of the spring is equal to its natural length. This leads to a particularly simple equation of motion, but there is otherwise no reason why the origin could not have been chosen at some other fixed point. One obvious alternative for the choice of origin would be at the fixed end of the spring. This leads to a slightly different equation of motion, as you are asked to show in the exercise below.

Exercise 3.1 ————————————————————

Figure 3.3 shows the same mechanical system as described in Example 3.1, but now the position x of the particle is to be measured from the fixed end of the spring (with the origin chosen to be at this point). Find the equation of motion for the particle in this case.

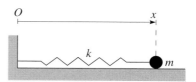

Figure 3.3

3.2 Solving the equation of motion

In the previous subsection we derived Equation (3.4) as the equation of motion for a particle attached to one end of a horizontal model spring, whose other end is fixed. The method of solving such a differential equation was described in *Unit 3*, but quite a lot can be deduced simply by looking at the form of the equation.

We now complete Procedure 3.1 of *Unit 6* for the problem stated in Example 3.1, by solving the differential equation and interpreting the solution.

Equation (3.4) has to be satisfied by a function $x(t)$ whose second derivative $\ddot{x}(t)$ is a negative constant multiple $(-k/m)$ of the function $x(t)$ itself. What functions satisfy this specification? There are at least two that come to mind, namely, the sine and the cosine functions. Hence functions of the form $x(t) = B\cos(\omega t)$ and $x(t) = C\sin(\omega t)$ (where B, C and ω are constants) are contenders to be solutions of the differential equation. Since we are dealing with a homogeneous linear differential equation, it follows from the principle of superposition that the sum of two such functions is also a contender.

◀Solve differential equation▶

See *Unit 3*, Theorem 1.1.

Exercise 3.2 ————————————————————

Show, by substitution, that $x(t) = B\cos(\omega t) + C\sin(\omega t)$ is a solution of the differential equation $m\ddot{x} + kx = 0$, where $\omega^2 = k/m$.

*Exercise 3.3 ————————————————————

By using the auxiliary equation, find the general solution of the differential equation

$$m\ddot{x} + kx = 0. \tag{3.4}$$

This method of solution is described in *Unit 3*.

As you found in Exercise 3.3, the general solution of Equation (3.4) is

◀Interpret solution▶

$$x(t) = B\cos(\omega t) + C\sin(\omega t), \tag{3.5}$$

where $\omega = \sqrt{k/m}$, and B and C are arbitrary constants. As usual with differential equations, the values of these arbitrary constants can be found if initial conditions are provided for the function $x(t)$. Motion of the type described by Equation (3.5) is known as **simple harmonic motion** (which is sometimes abbreviated to **SHM**). At this point it is useful to recall the terms used for describing oscillations that were introduced in Section 1. The quantity $\omega = \sqrt{k/m}$ is called the (natural) **angular frequency** of the motion. Simple harmonic motion is periodic with a **period**, τ, given by $\tau = 2\pi/\omega$, i.e. the motion repeats itself every $\tau = 2\pi/\omega$ seconds.

As the angle ωt is measured in radians, the SI units of the angular frequency ω are radians per second, abbreviated as $\mathrm{rad\,s^{-1}}$.

Since τ is the time for one cycle, the number f of cycles per unit time is equal to $1/\tau$. This is called the (natural) **frequency** of the motion and is given by

$$f = \frac{1}{\tau} = \frac{\omega}{2\pi},$$

so the angular frequency ω (in $\mathrm{rad\,s^{-1}}$) is equal to 2π times the frequency f (in Hz).

The SI unit for frequency is the *hertz*, where 1 hertz is 1 cycle per second and is abbreviated as Hz. Hence we have $1\,\mathrm{Hz} = 1\,\mathrm{s^{-1}}$.

We shall now demonstrate how particular values may be found for the arbitrary constants B and C when specific initial conditions are given.

Example 3.2

In a model of a vibrating system, the position $x(t)$ of a particle at time t is given by

$$x(t) = B \cos 10t + C \sin 10t.$$

The particle is set in motion at time $t = 0$, when its position is 0.2 metres and its velocity is $1\,\mathrm{m\,s^{-1}}$ in the direction of the positive x-axis (both measured relative to the given x-axis and origin).

Find the particular position function for the particle that corresponds to these initial conditions. Where is the particle after 0.5 seconds?

Solution

The initial conditions provided may be written as

$$x(0) = 0.2, \quad \dot{x}(0) = 1.$$

Since $x(t) = B \cos 10t + C \sin 10t$, we have

$$\dot{x}(t) = -10B \sin 10t + 10C \cos 10t.$$

Substituting $t = 0$ into these equations and using the given initial conditions, we have

$$x(0) = B = 0.2, \quad \dot{x}(0) = 10C = 1.$$

Hence $B = 0.2$ and $C = 0.1$, giving the particular position function

$$x(t) = 0.2 \cos 10t + 0.1 \sin 10t.$$

After 0.5 seconds, the particle is at

$$x(0.5) = 0.2 \cos 5 + 0.1 \sin 5 \simeq -0.04,$$

that is, 0.04 metres along the x-axis in the negative direction from the origin. ∎

*Exercise 3.4

For a particular case of the system shown in Figure 3.1, the model spring's stiffness is $k = 200\,\mathrm{N\,m^{-1}}$ and the particle's mass is $m = 0.5\,\mathrm{kg}$. The system is set in motion when $t = 0$, at which time the position is $x = 0.3$ metres and the velocity is $\dot{x} = 2\,\mathrm{m\,s^{-1}}$ in the direction of the positive x-axis. Find:
(a) the angular frequency ω and the period τ of the motion;
(b) the frequency f of the motion;
(c) the position function for the particle.

The mathematical description of simple harmonic motion,

$$x(t) = B \cos(\omega t) + C \sin(\omega t), \tag{3.5}$$

can be written in an alternative way as

$$x(t) = A \cos(\omega t + \phi), \tag{3.6}$$

where A and ϕ are arbitrary constants — except that, by convention, we take $A \geq 0$ and $-\pi < \phi \leq \pi$. The reason for choosing $A \geq 0$ is that in this case it has the simple interpretation of the **amplitude** of the motion. Here A and ϕ take on the roles previously occupied by B and C, since values for them can be obtained from a pair of initial conditions.

You showed how Equation (3.5) can be derived from Equation (3.6) in Exercise 1.3.

The quantity ϕ, which is called the **phase angle** or **phase** of the motion, has the interpretation that $A \cos \phi$ is the particle's position at time $t = 0$. Also, if ϕ is positive, then $-\phi/\omega$ gives the last time, prior to $t = 0$, at which the position x reaches its maximum value (see Figure 3.4). If ϕ is negative, then $-\phi/\omega$ is the first time after $t = 0$ at which the position x reaches its maximum value.

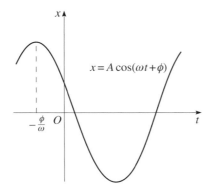

Figure 3.4

It is not hard to verify that Equation (3.6) again provides a solution of the differential equation $m\ddot{x} + kx = 0$, with $\omega^2 = k/m$. You saw in Exercise 1.3 that the equivalence of the expressions for $x(t)$ in Equations (3.5) and (3.6) is obtained by showing how the constants B and C in the first form are related to the constants A and ϕ in the second form. These linking relationships are

$$B = A \cos \phi, \quad C = -A \sin \phi. \tag{3.7}$$

These equations tell us how to find the values of B and C when we are given the values of A and ϕ. In order to proceed in the opposite direction, to obtain the values of A and ϕ from given values of B and C, we need to solve Equations (3.7) for A and ϕ. However, when written as

$$B = A \cos \phi, \quad -C = A \sin \phi,$$

these equations can be recognized as relating the Cartesian coordinates $(B, -C)$ of a point in the plane to its polar coordinates $\langle A, \phi \rangle$ (see Figure 3.5). Hence the amplitude A is given by

$$A = \sqrt{B^2 + C^2},$$

while the angle ϕ is the solution of the pair of equations

$$\cos \phi = B/A, \quad \sin \phi = -C/A.$$

Within the range $-\pi < \phi \le \pi$, the solution to these equations is unique.

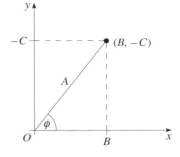

Figure 3.5

See *Unit 1* for the conversion from Cartesian to polar coordinates.

Exercise 3.5

In Exercise 3.4 you showed that the particular oscillation described there is represented by the equation

$$x(t) = 0.3 \cos 20t + 0.1 \sin 20t.$$

Find the amplitude and phase angle of this oscillation.

Before proceeding to summarize the important information about simple harmonic motion, it is worth pointing out a simple geometric way of visualizing the type of motion that is involved. This takes as its starting point the picture given in Figure 3.5, which shows the point with polar coordinates $\langle A, \phi \rangle$ and x-coordinate $B = x(0)$. Imagine a point that moves in the plane with polar coordinates $\langle A, \omega t + \phi \rangle$ at time t. This point starts moving when $t = 0$, at the point shown in Figure 3.5, and then moves anticlockwise around the origin on a circle of radius A, with constant angular velocity ω (see Figure 3.6).

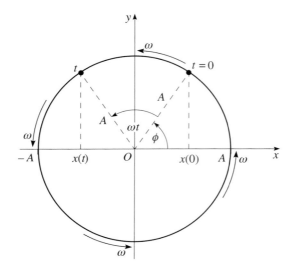

Figure 3.6

The x-coordinate of the point at time t is $x(t) = A \cos(\omega t + \phi)$, which is also the projection of the point in the plane onto the x-axis. Thus, as the point travels around the circle at a constant rate, its projection onto the x-axis undergoes simple harmonic motion between the extreme points $x = \pm A$.

Simple harmonic motion

The simple harmonic motion equation

$$\ddot{x} + \omega^2 x = 0$$

has a general solution which can be written in the form

$$x(t) = B \cos(\omega t) + C \sin(\omega t) \qquad (3.5)$$

or, alternatively, as

$$x(t) = A \cos(\omega t + \phi), \qquad (3.6)$$

where

$$A = \sqrt{B^2 + C^2}, \quad \cos \phi = B/A, \quad \sin \phi = -C/A.$$

The following names are given to quantities that are characteristic of simple harmonic motion:

- the *angular frequency* of the oscillations is ω;
- the *period* (time for one complete cycle) is $\tau = 2\pi/\omega$;
- the *frequency* (number of cycles per second) is $f = 1/\tau = \omega/(2\pi)$;
- the *amplitude* of the oscillations is A;
- the *phase angle* or *phase* of the oscillations is ϕ.

> This differential equation is equivalent to
> $$m\ddot{x} + kx = 0,$$
> where $\omega^2 = k/m$.

So far in this section, the equilibrium position of the particle has usually been taken as the origin of the x-axis, as this choice leads to the simplest equation of motion. We shall continue to adopt the same approach both here and in later mechanics units. However, in certain situations, it is more convenient to choose some other origin, so we shall look briefly now at how this affects the mathematical solution obtained.

In Exercise 3.1 you found the equation of motion for a particle at the end of a horizontal model spring, when the particle's position is measured from the fixed end of the spring (see Figure 3.7). The equation of motion was

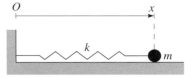

Figure 3.7

$$m\ddot{x} + kx = kl_0,$$

where k and l_0 are, respectively, the stiffness and the natural length of the spring. This differential equation is inhomogeneous, so its solution is the sum of two parts, a particular integral and the complementary function. A particular (constant) integral is given by

See *Unit 3*.

$$x_{\mathrm{p}} = l_0,$$

and the complementary function is, as before,

$$x_{\mathrm{c}} = A\cos(\omega t + \phi),$$

where $\omega = \sqrt{k/m}$. The general solution is therefore

$$x = x_{\mathrm{p}} + x_{\mathrm{c}},$$

i.e.

$$x = l_0 + A\cos(\omega t + \phi), \tag{3.8}$$

whose graph is shown in Figure 3.8.

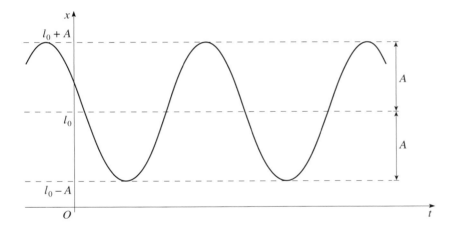

Figure 3.8

It is clear from this graph that l_0 is the average position of the particle, about which the oscillations take place. Apart from this, the motion is identical to that seen earlier, as you might expect.

Note how the solution (3.8) relates to the original situation of the glider on a frictionless horizontal air track. The particular integral $x_{\mathrm{p}} = l_0$ is the equilibrium position of the glider, while the complementary function $x_{\mathrm{c}} = A\cos(\omega t + \phi)$ describes all possible motions of the glider relative to its equilibrium position. The amplitude of such a motion depends on how the glider is set in motion, while the period (independent of the initial conditions) is $2\pi/\omega = 2\pi\sqrt{m/k}$, where k and m are, respectively, the stiffness of the spring and the mass of the glider.

Equation (3.8) can be written alternatively as

$$x = l_0 + B\cos(\omega t) + C\sin(\omega t), \tag{3.9}$$

where B and C are given in terms of A and ϕ by Equations (3.7).

115

Exercise 3.6 ————————————————————

For the system shown in Figure 3.7, the particle motion may be described by Equation (3.9). Find the particular solution that satisfies the initial conditions $x(0) = x_0$ and $\dot{x}(0) = v_0$.

End-of-section Exercise

Exercise 3.7 ————————————————————

Using the simple harmonic motion equation

$$\ddot{x} + \omega^2 x = 0,$$

show that for simple harmonic motion:

(a) the particle's position is zero whenever its velocity is a maximum or minimum;

(b) the particle's velocity is zero whenever its acceleration is a maximum or minimum.

4 Other oscillating systems

In this section we apply the methods developed in the previous section to oscillating systems that at first sight look more complicated, but also result in the particle moving in simple harmonic motion. Subsection 4.1 deals with the oscillations of a vertical model spring, and Subsection 4.2 looks at situations where the oscillations are caused by two springs.

4.1 Oscillations of a vertical spring

In this subsection we shall attempt to model the vibrating system of the experiment described in Section 1, and compare the predictions of the model with the experimental observations. This is a case where the 'model spring' is used to model an elastic string, always in tension, which shows some departure from 'model' behaviour.

As a start, let us take the direction of motion to be vertical (as in the real system). Figure 4.1 shows the relevant arrangement.

An important difference between the situations described by this figure and by Figure 3.1 is that here the equilibrium position does *not* correspond to the natural length of the spring, as it did in the earlier case. If the system in Figure 4.1 is to be in equilibrium, then the force exerted by the spring on the particle must balance the weight of the particle, which has magnitude mg. However, you will see that if we again measure the displacement of the particle from its equilibrium position, then the equation of motion takes a familiar form.

Figure 4.1

Exercise 4.1 ————————————————————

Find the length l_{eq} of the model spring of stiffness k and natural length l_0 shown in Figure 4.1, when the system is in equilibrium.

In Exercise 4.1 you showed that the length of the vertical spring in Figure 4.1 is $l_{eq} = l_0 + mg/k$ when the system is in equilibrium. This result was obtained by applying both Hooke's law (Equation (2.1)) and the condition for static equilibrium in the form $\mathbf{H} + \mathbf{W} = \mathbf{0}$, where $\mathbf{H}$ is the force exerted on the particle by the spring, and $\mathbf{W}$ is the weight of the particle. If we write $\mathbf{H}_{eq}$ rather than $\mathbf{H}$ here, to denote the *equilibrium* spring force, then, with the x-axis pointing downwards, we have

$$\mathbf{H}_{eq} = -\mathbf{W} = -mg\mathbf{i} = -k(l_{eq} - l_0)\mathbf{i}.$$

Figure 4.2(a) shows this same system after the particle has been moved away from its equilibrium position and released. The x-axis has again been chosen to point downwards, with its origin at the equilibrium position of the particle.

For any particle position x, the length of the spring is, using the result of Exercise 4.1,

$$l = l_{eq} + x = l_0 + \frac{mg}{k} + x,$$

so the force exerted on the particle by the spring is

$$\mathbf{H} = -k(l - l_0)\mathbf{i} = -k\left(\frac{mg}{k} + x\right)\mathbf{i} = -(mg + kx)\mathbf{i}.$$

The total force $\mathbf{F}$ acting on the particle, as illustrated in Figure 4.2(b), is then

$$\mathbf{F} = \mathbf{H} + \mathbf{W} = -(mg + kx)\mathbf{i} + mg\mathbf{i} = -kx\mathbf{i},$$

so Newton's second law, $m\ddot{\mathbf{r}} = \mathbf{F}$, takes the form

$$m\ddot{x}\mathbf{i} = -kx\mathbf{i}.$$

Resolving in the $\mathbf{i}$-direction and rearranging, we have

$$m\ddot{x} + kx = 0. \tag{3.4}$$

This is precisely the equation of motion derived earlier for a particle attached to a horizontal model spring. So the motion *relative* to the equilibrium position here is the same as it was in the horizontal case, but the equilibrium length of the spring is different. Hence, measured from its equilibrium position, the displacement of the particle in the vertical spring case is again a simple harmonic motion, with position function of the form

$$x(t) = A\cos(\omega t + \phi), \tag{3.6}$$

where $\omega^2 = k/m$, as before.

If the origin for position x were taken instead at the fixed (top) end of the spring, then the corresponding form of the position function would be

$$x(t) = l_{eq} + A\cos(\omega t + \phi) = l_0 + \frac{mg}{k} + A\cos(\omega t + \phi). \tag{4.1}$$

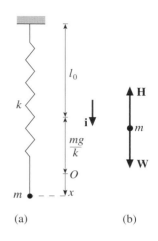

(a)   (b)

Figure 4.2

Note that
$$\mathbf{H} = \mathbf{H}_{eq} - kx\mathbf{i}.$$
This means that if the particle is moved from the origin (the equilibrium position) to position x, then the *change* in the force exerted on it by the spring is
$$\mathbf{H} - \mathbf{H}_{eq} = -kx\mathbf{i}.$$

In the horizontal case, the equilibrium length is $l_{eq} = l_0$.

Exercise 4.2

The system shown in Figure 4.1 features a model spring of natural length l_0 and equilibrium length $l_{eq} = l_0 + mg/k$.

(a) Show that the motion of this system has period $\tau = 2\pi\sqrt{(l_{eq} - l_0)/g}$.

(b) Suppose that a real spring is available that satisfies Hooke's law to a good approximation, even for small displacements from the free length of the spring. Describe a simple experiment that could be used, together with the formula derived in part (a), to estimate a value for g.

You found this expression for the equilibrium length in Exercise 4.1.

Exercise 4.3 —————————————————————————

(a) A bag of mass m is suspended from the ceiling by a model spring of stiffness k and natural length l_0. If the bag is allowed to oscillate vertically, show that the length x of the spring satisfies the differential equation

$$\ddot{x} + \omega^2 x = \omega^2 \left(l_0 + \frac{mg}{k} \right),$$

where $\omega^2 = k/m$.

(b) If the system is initially released from rest when the length of the spring is equal to its natural length, show that the subsequent motion of the bag is given by

$$x(t) = l_0 + \frac{mg}{k}(1 - \cos(\omega t)).$$

This is the equation of motion for the particle in Figure 4.1, if the x-axis is chosen to point vertically downwards with its origin at the top of the spring. The general solution is given by Equation (4.1).

We now revisit the experimental observations from Subsection 1.3, where a bag of coins oscillated vertically on the end of an elastic string. It was shown at the end of Section 2 that if the elastic string is to be represented by a model spring, then the appropriate parameter values obtained from measurements at static equilibrium are $l_0 \simeq 0.06$ metres for the natural length and $k \simeq 2.1 \,\mathrm{N\,m^{-1}}$ for the stiffness.

The model spring representation means that Equation (4.1) can be applied when the system oscillates. The prediction of the model is for simple harmonic motion with angular frequency $\omega = \sqrt{k/m}$, for which the corresponding period is

$$\tau = \frac{2\pi}{\omega} = 2\pi \sqrt{\frac{m}{k}}.$$

With the mass of the filled bag being made up of n coins, each of which has mass $0.01 \,\mathrm{kg}$, the predicted period becomes

$$\tau = 0.2\pi \sqrt{\frac{n}{k}}.$$

Calculating this for $n = 10, 15, 20$ and 25 (to make sure of being within the 'linear' range of the string extension), we obtain the approximate values shown in the second row of Table 4.1. The data given for τ_{expt} in the third row of this table are the corresponding experimental values from Table 1.2.

Table 4.1

Number of coins, n	10	15	20	25
Predicted period of oscillation, τ/seconds	1.37	1.68	1.94	2.17
Measured period of oscillation, τ_{expt}/seconds	1.25	1.6	1.8	2.1

The predicted figures are slightly on the high side when compared with the observed values, but the greatest error is less than 10%.

The model also predicts that τ^2 is proportional to the number of coins n, which you showed to be approximately the case for the experimental data in Exercise 1.4. Indeed, the model predicts that the constant of proportionality between τ^2 and n should be $(0.2\pi)^2/k \simeq 0.188$, which is somewhat higher than the value 0.168 obtained in Solution 1.4.

To sum up, the predictions obtained by modelling the elastic string by a model spring are:

(a) a period that remains constant throughout the motion with a particular number of coins in the bag;

(b) a period that increases as the square root of the number of coins in the bag;

(c) a constant-amplitude motion about the equilibrium position, once the system is released with particular initial conditions.

Of these three predictions, the first two agree quite well with experimental observations. The third does not; all one can say is that the prediction holds for only very short periods of time, and not accurately even then (see Figure 1.3). The model spring is therefore inadequate in this respect as a representation of the elastic string. The discrepancy is due mainly to the model's neglect of damping effects such as air resistance. This is a matter that needs more attention, and it will be investigated further in *Unit 17*.

4.2 Systems with two springs

This subsection extends the treatment of simple oscillatory systems by applying the modelling techniques used so far to systems that include a pair of model springs.

Exercise 4.4

The system shown in Figure 4.3 features a particle attached to two model springs and in contact with a frictionless horizontal track. The distance between the two fixed vertical surfaces is 0.8 metres. The left-hand spring (spring 1) has natural length 0.3 metres and stiffness $200 \, \text{N} \, \text{m}^{-1}$, while the right-hand spring (spring 2) has natural length 0.4 metres and stiffness $300 \, \text{N} \, \text{m}^{-1}$. The particle has mass 2 kg.

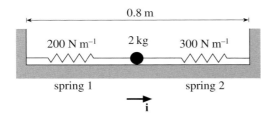

Figure 4.3

(a) Show, by applying Hooke's law, that the forces exerted by the two springs on the particle are

$$\mathbf{H}_1 = -200(l_1 - 0.3)\mathbf{i},$$
$$\mathbf{H}_2 = 300(l_2 - 0.4)\mathbf{i},$$

where l_1 and l_2 are the lengths of the springs, and the unit vector $\mathbf{i}$ is directed from left to right. Write the expression for $\mathbf{H}_2$ in terms of l_1 and $\mathbf{i}$.

The first two parts of this exercise require an approach similar to that used in Example 2.2.

(b) Determine the position, relative to the fixed surfaces, at which the particle can remain at rest.

(c) Consider the linear oscillations of this system. If the x-axis is chosen directed from left to right, with its origin at the particle's equilibrium position, show that the equation of motion for the particle is

$$\ddot{x} + 250x = 0.$$

As illustrated by the previous exercise, for two-spring systems the simplest equation of motion again arises when the particle's displacement is measured from its equilibrium position. This is true in general — measuring from the equilibrium position gives a homogeneous differential equation. The reason for this is that a particle which is stationary at the equilibrium position corresponds to a solution of the differential equation. If we measure from equilibrium, then this means that $x = 0$ (together with $\dot{x} = 0$ and $\ddot{x} = 0$) is a solution of the differential equation. But if $x = \dot{x} = \ddot{x} = 0$, then the left-hand side of the differential equation is zero, so the right-hand side must be zero also. Hence the differential equation is homogeneous.

We shall use the fact that the simplest equation of motion is obtained by measuring from equilibrium when considering more complicated spring systems in *Units 17* and *18*.

We conclude this section by asking you to investigate a two-spring system that is aligned vertically rather than horizontally.

Exercise 4.5

A block of mass m oscillates vertically under the influence of gravity and of two identical springs, each of stiffness k and natural length l_0 (see Figure 4.4). The springs are aligned vertically, with one attached to the floor and the other attached to the ceiling of a room of height $5l_0$. Assume that the block may be modelled as a particle.

(a) Show that the height x of the block from the floor at time t during the vertical oscillations satisfies the differential equation

$$m\ddot{x} + 2kx = 5kl_0 - mg.$$

(b) Hence find the height at which the block could remain in equilibrium.

(c) Find the period τ of the block's oscillations.

Suppose that the block is initially (at $t = 0$) released from rest at height $3l_0$.

(d) Find an expression for the height x of the block at time t.

(e) What are the minimum and maximum heights of the block during its motion?

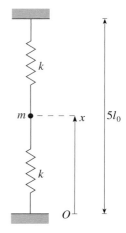

Figure 4.4

End-of-section Exercises

Exercise 4.6

A particle of mass 0.5 kg is suspended from the ceiling by a model spring of stiffness $50\,\text{N m}^{-1}$ and natural length 0.2 m. At time $t = 0$, the length of the spring is equal to its natural length, and the particle is moving vertically downwards at a speed of $1\,\text{m s}^{-1}$.

(a) Show that the length x of the spring satisfies the differential equation

$$\ddot{x} + 100x = 29.81.$$

(b) Find the length x_{eq} of the spring in the equilibrium position.

(c) For the given initial conditions, find the length of the spring in terms of time t.

(d) Find the period $\tau = 2\pi/\omega$, amplitude A and phase ϕ of the oscillations of the particle, and express the length of the spring at time t in the form

$$x(t) = x_{\text{eq}} + A\cos(\omega t + \phi).$$

(e) After $t = 0$, when does the particle first reach its lowest point, and what is the maximum length of the spring during the motion?

Exercise 4.7

A particle of mass m is hung from the ceiling by a model spring of stiffness k and natural length l_0. Take the equilibrium position of the particle as the origin, with the positive x-axis downwards. The particle is pulled a distance $\frac{1}{4}l_0$ below its equilibrium position and then released from rest.

(a) Given that the equation of motion for the particle is

$$m\ddot{x} + kx = 0,$$

find the particular solution of the equation of motion that satisfies the given initial conditions.

(b) What are the amplitude and phase of oscillations of the particle?

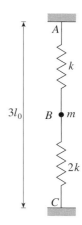

Exercise 4.8

Figure 4.5 shows a particle B of mass m, attached via two model springs to fixed points A and C, where C is a distance $3l_0$ vertically below A. Each spring has natural length l_0. Spring AB has stiffness k, and spring BC has stiffness $2k$.

(a) Find the height of the particle B above C when the system is in equilibrium.

(b) Obtain the equation of motion for the vertical oscillations of the particle in terms of the height x of the particle above its equilibrium position.

Figure 4.5

Exercise 4.9

Figure 4.6 shows the uniform cross-section of a rectangular pontoon that floats on water. The displacement x of the upper surface of the pontoon is measured upwards from its equilibrium position.

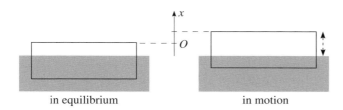

in equilibrium   in motion

Figure 4.6

It is a consequence of suitable modelling assumptions, and in particular of *Archimedes' Principle*, that, when bobbing up and down on flat water, the pontoon has equation of motion

$$M\ddot{x} + A\rho gx = 0,$$

where M is the mass of the pontoon, A is its uniform horizontal cross-sectional area, ρ is the density of water, and g is the magnitude of the acceleration due to gravity. According to this model, the 'bobbing up and down' is therefore a simple harmonic motion.

Archimedes' Principle states that if an object is wholly or partly immersed in a liquid, then the resulting buoyancy force on the object is directed vertically upwards and is equal in magnitude to the weight of liquid displaced by the object.

(a) Show that this model predicts, for a pontoon of given dimensions, that the period τ of the oscillations is proportional to $\sqrt{M}$, and hence increases with the mass of the pontoon. Do you think that there is any limit to the period that could be attained, for a suitably massive pontoon?

(b) A small object, whose mass m is negligible compared with that of the pontoon, is placed on the pontoon's upper surface. Suppose that the pontoon undergoes oscillations with amplitude 10 cm and period 1 second. Show that the small object remains in contact with the surface throughout the motion of the pontoon.

(c) Suppose that, for the situation described in part (b), the period is now 0.5 seconds. Show that the small object is predicted to leave the upper surface of the pontoon as the latter rises and at about 6 cm above the surface's equilibrium position.

Outcomes

After studying this unit you should be able to:

• apply the force law (Hooke's law) for a model spring, in statics and dynamics problems;

• find the equilibrium position of a particle that is acted on by model springs and gravity;

• derive an equation of motion for a system involving model springs and gravity, with the origin taken either at an equilibrium position or at some other appropriate fixed point;

• understand the basic features of simple harmonic motion, and use the terminology associated with it;

• find the amplitude, phase, angular frequency and period of a simple harmonic motion.

Solutions to the exercises

Section 1

1.1 (a) If $n = 22$, then Equation (1.1) gives
$$d_{22} \simeq 0.06 + 0.046 \times 22 = 1.072,$$
so the static depth of the bag is about 1.07 metres.

(b) If there are n coins in the bag and $d_n = 0.66$, then Equation (1.1) gives
$$0.66 \simeq 0.06 + 0.046n.$$
Solving for n, we obtain
$$n = \frac{0.66 - 0.06}{0.046} \simeq 13.0,$$
so there are 13 coins in the bag.

1.2 (a) The period of the oscillations is $\frac{2\pi}{5}$.

(b) We know that $A\cos 5t$ varies between $\pm A$. So $10 + A\cos 5t$ varies between $10 - A$ and $10 + A$. Its value would become negative at times if $10 - A$ were less than 0, so for $x \geq 0$ we know that A must not exceed 10.

1.3 Using a trigonometric identity from the Handbook,
$$A\cos(\omega t + \phi) = A(\cos(\omega t)\cos\phi - \sin(\omega t)\sin\phi).$$
Comparing this with
$$B\cos(\omega t) + C\sin(\omega t),$$
we see that it is of the same form, with
$$B = A\cos\phi \quad \text{and} \quad C = -A\sin\phi.$$

1.4 The values of τ^2 are given in the table below.

n	5	10	15	20	25
τ^2	0.49	1.56	2.56	3.24	4.41

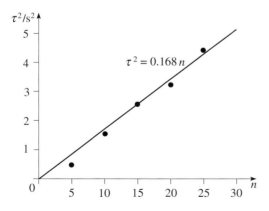

As you can see from the graph above, a straight line through the origin agrees fairly well with the data for $n > 5$, indicating direct proportionality between τ^2 and n.

(As you will see in *Unit 9*, the best least squares estimate for the slope of this line is given by
$$\frac{\text{sum of } \tau^2}{\text{sum of } n} = \frac{1.56 + 2.56 + 3.24 + 4.41}{10 + 15 + 20 + 25} \simeq 0.168.$$
So the best fit line is $\tau^2 = 0.168n$.)

Section 2

2.1 (a) When $l = 0.35$, the spring is extended by an amount $e = 0.05$, so the magnitude of the spring force is $0.05 \times 200 = 10$ (newtons). Since the spring is in tension, the force on the object at the end is directed towards the centre of the spring.

(b) When $l = 0.2$, the spring is compressed by an amount $c = 0.1$, so the magnitude of the spring force is $0.1 \times 200 = 20$ (newtons). Since the spring is in compression, the force on the object at the end is directed away from the centre of the spring.

2.2 In each case we have $k = 200$ and $l_0 = 0.3$. Take $\widehat{\mathbf{s}}$ to be a unit vector in the direction from the centre of the spring towards the object.

(a) With $l = 0.35$, the force acting on the object is
$$\mathbf{H} = -200(0.35 - 0.3)\widehat{\mathbf{s}} = -10\widehat{\mathbf{s}},$$
with magnitude 10 N and direction given by $-\widehat{\mathbf{s}}$, that is, towards the centre of the spring.

(b) When $l = 0.2$, the force acting on the object is
$$\mathbf{H} = -200(0.2 - 0.3)\widehat{\mathbf{s}} = 20\widehat{\mathbf{s}},$$
with magnitude 20 N and direction given by $\widehat{\mathbf{s}}$, that is, away from the centre of the spring.

2.3 Let the length of each spring be l_1 when there is no baby in the baby bouncer. Assume that the two springs may be modelled satisfactorily by model springs, each with stiffness k and natural length l_0. Choose the **i**-direction to be vertically downwards.

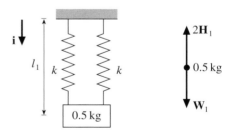

Each spring exerts a force
$$\mathbf{H}_1 = -k(l_1 - l_0)\widehat{\mathbf{s}} = -k(l_1 - l_0)\mathbf{i}.$$
The weight of the seat plus straps is $\mathbf{W}_1 = 0.5g\mathbf{i}$. The system is in equilibrium, so
$$\mathbf{W}_1 + 2\mathbf{H}_1 = \mathbf{0}.$$
Resolving in the **i**-direction gives
$$2k(l_1 - l_0) = 0.5g. \tag{S.1}$$
With the baby strapped into the seat, the length of each spring becomes $l_1 + 0.03$ (in metres).

Now each spring exerts a force

$$\mathbf{H}_2 = -k(l_1 + 0.03 - l_0)\mathbf{i},$$

while the total weight of the baby, seat and straps is $\mathbf{W}_2 = 8g\mathbf{i}$. The system is again in equilibrium, so

$$\mathbf{W}_2 + 2\mathbf{H}_2 = \mathbf{0}.$$

Resolving in the **i**-direction gives

$$2k(l_1 + 0.03 - l_0) = 8g. \tag{S.2}$$

We have $2k(l_1 - l_0) = 0.5g$ from Equation (S.1), and subtracting this from Equation (S.2) gives $0.06k = 7.5g$. Hence the stiffness of each spring is

$$k = 125g \simeq 1226\,\mathrm{N\,m^{-1}}.$$

(This problem can also be tackled without going through the full procedure above. The stiffness of a model spring describes the *increase* in force magnitude exerted by the spring per unit *increase* in length (if the spring is already extended). Here the total increase in force magnitude as a result of putting the baby into the bouncer is $7.5g\,\mathrm{N}$, which is shared equally between the two springs ($7.5g/2\,\mathrm{N}$ each). The corresponding increase in length of $0.03\,\mathrm{m}$ arises therefore from a stiffness of $k = 7.5g/(2 \times 0.03) \simeq 1226\,\mathrm{N\,m^{-1}}$.)

2.4 As before, the object is modelled as a particle. In Example 2.2, the distance between the fixed points was greater than the sum of the natural lengths of the two springs, and hence, in equilibrium, each spring was extended. Here the distance between the fixed points is less than the sum of the natural lengths of the two springs, and hence, in equilibrium, each spring is compressed. However, this does not greatly affect the form of the solution.

◀Choose axes▶

We again choose the x-axis to point from left to right, with origin at the left-hand fixed point.

◀Apply law(s)▶

Then the lengths of the two springs are x (left spring) and $0.3 - x$ (right spring), so the forces exerted by them are

$$\mathbf{H}_{\mathrm{left}} = -40(x - 0.3)\mathbf{i},$$

$$\mathbf{H}_{\mathrm{right}} = -60((0.3 - x) - 0.2)(-\mathbf{i}) = 60(0.1 - x)\mathbf{i}.$$

Since the particle is held in equilibrium by these two forces plus the weight $\mathbf{W}$ of the particle and the normal reaction $\mathbf{N}$ on it (both acting vertically), we have

$$\mathbf{W} + \mathbf{N} + \mathbf{H}_{\mathrm{left}} + \mathbf{H}_{\mathrm{right}} = \mathbf{0}. \tag{S.3}$$

◀Solve equation(s)▶

Resolving in the (horizontal) **i**-direction gives

$$60(0.1 - x) - 40(x - 0.3) = 0.$$

The solution of this equation is $x = 0.18$, so we conclude that the particle is $0.18\,\mathrm{m}$ from the left-hand fixed point (and hence $0.12\,\mathrm{m}$ from the right-hand fixed point).

Resolving Equation (S.3) in the **i**-direction also tells us that the magnitudes of the compressive forces in the two springs are the same. This magnitude is

$$|\mathbf{H}_{\mathrm{left}}| = -40(0.18 - 0.3) = 4.8,$$

i.e. $4.8\,\mathrm{N}$.

2.5 Model the object as a particle.

◀Choose axes▶

Choose the x-axis to point vertically upwards, with origin at A. Then the weight of the particle is

$$\mathbf{W} = -1.5g\mathbf{i}.$$

◀Apply law(s)▶

The springs have lengths x (lower spring) and $2.1 - x$ (upper spring), so the forces exerted by them are

$$\mathbf{H}_{\mathrm{lower}} = -50(x - 0.5)\mathbf{i},$$

$$\mathbf{H}_{\mathrm{upper}} = -20((2.1 - x) - 0.3)(-\mathbf{i}) = 20(1.8 - x)\mathbf{i}.$$

In equilibrium, we have

$$\mathbf{H}_{\mathrm{lower}} + \mathbf{H}_{\mathrm{upper}} + \mathbf{W} = \mathbf{0}.$$

◀Solve equation(s)▶

Resolving in the **i**-direction, we obtain

$$-50(x - 0.5) + 20(1.8 - x) - 1.5g = 0,$$

so $70x = 61 - 1.5g$. The solution of this equation is $x \simeq 0.66$.

◀Interpret solution▶

So we conclude that the object is about $0.66\,\mathrm{m}$ above the floor.

2.6 **(a)** In order to carry out the function intended for the dish dispenser, the spring must compress by a distance $0.007\,\mathrm{m}$ for each additional mass $0.59\,\mathrm{kg}$ placed on it. This extra mass corresponds to an additional force (weight) of magnitude $0.59g\,\mathrm{N}$, hence the stiffness required (in $\mathrm{N\,m^{-1}}$) is

$$\frac{0.59g}{0.007} \simeq 827.$$

(b) If the alternative dishes have the same diameter as the originals and are made of a material of similar density, then their weight per unit thickness will be much the same. In these circumstances, the dish dispenser might well continue to function satisfactorily. However, dishes with a smaller diameter will be less heavy for a given thickness. Hence, if a pile of side plates is placed on a dish dispenser designed for use with dinner plates, one could expect the level of the top of the pile to be raised with each plate added.

2.7 Suppose that the original spring, when hung vertically from a fixed point, supported an object of mass m with equilibrium length l, i.e. $k(l - l_0) = mg$ (see Equation (2.2)). The original spring can be thought of as being made up of the two shorter springs connected at their ends and, while supporting the weight of the same object in equilibrium, each will have length $\frac{1}{2}l$ and hence extension $\frac{1}{2}(l - l_0)$. The stiffness of each shorter spring is therefore

$$\frac{mg}{\frac{1}{2}(l - l_0)} = \frac{k(l - l_0)}{\frac{1}{2}(l - l_0)} = 2k.$$

Each of the shorter springs is twice as stiff as the original. (This illustrates that stiffness depends on the natural length of a spring and is not just a characteristic of other features of the spring.)

2.8 Once the battery has been placed in its holder, the sum of the spring lengths is

$(5.5 - 5)\,\text{cm} = 0.5\,\text{cm} = 0.005\,\text{m}.$

◄Choose axes►

Take the x-axis to be from left to right, with origin at the left-hand end of the battery holder (see Figure 2.13). Suppose that the spring at the left-hand side of the battery has length x. Then the length of the right-hand spring is $0.005 - x$.

◄Apply law(s)►

The forces exerted by the two springs are

$\mathbf{H}_{\text{left}} = -30(x - 0.004)\mathbf{i},$

$\mathbf{H}_{\text{right}} = -10((0.005 - x) - 0.003)(-\mathbf{i})$
$= 10(0.002 - x)\mathbf{i}.$

Since the battery is held in equilibrium by these two forces plus the weight $\mathbf{W}$ of the battery and the normal reaction $\mathbf{N}$ on it (both acting vertically), we have

$\mathbf{W} + \mathbf{N} + \mathbf{H}_{\text{left}} + \mathbf{H}_{\text{right}} = \mathbf{0}.$

◄Solve equation(s)►

Resolving in the (horizontal) $\mathbf{i}$-direction gives

$-30(x - 0.004) + 10(0.002 - x) = 0,$

with solution $x = 0.0035$ (metres). Resolving in the $\mathbf{i}$-direction also tells us that the magnitudes of the (compressive) spring forces are equal. This magnitude is

$|\mathbf{H}_{\text{left}}| = 30 \times 0.0005 = 0.015,$

i.e. $0.015\,\text{N}.$

Section 3

3.1 ◄Draw picture► ◄Choose axes►

◄Draw force diagram►

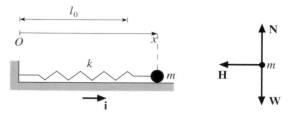

The length of the model spring is x. We omit from further consideration the weight $\mathbf{W}$ and the normal reaction $\mathbf{N}$, since these forces cancel each other ($\mathbf{W} + \mathbf{N} = \mathbf{0}$).

◄Apply Newton's 2nd law►

The force $\mathbf{H}$ exerted by the spring on the particle is given by

$$\mathbf{H} = -k(l - l_0)\widehat{\mathbf{s}}, \qquad (2.1)$$

where l is the length of the spring and $\widehat{\mathbf{s}}$ is a unit vector directed from the centre of the spring towards the particle. Here we have $l = x$ and $\widehat{\mathbf{s}} = \mathbf{i}$, which gives

$\mathbf{H} = -k(x - l_0)\mathbf{i}.$

This is also the total force that acts on the particle, so Newton's second law (3.1) becomes

$m\ddot{x}\mathbf{i} = -k(x - l_0)\mathbf{i}.$

◄Solve equation(s)►

Resolving in the $\mathbf{i}$-direction gives

$m\ddot{x} = -k(x - l_0),$

that is,

$m\ddot{x} + kx = kl_0.$

(Notice the similarities, and the difference, between this equation of motion and Equation (3.4) derived in Example 3.1 for a displacement from the equilibrium position.)

3.2 If $x(t) = B\cos(\omega t) + C\sin(\omega t)$, then
$\dot{x}(t) = -B\omega\sin(\omega t) + C\omega\cos(\omega t),$
$\ddot{x}(t) = -B\omega^2\cos(\omega t) - C\omega^2\sin(\omega t) = -\omega^2 x(t).$
Putting $\omega^2 = k/m$ and writing x for $x(t)$, we have
$\ddot{x} = -kx/m,$
that is,
$m\ddot{x} + kx = 0.$
Hence $x(t) = B\cos(\omega t) + C\sin(\omega t)$ is a solution of this last differential equation.

3.3 Write the differential equation in the form

$$\ddot{x} + \omega^2 x = 0,$$

where $\omega^2 = k/m$. Then the auxiliary equation is

$$\lambda^2 + \omega^2 = 0,$$

with solutions $\lambda = \pm i\omega$. So the general solution is

$$x(t) = e^0(B\cos(\omega t) + C\sin(\omega t))$$
$$= B\cos(\omega t) + C\sin(\omega t),$$

where B and C are arbitrary constants.

3.4 (a) The angular frequency is

$$\omega = \sqrt{k/m} = \sqrt{200/0.5} = 20,$$

i.e. $20\,\text{rad}\,\text{s}^{-1}$.

The period is

$$\tau = 2\pi/\omega = 2\pi/20 \simeq 0.314,$$

i.e. about $0.314\,\text{s}$.

(b) The frequency is

$$f = \omega/(2\pi) = 20/(2\pi) \simeq 3.18,$$

i.e. about $3.18\,\text{Hz}$.

(c) With $\omega = 20$, we have

$$x(t) = B\cos 20t + C\sin 20t,$$

whose derivative is

$$\dot{x}(t) = -20B\sin 20t + 20C\cos 20t.$$

Now $x = 0.3$ and $\dot{x} = 2$ when $t = 0$, so

$$0.3 = B, \quad 2 = 20C.$$

Hence $B = 0.3$ and $C = 0.1$. The position function for the particle is

$$x(t) = 0.3\cos 20t + 0.1\sin 20t.$$

3.5 With the usual notation, we have

$$A = \sqrt{B^2 + C^2}$$
$$= \sqrt{0.3^2 + 0.1^2} = \sqrt{0.1} \simeq 0.316.$$

The equations to be solved for ϕ (from Equations (3.7)) are

$$\cos\phi = 0.3/A, \quad \sin\phi = -0.1/A.$$

With $\cos\phi > 0$ and $\sin\phi < 0$, the angle ϕ lies in the fourth quadrant (where $-\frac{\pi}{2} < \phi < 0$), so

$$\phi = \arcsin\left(\frac{-0.1}{\sqrt{0.1}}\right) \simeq -0.322.$$

Thus the oscillation has amplitude $0.316\,\text{m}$ and phase angle -0.322 radians, i.e. it may be described by the equation

$$x(t) \simeq 0.316\cos(20t - 0.322).$$

3.6 Since $x = l_0 + B\cos(\omega t) + C\sin(\omega t)$, we have

$$\dot{x} = -\omega B\sin(\omega t) + \omega C\cos(\omega t).$$

Initially $x(0) = x_0$ and $\dot{x}(0) = v_0$, which lead to

$$x_0 = l_0 + B, \quad v_0 = \omega C.$$

Hence $B = x_0 - l_0$ and $C = v_0/\omega$, so the required solution is

$$x = l_0 + (x_0 - l_0)\cos(\omega t) + (v_0/\omega)\sin(\omega t).$$

3.7 (a) We start from the simple harmonic motion equation

$$\ddot{x} + \omega^2 x = 0.$$

Writing $\ddot{x}$ as the derivative of the velocity, v, of the particle and rearranging gives

$$\dot{v} = -\omega^2 x. \tag{S.4}$$

Now suppose that the velocity of the particle is a maximum or minimum: then $\dot{v} = 0$. So by Equation (S.4), $x = 0$, i.e. the particle is at the equilibrium position. [Conversely, if the particle is at the equilibrium position, then $x = 0$. So by Equation (S.4), $\dot{v} = 0$, i.e. the velocity is a maximum or minimum.]

(b) Again we start from the simple harmonic motion equation

$$\ddot{x} + \omega^2 x = 0.$$

Differentiation and rearrangement of this equation gives

$$\frac{d\ddot{x}}{dt} = -\omega^2\frac{dx}{dt} = -\omega^2\dot{x}.$$

If the acceleration $\ddot{x}$ is a maximum or minimum, then $d\ddot{x}/dt = 0$, and the last equation shows that this occurs precisely when the velocity $\dot{x}$ is zero.

Section 4

4.1   ◀Draw picture▶   ◀Draw force diagram▶

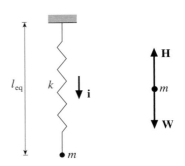

◀Choose axes▶

Suppose that the **i**-direction is chosen to point downwards, as shown above. The length of the spring in equilibrium is l_{eq}.

◀Apply Hooke's law and the equilibrium condition▶

The force exerted on the particle by the model spring is then

$$\mathbf{H} = -k(l_{\text{eq}} - l_0)\hat{\mathbf{s}},$$

where $\hat{\mathbf{s}}$ is a unit vector directed from the centre of the spring towards the particle, i.e. $\hat{\mathbf{s}} = \mathbf{i}$. The weight of the particle is $\mathbf{W} = mg\mathbf{i}$. As the particle is in equilibrium, we have $\mathbf{H} + \mathbf{W} = \mathbf{0}$, so

$$-k(l_{\text{eq}} - l_0) + mg = 0.$$

Hence

$$l_{\text{eq}} = l_0 + mg/k.$$

(This formula was also established in Example 2.3.)

4.2 (a) The oscillation is given by

$$x(t) = A\cos(\omega t + \phi), \tag{3.6}$$

where $\omega = \sqrt{k/m}$. This oscillation has period

$$\tau = 2\pi/\omega = 2\pi\sqrt{m/k}.$$

Also, $l_{eq} = l_0 + mg/k$, so

$$\tau = 2\pi\sqrt{(l_{eq} - l_0)/g}.$$

(b) This last formula can be used to estimate a value for g if we have values for l_0, l_{eq} and τ. Suppose that a spring, which obeys Hooke's law closely, is suspended from a fixed support. Take l_0 as the measured length of this spring when there is no load on it, i.e. the free length. Then hang a load from its lower end, and take l_{eq} to be the measured length of the spring when at rest. Finally, time small oscillations of the spring, with the same load supported as before, to obtain a value for τ.

4.3 (a) ◀Draw force diagram▶

The force diagram is as shown in Figure 4.2(b).

◀Apply Newton's 2nd law▶

We again have $\mathbf{W} = mg\mathbf{i}$, but now the force exerted by the spring is expressed as

$$\mathbf{H} = -k(l - l_0)\mathbf{i} = -k(x - l_0)\mathbf{i}.$$

Newton's second law then gives

$$m\ddot{x}\mathbf{i} = \mathbf{H} + \mathbf{W}$$
$$= -k(x - l_0)\mathbf{i} + mg\mathbf{i} = (-kx + kl_0 + mg)\mathbf{i}.$$

Resolving in the $\mathbf{i}$-direction, we have

$$m\ddot{x} + kx = kl_0 + mg.$$

Dividing through by m, we can rewrite this differential equation as

$$\ddot{x} + \omega^2 x = \omega^2\left(l_0 + \frac{mg}{k}\right),$$

where $\omega^2 = k/m$.

(b) ◀Solve differential equation▶

The differential equation is inhomogeneous. A particular integral is

$$x_p = l_0 + \frac{mg}{k}.$$

(This is just the equilibrium length l_{eq} of the spring.) The complementary function is

$$x_c = B\cos(\omega t) + C\sin(\omega t),$$

so the general solution is

$$x(t) = l_0 + \frac{mg}{k} + B\cos(\omega t) + C\sin(\omega t)$$

(which is equivalent to Equation (4.1)).

◀Interpret solution▶

The given initial conditions are $x(0) = l_0$ and $\dot{x}(0) = 0$. These lead to

$$l_0 = l_0 + \frac{mg}{k} + B, \quad 0 = \omega C.$$

Hence $B = -mg/k$ and $C = 0$, so the required solution is

$$x(t) = l_0 + \frac{mg}{k}(1 - \cos(\omega t)).$$

4.4 (a) Using Hooke's law (2.1), the forces exerted by the two springs on the particle are

$$\mathbf{H}_1 = -200(l_1 - 0.3)\hat{\mathbf{s}}_1, \quad \text{where } \hat{\mathbf{s}}_1 = \mathbf{i},$$
$$\mathbf{H}_2 = -300(l_2 - 0.4)\hat{\mathbf{s}}_2, \quad \text{where } \hat{\mathbf{s}}_2 = -\mathbf{i}.$$

These give the results stated in the question. We also have $l_1 + l_2 = 0.8$, so $l_2 = 0.8 - l_1$, since the distance between the fixed surfaces is 0.8 m and the particle has no dimensions. Hence we may write

$$\mathbf{H}_1 = -200(l_1 - 0.3)\mathbf{i},$$
$$\mathbf{H}_2 = 300(0.8 - l_1 - 0.4)\mathbf{i} = 300(0.4 - l_1)\mathbf{i}.$$

(b) When the particle is in equilibrium, we have the condition $\mathbf{W} + \mathbf{N} + \mathbf{H}_1 + \mathbf{H}_2 = \mathbf{0}$, where $\mathbf{W}$ is the weight of the particle and $\mathbf{N}$ is the normal reaction on it. On resolving in the $\mathbf{i}$-direction, this gives

$$-200(l_1 - 0.3) + 300(0.4 - l_1) = 0,$$

whose solution is $l_1 = 0.36$. Hence the particle is in equilibrium at a point 0.36 m from the left-hand fixed surface (and 0.44 m from the right-hand surface).

(c)

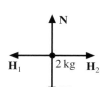

From part (b), the lengths of the springs in equilibrium are, respectively, 0.36 m and 0.44 m. If the particle is displaced by x from its equilibrium position (with the x-axis directed from left to right, as shown above), then the length of spring 1 becomes $l_1 = 0.36 + x$.

The forces exerted on the particle by the two springs are now

$$\mathbf{H}_1 = -200(l_1 - 0.3)\mathbf{i} = -200(0.06 + x)\mathbf{i},$$
$$\mathbf{H}_2 = 300(0.4 - l_1)\mathbf{i} = 300(0.04 - x)\mathbf{i}.$$

As before, the weight $\mathbf{W}$ of the particle is balanced by the normal reaction $\mathbf{N}$ on it, i.e. $\mathbf{W} + \mathbf{N} = \mathbf{0}$. Newton's second law (with $m = 2$ kg) then gives

$$2\ddot{x}\mathbf{i} = \mathbf{H}_1 + \mathbf{H}_2$$
$$= -200(0.06 + x)\mathbf{i} + 300(0.04 - x)\mathbf{i}$$
$$= -500x\mathbf{i},$$

which, after resolving in the $\mathbf{i}$-direction, leads to the equation

$$\ddot{x} + 250x = 0,$$

as required.

4.5 (a)   ◄Draw picture►   ◄Choose axes►

◄Draw force diagram►

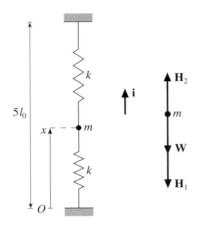

The force diagram above is drawn for the case where both springs are extended.

◄Apply Newton's 2nd law►

Regard the lower spring as spring 1 and the upper spring as spring 2. These springs have respective lengths x and $5l_0 - x$, so the forces they exert are (by Hooke's law)

$$\mathbf{H}_1 = -k(x - l_0)\mathbf{i},$$
$$\mathbf{H}_2 = -k(5l_0 - x - l_0)(-\mathbf{i}) = k(4l_0 - x)\mathbf{i}.$$

From Newton's second law, we have

$$
\begin{aligned}
m\ddot{x}\mathbf{i} &= \mathbf{H}_1 + \mathbf{H}_2 + \mathbf{W} \\
&= -k(x - l_0)\mathbf{i} + k(4l_0 - x)\mathbf{i} - mg\mathbf{i} \\
&= (5kl_0 - 2kx - mg)\mathbf{i}.
\end{aligned}
$$

Resolving in the **i**-direction and rearranging, we obtain the equation

$$m\ddot{x} + 2kx = 5kl_0 - mg, \qquad (\text{S.5})$$

as required.

(b)   ◄Solve differential equation►

In equilibrium, with $x = x_{\text{eq}}$ say, we have $\dot{x} = 0$ and $\ddot{x} = 0$. Substituting the second of these into the equation of motion (S.5) gives

$$2kx_{\text{eq}} = 5kl_0 - mg,$$

so the equilibrium height is

$$x_{\text{eq}} = \frac{5l_0}{2} - \frac{mg}{2k}.$$

(As you might expect, this is below the half-way point between the floor and the ceiling.)

(c)   The general solution of the equation of motion (S.5) is

$$x = B\cos(\omega t) + C\sin(\omega t) + x_{\text{eq}},$$

where the angular frequency ω is $\sqrt{2k/m}$. The period of the vertical oscillations is

$$\tau = \frac{2\pi}{\omega} = 2\pi\sqrt{\frac{m}{2k}} = \pi\sqrt{\frac{2m}{k}}.$$

(d)   The initial conditions are $x(0) = 3l_0$ and $\dot{x}(0) = 0$. So we have

$$3l_0 = B + \frac{5l_0}{2} - \frac{mg}{2k}, \quad 0 = C\omega.$$

Hence $B = l_0/2 + mg/(2k)$ and $C = 0$, giving the particular solution

$$x(t) = \left(\frac{l_0}{2} + \frac{mg}{2k}\right)\cos(\omega t) + \frac{5l_0}{2} - \frac{mg}{2k}.$$

(e)   The minimum and maximum heights are attained, respectively, when $\cos(\omega t) = -1$ and when $\cos(\omega t) = 1$. So

$$x_{\min} = -\left(\frac{l_0}{2} + \frac{mg}{2k}\right) + \frac{5l_0}{2} - \frac{mg}{2k} = 2l_0 - \frac{mg}{k},$$

$$x_{\max} = \frac{l_0}{2} + \frac{mg}{2k} + \frac{5l_0}{2} - \frac{mg}{2k} = 3l_0.$$

(As expected, x_{eq} lies half-way between $x_{\min}$ and $x_{\max}$.)

4.6 (a)   ◄Draw picture►   ◄Choose axes►

◄Draw force diagram►

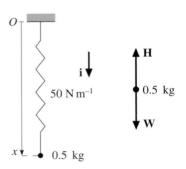

◄Apply Newton's 2nd law►

The force exerted on the particle by the spring is, from Hooke's law (2.1),

$$\mathbf{H} = -k(l - l_0)\mathbf{i} = -50(x - 0.2)\mathbf{i}.$$

From Newton's second law, we have

$$
\begin{aligned}
0.5\ddot{x}\mathbf{i} &= \mathbf{H} + \mathbf{W} \\
&= -50(x - 0.2)\mathbf{i} + 0.5g\mathbf{i} \\
&= (-50x + 10 + 0.5g)\mathbf{i}.
\end{aligned}
$$

On resolving in the **i**-direction and rearranging, we obtain

$$\ddot{x} + 100x = 20 + g \simeq 29.81, \qquad (\text{S.6})$$

as required.

(b)   ◄Solve differential equation►

When in equilibrium, with $x = x_{\text{eq}}$, we have $\ddot{x} = 0$, so

$$100x_{\text{eq}} = 29.81, \quad \text{or} \quad x_{\text{eq}} = 0.2981 \simeq 0.30.$$

The length of the spring in the equilibrium position is therefore 0.30 m (to 2 d.p.).

(c)   The general solution of the equation of motion (S.6) is approximately

$$x(t) = 0.3 + B\cos 10t + C\sin 10t.$$

The initial conditions are $x(0) = 0.2$ and $\dot{x}(0) = 1$.

Hence we obtain

$$0.2 = 0.3 + B, \quad 1 = 10C,$$

which lead to $B = -0.1$ and $C = 0.1$. The spring length for this particular motion is given by

$$x(t) = 0.3 - 0.1\cos 10t + 0.1\sin 10t.$$

(d) The angular frequency of the simple harmonic motion is $\omega = \sqrt{100} = 10$. So the period is

$$\tau = 2\pi/\omega = 0.2\pi \simeq 0.63 \text{ seconds.}$$

The amplitude of the oscillations is

$$A = \sqrt{B^2 + C^2} = \sqrt{0.02} \simeq 0.14 \text{ metres.}$$

The phase of the oscillations is (from Equations (3.7)) the solution of the equations

$$\cos\phi = \frac{B}{A} = \frac{-0.1}{\sqrt{0.02}} = -\frac{1}{\sqrt{2}},$$

$$\sin\phi = -\frac{C}{A} = -\frac{0.1}{\sqrt{0.02}} = -\frac{1}{\sqrt{2}}.$$

Since both $\cos\phi$ and $\sin\phi$ are negative, the angle ϕ lies in the third quadrant ($-\pi < \phi < -\frac{\pi}{2}$), so it is given by

$$\phi = \arctan 1 - \pi = -\frac{3\pi}{4}.$$

The spring length can therefore be re-expressed as

$$x(t) \simeq 0.3 + 0.14\cos(10t - \tfrac{3\pi}{4}).$$

(e) The maximum length of the spring is the length at which the particle reaches its lowest point, namely,

$$x_{\text{eq}} + A \simeq 0.44 \text{ metres.}$$

The particle first reaches this point at the smallest positive value of t for which $\cos(10t - \frac{3\pi}{4}) = 1$, i.e. when $t = 3\pi/40 \simeq 0.24$ seconds.

4.7 (a) The general solution of the given equation of motion is

$$x(t) = B\cos(\omega t) + C\sin(\omega t),$$

where $\omega^2 = k/m$. Suppose that the particle is released at $t = 0$. Then the initial conditions are

$$x(0) = \tfrac{1}{4}l_0, \quad \dot{x}(0) = 0,$$

which give $B = \tfrac{1}{4}l_0$ and $C = 0$. Hence the required particular solution is

$$x(t) = \tfrac{1}{4}l_0\cos(\omega t).$$

(b) On comparing the particular solution above with the standard expression $A\cos(\omega t + \phi)$, we see that the oscillations of the particle have amplitude $A = \tfrac{1}{4}l_0$ and phase $\phi = 0$.

4.8 (a) ◄Draw picture► ◄Choose axes►
◄Draw force diagram►

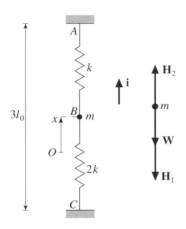

◄Apply Newton's 2nd law►

Regard the lower spring as spring 1 (of length l_1) and the upper spring as spring 2 (of length l_2), and choose the x-axis directed upwards as shown. Then the forces exerted on the particle by the two springs are

$$\mathbf{H}_1 = -2k(l_1 - l_0)\mathbf{i},$$

$$\mathbf{H}_2 = -k(l_2 - l_0)(-\mathbf{i}) = k(l_2 - l_0)\mathbf{i}.$$

Since $l_1 + l_2 = 3l_0$, the force from the second spring can also be written as

$$\mathbf{H}_2 = k(2l_0 - l_1)\mathbf{i}.$$

In equilibrium, we have $l_1 = l_{1,\text{eq}}$ and

$$\mathbf{H}_1 + \mathbf{H}_2 + \mathbf{W} = \mathbf{0},$$

so

$$-2k(l_{1,\text{eq}} - l_0)\mathbf{i} + k(2l_0 - l_{1,\text{eq}})\mathbf{i} - mg\mathbf{i} = \mathbf{0}.$$

On solving for $l_{1,\text{eq}}$, we find

$$l_{1,\text{eq}} = \tfrac{4}{3}l_0 - mg/(3k).$$

(b) In motion, with $l_1 = l_{1,\text{eq}} + x$, Newton's second law gives

$$\begin{aligned}
m\ddot{x}\mathbf{i} &= \mathbf{H}_1 + \mathbf{H}_2 + \mathbf{W} \\
&= -2k(l_{1,\text{eq}} + x - l_0)\mathbf{i} + k(2l_0 - l_{1,\text{eq}} - x)\mathbf{i} - mg\mathbf{i} \\
&= -3kx\mathbf{i},
\end{aligned}$$

that is,

$$m\ddot{x} + 3kx = 0.$$

4.9 **(a)** The given equation of motion is equivalent to
$$\ddot{x} + \omega^2 x = 0,$$
where $\omega^2 = A\rho g/M$. The period τ is therefore given by
$$\tau = \frac{2\pi}{\omega} = 2\pi\sqrt{\frac{M}{A\rho g}} = C\sqrt{M},$$
where $C = 2\pi/\sqrt{A\rho g}$ is constant if A is fixed.

If the mass M is increased progressively, for given dimensions of the pontoon, then eventually the pontoon will sink! The quoted equation of motion then no longer applies.

(If the total height of the pontoon is H, then we must have $M < AH\rho$ if the pontoon is to float. This gives an upper limit $2\pi\sqrt{H/g}$ for the period of oscillations.)

(b)

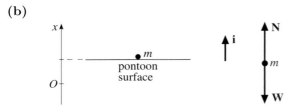

Since the mass m of the object is negligible compared with that of the pontoon, it cannot alter the motion of the latter. Hence if the object (considered as a particle) remains in contact with the surface, its position x above the surface's equilibrium position must satisfy the equation
$$\ddot{x} + \omega^2 x = 0, \tag{S.7}$$
as in part (a).

The particle is acted on by two forces: its weight $\mathbf{W}$ and the normal reaction $\mathbf{N}$ exerted on it by the surface of the pontoon. The normal reaction force $\mathbf{N}$ is a push rather than a pull and therefore must be of the form $\mathbf{N} = |\mathbf{N}|\mathbf{i}$ with $|\mathbf{N}| \geq 0$.

Newton's second law applied to the object gives
$$m\ddot{x}\mathbf{i} = \mathbf{N} + \mathbf{W}$$
$$= |\mathbf{N}|\mathbf{i} - mg\mathbf{i}.$$
Resolving this equation in the $\mathbf{i}$-direction and rearranging gives
$$|\mathbf{N}| = mg + m\ddot{x}.$$
But $|\mathbf{N}| \geq 0$, so $mg + m\ddot{x} \geq 0$, i.e. $g + \ddot{x} \geq 0$ since m is positive.

Now we use Equation (S.7) to substitute for $\ddot{x}$ and obtain
$$g - \omega^2 x \geq 0,$$
i.e.
$$x \leq g/\omega^2. \tag{S.8}$$
If $\tau = 1$, then $\omega = 2\pi$ and $g/\omega^2 \simeq 0.25$. For an amplitude of $10\,\mathrm{cm}$, we have $x \leq 0.1$. Hence, in this case, the condition (S.8) is satisfied, and the object never leaves the surface.

(c) If $\tau = 0.5$, then $\omega = 4\pi$ and $g/\omega^2 \simeq 0.06$. In this case, there are values of x less than 0.1 for which the inequality (S.8) is not satisfied, so the object must leave the surface during the motion.

It will do so where $x = g/\omega^2 \simeq 0.06$, i.e. $6\,\mathrm{cm}$ above the surface's equilibrium position. This takes place when the pontoon is rising, because then x is increasing and hence $N = m(g - \omega^2 x)$ is decreasing towards zero.

UNIT 8   *Energy and consolidation*

Study guide for Unit 8

This unit has two roles: the first is to introduce the topic of energy in mechanical systems; the second is to consolidate the mechanics covered in *Units 5, 6* and *7*.

Sections 1 and 2 contain new material and should be studied in numerical order. Sections 3, 4 and 5 contain revision material and can be studied at any point.

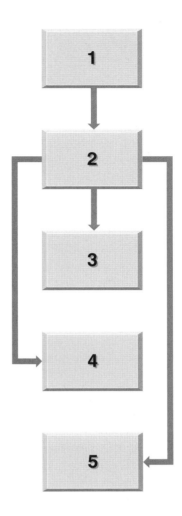

Introduction

Energy is an important concept in physics. What we mean by mechanical energy will be formally defined in Section 1, but for now we shall use the everyday notion. It is a relatively new concept when compared to the concepts of mass and force. The concept of energy that can be converted from one form to another came to the fore when James Joule did experiments converting mechanical energy into heat in 1843. What Joule found was that energy can be neither created nor destroyed: it can merely be converted from one form to another. A precise statement of this fact will be given in Section 1 as the law of conservation of mechanical energy.

In Section 1 you will see that the use of conservation of mechanical energy to solve mechanics problems is entirely equivalent to using Newton's second law of motion. It is possible to derive the law of conservation of mechanical energy from Newton's second law, and vice versa. So, in a sense, no new problems can be solved using conservation of energy — every problem could equally well be solved by appealing to Newton's second law.

So why teach about energy? There are many answers to this. One answer is that in some situations it is far quicker to solve problems by considering energy, as you will see in this unit.

A second reason to introduce energy is that it is a physical concept that is important in many fields other than mechanics. In this course we shall concentrate on mechanical energy and heat. By introducing other forms of energy, such as electromagnetic, chemical, and so on, conservation of energy can be extended beyond the field of mechanics, and becomes one of the fundamental principles of physics.

A third reason to introduce energy is that it leads the way from Newtonian mechanics to Lagrangian and Hamiltonian mechanics. These other methods for solving mechanics problems have richer mathematical structures than Newtonian mechanics. This richer structure makes the generalization to relativistic and quantum mechanics easier.

The first half of this unit is devoted to energy. The law of conservation of mechanical energy is developed in Section 1. In Section 2 it is applied to systems involving gravity and springs. For this first look at energy, the discussion will (mostly) be limited to one-dimensional problems.

The second half of this unit comprises three sections, each containing a set of exercises for one of the earlier mechanics units. These exercises are designed to give you a quick refresher course in the contents of the relevant unit. Each set of exercises follows broadly the sequence in which topics are introduced in the corresponding unit. In fact, although we use the title 'exercise' throughout for uniformity, many of the exercises would be better regarded as self-assessment questions. Some of them take the same form as exercises in the units, where you are asked to solve a problem in mechanics, for example. Others are intended to make you think again about the concepts and procedures introduced in the relevant unit: you might be asked, for example, to quote Newton's laws of motion. Of course, it is easy to look up the answers to such questions in the unit or the Handbook, but to do so without having first tried to provide the answer from your own memory would defeat the object.

You may not feel that you need to work through all of the exercises, or you may not have time to do so. We offer two kinds of help towards making a selection to suit your own requirements. On the one hand, we have made a

(© Science Photo Library)
James Joule (1818–1889) was an amateur physicist who did many experiments over a forty-year period that established laws about conversion of many types of energy, including mechanical energy, heat and electrical energy. It is for this reason that the SI unit of energy is named after him.

Heat is studied in *Unit 15*.

Lagrangian and Hamiltonian mechanics are third-level applied mathematics topics.

Two- and three-dimensional problems are studied in *Unit 24*.

choice of about half-a-dozen questions on each unit which we think are the ones that cover the most important topics; these exercises are indicated with an asterisk. On the other hand, your aim may well be to concentrate on those parts of the course about which you feel least confident. To help you spot where a topic occurs, we have put a marker in italics in the margin the first time it appears. Thus if you feel you need practice with problems involving air resistance, for example, look through the exercises on *Unit 6* until you find the phrase '*Air resistance*' in the margin (it's beside Exercise 4.12); that exercise and the ones immediately following will provide you with the practice you want.

1 Energy: definitions

In this section an alternative approach to solving a certain class of mechanics problems is introduced. This approach is based on the concept of *mechanical energy* which is introduced in this section. The application of this concept to solving mechanics problems is based on the constancy or *conservation* of mechanical energy, which is introduced below. More detailed discussion of applying conservation of energy to solve mechanics problems is deferred to Section 2.

In this section we introduce a method for solving mechanics problems for systems where the forces *depend only on the position* of the particle. Such forces are very common. For example, the force acting on a steel pin due to the attraction of a magnet depends on the distance between the pin and the magnet. In fact, the magnitude of this force increases as the pin is brought closer to the magnet. On the other hand, a dog tethered to a tree by a length of elastic rope feels a restraining force, once the elastic is taut, whose magnitude increases as the dog moves away from the tree. In either case, we can consider a one-dimensional situation and define the **i**-direction to be the direction of the force, and then we have

$$\mathbf{F} = F\mathbf{i} = F(x)\,\mathbf{i},$$

where we have written $F(x)$ in the last expression to emphasize that the **i**-component of the force depends on x alone. We shall assume that the form of the function $F(x)$ is known, and use this knowledge to answer questions about the motion. It is possible here for $F(x)$ to be a constant function, so, in saying that 'F depends only on position', we really mean that F depends *at most* on position, that is, it does not depend directly on other variables of the motion, such as the velocity $\mathbf{v}$, the acceleration $\mathbf{a}$ or the time t.

The starting point for introducing energy is to define one of its basic forms.

Kinetic energy

As mentioned in the Introduction, the concept of energy is grounded in experimental results. So, to start our discussion, consider the following thought experiment. Imagine an object hitting a wall. What quantifies how much damage the object will do? Obviously, the faster the object is travelling, the more damage will be done (for example, there might be a bigger dent in the wall). Similarly, the heavier the object, the more damage is done.

You will appreciate that in reality these thought experiments are hard to do. How do you quantify the 'amount of damage'? The results also depend on the materials that the object is made of. Forget such experimental details

If you prefer to think of a specific experiment, then imagine ball-bearings of various masses being fired at a steel plate at various speeds. The 'amount of damage' could then be quantified by the maximum depth of the impact crater.

for a moment, and focus on the general trends that are found. There is some experimental evidence that doubling the mass of the object doubles the 'amount of damage' (however this is quantified). The same is not true for the speed of the object: doubling the speed of impact quadruples the 'amount of damage'.

From this experimental evidence, the 'amount of damage' is quantified by something that is proportional to the mass, m, of the object multiplied by the speed, v, of the object squared, i.e. mv^2. This motivates us to look at a quantity of this kind, so we make the following definition.

Kinetic energy

The kinetic energy, T, of a particle of mass m moving with speed v is given by

$$T = \tfrac{1}{2}mv^2.$$

It is conventional to use T for the kinetic energy, because E is usually reserved for the total energy, as you will see later. We choose $\frac{1}{2}$ as the constant of proportionality for reasons that will become clear later.

The word *kinetic* in the term *kinetic energy* emphasizes that the energy is due to the motion of the object.

The SI unit for energy is the *joule* (J). So a particle of mass 4 kg moving with speed $5\,\mathrm{m\,s^{-1}}$ has kinetic energy $\frac{1}{2} \times 4 \times 5^2 = 50$ joules.

$1\,\mathrm{J} = 1\,\mathrm{kg\,m^2\,s^{-2}}$

The case of constant forces

As alluded to above, there are many forms of energy other than kinetic energy. To motivate the definition of another form, we first consider a special case of a general mechanical system: the case where all the forces acting on the particle are constant (for example, a projectile moving under gravity alone).

Consider a particle of mass m acted upon by a total force $\mathbf{F}$ that is constant. Choose $\mathbf{i}$ to be a unit vector in the direction of the force, i.e. $\mathbf{F} = F\mathbf{i}$ for some constant F.

It is natural to begin by writing down Newton's second law,

$$\mathbf{F} = m\mathbf{a},$$

where, as usual, $\mathbf{a}$ is the acceleration of the particle. The motion is one-dimensional and we have $\mathbf{a} = \ddot{x}\mathbf{i}$, so the above equation can be resolved in the $\mathbf{i}$-direction to obtain

$$F = m\ddot{x}. \tag{1.1}$$

If F is constant, then Equation (1.1) tells us that the acceleration $\ddot{x} = F/m$ is constant. Motion of a particle in one dimension with constant acceleration was considered in *Unit 6*. It was shown there that if the constant acceleration is $a_0\mathbf{i}$, then the position $x\mathbf{i}$ and velocity $v\mathbf{i}$ of the particle are related by an equation

$$v^2 = v_0^2 + 2a_0(x - x_0),$$

where x_0 and v_0 are, respectively, the values of x and v at time $t = 0$. In our case a_0 is given by F/m, so we have

$$v^2 = v_0^2 + 2\frac{F}{m}(x - x_0).$$

Multiplying by $\frac{1}{2}m$ gives

$$\tfrac{1}{2}mv^2 = \tfrac{1}{2}mv_0^2 + F(x - x_0).$$

Now we can rearrange the equation by moving all the variables to the left and all the constants to the right, to obtain

$$\tfrac{1}{2}mv^2 - Fx = \tfrac{1}{2}mv_0^2 - Fx_0. \tag{1.2}$$

This equation has a useful symmetry: both sides of the equation involve the expression $\tfrac{1}{2}mv^2 - Fx$; the only difference is that the left-hand side involves variables describing the particle's motion at time t, and the right-hand side involves the initial values of those variables. The right-hand side of this equation is a constant, which we shall call E, the **total mechanical energy** of the particle. So we have

$$E = \tfrac{1}{2}mv^2 - Fx \quad \text{(for constant F)}. \tag{1.3}$$

The first term in the above expression is the kinetic energy of the particle. The second term is also given a name: it is called the **potential energy function** of the particle, with the following definition.

We call the second term on the right-hand side of Equation (1.3) the potential energy *function* to emphasize that it is dependent on the position of the particle.

Potential energy function (for a constant force)

The potential energy function, $U(x)$, of a particle at position $\mathbf{r} = x\mathbf{i}$ under the influence of a constant force $\mathbf{F} = F\mathbf{i}$ is

$$U(x) = -Fx.$$

Equation (1.3) can now be reinterpreted as saying that the total mechanical energy of a particle is the sum of its kinetic energy and potential energy, $E = T + U$. The fact that E is constant throughout the motion of the particle means that the particle *does not lose or gain mechanical energy*. For this reason Equation (1.3) is called the **law of conservation of mechanical energy**, and we re-state this now for future reference.

Law of conservation of mechanical energy

The total mechanical energy of a particle is given by the sum of its kinetic and potential energies, i.e.

$$E = \tfrac{1}{2}mv^2 + U(x). \tag{1.4}$$

If the force on the particle depends only on the particle's position, then the total mechanical energy of the particle is constant.

The potential energy is written as $U(x)$ rather than $-Fx$ in Equation (1.4) because, as you will see later, there are other expressions for $U(x)$ that apply to non-constant forces.

To see the reasonableness of this, consider the familiar example of an object falling vertically downwards under gravity. As the object speeds up (and gains kinetic energy), it loses height (and loses potential energy). On the other hand, if the object is rising (gaining potential energy), then it is also slowing down (losing kinetic energy). So conservation of mechanical energy says that a gain in kinetic energy must be accompanied by a loss of potential energy, and vice versa.

There is a subtle point that may be troubling you. The potential energy $U(x)$ depends on the distance x *measured from the origin*. However, as we have stated previously, the location of the origin is a free choice for the problem solver and does not affect any physical aspect of the system. The resolution of this apparent conflict can be seen by looking at Equation (1.2), where the distance from the origin appears symmetrically on both sides of the equation. If we choose a different origin a distance d along the positive x-axis, then we have

$$\tfrac{1}{2}mv^2 - F(x - d) = \tfrac{1}{2}mv_0^2 - F(x_0 - d),$$

and the d terms cancel to give Equation (1.2) again.

Although the choice of origin does not affect the predictions made by using the law of conservation of mechanical energy, it does affect the numerical value of the potential energy (and hence value of the the total mechanical energy also). The upshot of this is that when using potential energy we must state where the zero of potential energy is to be taken. This position is called the **datum**. Most frequently we take the datum to be the origin, as in the above discussion.

Energy conservation is useful in solving problems that involve only the speed and position of objects, rather than, say, the position of the object at specific times. This is illustrated in the following example and exercise.

Example 1.1

A stone of mass m is thrown vertically upwards from ground level with initial speed $15\,\text{m s}^{-1}$. Assuming that gravity is the only force acting on the stone, find:

(a) the speed of the stone when its height is 5 metres;

(b) the maximum height of the stone.

Section 2 looks in more detail at using energy conservation to solve problems like this.

Solution

Choose an x-axis pointing upwards, with the origin (and datum) at the point of projection (see Figure 1.1). The only force acting on the stone is gravity, which is constant, so Equation (1.3) applies. In this case the total force $\mathbf{F}$ acting on the stone is $\mathbf{F} = \mathbf{W} = -mg\mathbf{i}$, so we have $F = -mg$ and Equation (1.3) becomes

$$E = \tfrac{1}{2}mv^2 + mgx.$$

Initially $v = 15$ when $x = 0$, so

$$E = \tfrac{1}{2}m \times 15^2 + m \times 9.81 \times 0 = 112.5m.$$

Hence, throughout the motion, we have

$$\tfrac{1}{2}v^2 + gx = 112.5. \qquad (1.5)$$

(a) When $x = 5$, Equation (1.5) gives

$$\tfrac{1}{2}v^2 + 9.81 \times 5 = 112.5.$$

Hence

$$v^2 = 2 \times (112.5 - 9.81 \times 5) = 126.9.$$

So $v = \pm\sqrt{126.9}$, and the speed of the stone at height $x = 5$ is

$$|v| = \sqrt{126.9} \simeq 11.3.$$

This speed of about $11.3\,\text{m s}^{-1}$ is the same whether the stone is moving up or down. The sign of the velocity will depend on the direction of motion.

(b) At maximum height, we have $v = 0$. Substituting $v = 0$ into Equation (1.5) produces

$$gx = 112.5 \quad \text{or} \quad x = 112.5/9.81 \simeq 11.5,$$

so the maximum height attained by the stone is approximately 11.5 metres. ∎

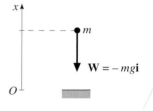

Figure 1.1

Notice that the m terms cancel, so this equation applies to a stone of any mass; all stones will follow the same trajectory.

*Exercise 1.1

(a) A marble, initially at rest, is dropped from the Clifton Suspension Bridge and falls into the River Avon, 77 metres below (see Figure 1.2).

You considered this situation in *Unit 6*.

Assuming that the only force acting on the marble is the force of gravity, use energy conservation to estimate the speed of the marble just before it hits the water. How far has it fallen when its speed reaches $20\,\mathrm{m\,s^{-1}}$?

(Choose a downward-pointing x-axis with origin at the point of release, and take this origin as the datum of potential energy. Take care with the sign of the potential energy function.)

(b) Why can the law of conservation of mechanical energy not be used if air resistance is taken into account in the situation above?

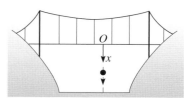

Figure 1.2

The case of position-dependent forces

So far we have considered only constant forces; now we generalize to any force that is a function of position only. Since we are still considering only one-dimensional problems, such a force can be written as

$$\mathbf{F} = F(x)\,\mathbf{i}.$$

Consider the case of a particle moving from the origin, which we shall take as the datum, to the point a. Divide the interval $[0, a]$ into n equal parts of length $h = a/n$. Define a function $\widetilde{F}(x)$ that approximates $F(x)$ by its value at the start of each subinterval, as shown in Figure 1.3.

The case of a particle moving in two or three dimensions is considered in *Unit 24*.

It makes no difference to the argument if the value at the midpoint or end of each interval is used, since later we take the limit as h tends to zero.

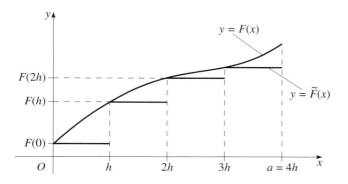

Figure 1.3   Approximating $F(x)$. (For ease of representation, the diagram shows the case $n = 4$.)

The Appendix on page 161 shows how to define a potential energy function $\widetilde{U}(x)$ for $\widetilde{F}(x)$ so that energy is conserved for the interval $[0, a]$. It is shown that the potential energy at $x = a$ is given by

$$\widetilde{U}(a) = -F(0)h - F(h)h - \cdots - F((n-1)h)h$$
$$= -\sum_{r=0}^{n-1} F(rh)h.$$

This sum is reminiscent of the sum over subintervals that is sometimes used as the definition of an integral. If the number of intervals, n, tends to infinity (or, equivalently, h tends to zero), then the above sum tends to an integral, which gives the result

$$U(a) = -\int_0^a F(x)\,dx.$$

The above result is a definite integral with lower limit 0, which was the chosen datum. If a datum is not specified, then the result is the same, but with an arbitrary constant added (representing the value of the potential energy at the start of the interval). The result can then be more easily written as an indefinite integral, and we take this as the definition of potential energy for a non-constant force.

Example 6.4 of *Unit 1* has a similar argument where an integral is obtained as a limit of a sum over small subintervals.

Note that $\widetilde{F}(x)$ approximates $F(x)$ more and more closely as $h \to 0$. Correspondingly, the potential energy function $\widetilde{U}(x)$ tends to $U(x)$, the potential energy function of $F(x)$, as $h \to 0$.

Potential energy function (general case)

For a particle moving along the x-axis under the influence of a force with **i**-component $F(x)$, the potential energy function $U(x)$ is given by

$$U(x) = -\int F(x)\,dx, \qquad (1.6)$$

or, equivalently,

$$F(x) = -\frac{dU}{dx}.$$

The potential energy function is defined in Equation (1.6) as an indefinite integral, so it is defined only to within a constant of integration. In practice, however, the value of this constant is unimportant, because it can be absorbed into the constant E appearing in Equation (1.4). The constant of integration in the definition of the potential energy function can therefore be chosen to have any convenient value. In other words, we can choose the value of the potential energy function $U(x)$ to be zero at any convenient point. As defined earlier, this point is called the **datum** of the potential energy function. Thus, if x_0 is the chosen datum, then $U(x_0) = 0$.

> You saw a similar situation in *Unit 2*, where the integrating factor for a first-order linear differential equation was defined in terms of an indefinite integral.

Equivalence with Newton's second law

Now we are going to show that the law of conservation of energy is formally equivalent to applying Newton's second law for forces which depend only on position. Suppose that we have a force $\mathbf{F} = F(x)\,\mathbf{i}$ that depends only on the position of a particle. By the previous results, the total mechanical energy of the particle, E, is constant, i.e.

$$E = \tfrac{1}{2}mv^2 - \int F(x)\,dx.$$

Now differentiate both sides of this equation. The left-hand side is zero since E is constant, so we have

$$0 = \tfrac{1}{2}m\frac{d}{dx}(v^2) - F(x), \qquad (1.7)$$

where we have also used the fact that differentiation is the inverse of integration.

On applying the Chain Rule for differentiation to the remaining derivative, we obtain

> The Chain Rule (Composite Rule) was revised in *Unit 1*.

$$\frac{d}{dx}(v^2) = 2v\frac{dv}{dx} = 2\frac{dx}{dt}\frac{dv}{dx} = 2\frac{dv}{dt} = 2\ddot{x}.$$

Substituting this into Equation (1.7) and rearranging gives

> You saw in *Unit 6* that $v(dv/dx)$ is one of the alternative expressions for the acceleration.

$$F(x) = m\ddot{x},$$

which is a statement of Newton's second law.

So conservation of total mechanical energy implies Newton's second law when the total force depends only on position. Conversely, if we start with Newton's second law, then we can obtain the law of conservation of energy by integration. This shows that the two approaches are equivalent for position-dependent forces: any problem that can be solved using conservation of energy can also be solved using Newton's second law, and vice versa.

Calculating potential energy functions

You will see how the conservation law may be applied in Section 2. For the remainder of this subsection, we ask you to concentrate on the process of finding the potential energy function $U(x)$ for a known force with x-component $F(x)$. Try the following exercises; the results will be discussed afterwards.

*Exercise 1.2 _____

Using an x-axis pointing vertically upwards (see Figure 1.4) and Equation (1.6), verify that the potential energy function for the force due to gravity acting on a particle of mass m is

$$U(x) = mgx,$$

where the datum for this function is taken to be the origin $x = 0$.

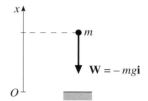

Figure 1.4

*Exercise 1.3 _____

Consider the motion of a particle of mass m along a straight frictionless track that is at an angle θ to the horizontal. Using an x-axis pointing up the slope, verify that the potential energy function for the total force acting on the particle is

$$U(x) = mgx \sin\theta,$$

where the datum is taken to be the origin $x = 0$.

*Exercise 1.4 _____

Figure 1.5 shows a model spring of stiffness k and natural length l_0 deformed by a distance x (where $x > 0$ for an extension and $x < 0$ for a compression).

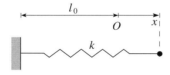

Figure 1.5

Verify that the potential energy function for the force exerted by the spring is

$$U(x) = \tfrac{1}{2}kx^2,$$

where the datum is taken to be the point of zero deformation, $x = 0$.

In Exercise 1.2, you showed that, for a suitable choice of datum ($x = 0$), the potential energy function is $U(x) = mgx$, if the x-axis is directed vertically upwards. So for positions above the datum the potential energy function is positive, and for those below the datum the potential energy function is negative.

Now consider what happens if the x-axis is pointing in the opposite direction, i.e. vertically downwards, as shown in Figure 1.6. This leads to the potential energy function $U(x) = -mgx$. Now if the particle is above the datum, then the coordinate x is negative, so $U(x)$ is again positive. Conversely, if the particle is below the datum, then x is positive, so $U(x)$ is negative. These signs are the same as for the potential energy function with an upward pointing x-axis. This leads to the following memorable result for the potential energy function due to gravity, henceforth called the gravitational potential energy.

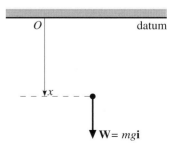

Figure 1.6

139

Gravitational potential energy

The gravitational potential energy of a particle of mass m is given by

$$U = mg \times \text{height above datum},$$

where the height is measured vertically from some chosen datum and g is the magnitude of the acceleration due to gravity.

The result stated for gravitational potential energy applies even when the direction of motion of the particle is not vertical. For example, in Exercise 1.3 you showed that for a particle moving on a slope at an angle θ to the horizontal, with the x-axis pointing up the slope, the potential energy function is $U(x) = mgx \sin\theta$. Since the vertical height of the particle above the datum is $x \sin\theta$, we again have $U(x) = mg \times \text{height}$.

For the model spring force in Exercise 1.4, you showed the following, which we state for future reference.

Potential energy stored in a spring

The potential energy stored in a model spring is

$$U = \tfrac{1}{2} \times \text{stiffness} \times (\text{deformation})^2,$$

where the datum is chosen to be at the natural length of the spring.

As before, 'deformation' refers to either extension or compression, as appropriate.

The next set of exercises investigates what happens to the potential energy function when the force acting on a particle is the sum of two forces. Try the exercises, then read the discussion that follows.

*Exercise 1.5

Find the potential energy function for each of the following forces (where a and b are constants). State, in each case, the datum you are using.

(a) $F(x) = -ax^2$

(b) $F(x) = b/x^2 \ (x > 0)$

*Exercise 1.6

(a) Suppose that the potential energy functions $U_1(x)$ and $U_2(x)$ correspond to the forces $F_1(x)$ and $F_2(x)$, respectively. Show that a potential energy function corresponding to the force $F(x) = F_1(x) + F_2(x)$ is

$$U(x) = U_1(x) + U_2(x).$$

Note that $U(x) + C$ is also a potential energy function, for any constant C.

(b) Using the result of part (a) and your answers to Exercise 1.5, write down a potential energy function for the force

$$F(x) = -ax^2 + b/x^2 \quad (x > 0),$$

where a and b are constants.

Exercise 1.7 _____

Find the force that gives rise to the potential energy function

$$U(x) = ax^2 + bx^{-2} \quad (x > 0),$$

where a and b are constants.

_____

Exercise 1.6 raises the question of what occurs when two potential energy functions that have different datum points are added together. In this case, it is possible to set up a fresh datum at any desired point for the combined potential energy function, by adding an appropriate constant to the expression for $U(x)$, since the potential energy is defined in terms of an indefinite integral (Equation (1.6)). Specifying a datum amounts to pinning down a value for the arbitrary constant in the indefinite integral, but, while this may sometimes be convenient, it is not essential to do it. Indeed, it is not necessary for the potential energy to take the value zero at any point.

End-of-section Exercise

Exercise 1.8 _____

A bad-tempered professional tennis player, in a fit of annoyance when his first serve is judged out though he thought it was good, commits an act of 'ball abuse': he takes a swipe with his racket at the ball he is holding, and hits it as hard as he can vertically up into the air. When the ball is struck by the racket it is 1 metre above the ground. The ball leaves the racket with a speed of $20\,\mathrm{m\,s^{-1}}$. Assuming that the ball moves under gravity alone, calculate how high above the ground the ball goes, and its speed when it reaches the ground on its return journey.

_____

2 Applying energy conservation

In the previous section we concentrated mainly on the relationship between the potential energy function $U(x)$ and the force component $F(x)$. Now we look at how to use energy conservation to solve problems.

Example 1.1 on page 136 is typical of many problems that can be solved by using the law of conservation of mechanical energy. There are two reasons why this problem is particularly suitable. First, it involves a force, gravity, that depends only on position (in this case, of course, the force is a constant function of position). This is crucial, because the law of conservation of mechanical energy applies only to such forces. Secondly, the problem asks for a relationship between position and speed, which is ideal because the conservation law immediately gives the desired relationship.

Procedure 2.1   Applying conservation of energy

This procedure may be applied to a mechanics problem involving the one-dimensional motion of a particle, in which:

- the total force depends only on the position of the particle (or is constant);
- the question to be answered refers to a relationship between the position and the velocity of the particle.

It uses the law of conservation of mechanical energy,

$$E = \tfrac{1}{2}mv^2 + U(x), \tag{1.4}$$

where m, x**i** and v**i** are, respectively, the mass, position and velocity of the particle, and $U(x)$ is the potential energy function.

The procedure is as follows.

(a) Drawing a picture is always the first step in solving a mechanics problem. ◀Draw picture▶

(b) The next step is to choose a datum. For gravitational potential energy it is usual to choose the origin. For springs, the datum is usually chosen to be the point of zero deformation. (For other forces this step could be deferred until the potential energy function is known: choose the datum to simplify the expression.) ◀Choose datum▶

(c) Identify the x-component $F(x)$ of the total force acting on the particle, then apply the potential energy function definition ◀Find potential energy▶

$$U(x) = -\int F(x)\,dx. \tag{1.6}$$

(It may not be necessary to do the integration to obtain $U(x)$ if the total force is a sum of forces for which the potential energy function is already known, as with gravity or model springs — simply add together the corresponding potential energy functions.)

(d) Use Equation (1.4) and the initial conditions to calculate the value of the constant E, the total mechanical energy of the system. ◀Find E▶

(e) Solve the resulting version of Equation (1.4), either for x (at a specified value of v) or for v (at a specified value of x). ◀Find x or v▶

(f) Interpret the solution in terms of the original problem. ◀Interpret solution▶

The steps outlined in Procedure 2.1 are used in the following example.

Example 2.1

A toy manufacturer is testing a trampoline and wants to estimate the largest mass of child that can safely use it. An experiment is devised in which a sandbag of mass m is dropped from a height h, and the maximum deformation d of the trampoline is measured.

(a) Model the trampoline as a model spring of stiffness k. Find an equation relating the above parameters and g. You may assume that no energy is lost in the impact.

(b) It is observed that when a 20 kg sandbag is dropped from a height of 1 metre above the trampoline, the maximum deformation of the trampoline is 25 cm. Use these data to calculate the stiffness of the model spring.

A better approach would be to collect more data so that a better estimate could be made and the model could be tested.

(c) If the maximum safe deformation is 30 cm, estimate the maximum mass that may be dropped on the trampoline from a height of 1 metre.

Solution

(a) Figure 2.1 shows pictures of the sandbag at the top and bottom of its motion.   ◄Draw picture►

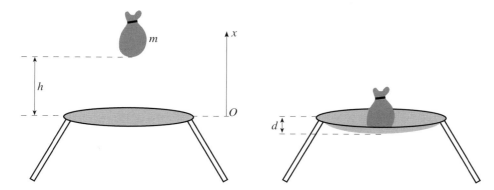

Figure 2.1

Choose an x-axis pointing upwards with origin at the height of the undeformed trampoline, as shown in Figure 2.1.

Take the origin as the datum for the gravitational potential energy.   ◄Choose datum►
Then the potential energy function due to the weight is

$$U_{\text{grav}}(x) = mgx.$$ ◄Find potential energy►

Take the origin as the datum for the spring potential energy function (as this corresponds to the point of zero deformation of the spring). The trampoline exerts a force only when the sandbag is in contact with it, so the potential energy is stored in the spring only if $x < 0$. So the potential energy stored in the spring is

$$U_{\text{spring}}(x) = \begin{cases} 0, & x \geq 0, \\ \frac{1}{2}kx^2, & x < 0. \end{cases}$$

To find the total potential energy we add together the two contributions:

$$U(x) = U_{\text{spring}}(x) + U_{\text{grav}}(x) = \begin{cases} mgx, & x \geq 0, \\ \frac{1}{2}kx^2 + mgx, & x < 0. \end{cases}$$

Initially the sandbag is at rest ($v = 0$) at a height $x = h > 0$ above the   ◄Find E►
trampoline, so using Equation (1.4) gives

$$E = \tfrac{1}{2}m0^2 + mgh = mgh.$$

At the bottom of the motion, the sandbag is again at rest, at the point   ◄Find x or v►
$x = -d$ (where $d > 0$ is the deformation of the trampoline). At this point we have

$$E = \tfrac{1}{2}m0^2 + U(-d) = \tfrac{1}{2}kd^2 - mgd.$$

This gives the desired relationship

$$mgh = \tfrac{1}{2}kd^2 - mgd. \tag{2.1}$$

(b) To calculate k, rearrange Equation (2.1) to make k the subject, then   ◄Interpret solution►
substitute in the known values:

$$k = \frac{2mg(h+d)}{d^2} = \frac{2 \times 20 \times 9.81 \times (1 + 0.25)}{0.25^2} \simeq 7848.$$

So the spring has stiffness approximately $8000\,\text{N m}^{-1}$.

(c) To calculate the mass that corresponds to the maximum deformation of the trampoline, rearrange Equation (2.1) to make m the subject, then substitute in the known values:

$$m = \frac{kd^2}{2g(h+d)} = \frac{7848 \times 0.3^2}{2 \times 9.81 \times (1+0.3)} \simeq 27.7.$$

So the maximum safe mass is approximately 27 kg. ∎

Note that here we round *down* rather than to the nearest integer (because 28 kg is *above* the safe maximum mass).

Now try applying the law of conservation of energy yourself by attempting the following exercises.

Exercise 2.1

A particle of mass m moves without friction down a slope inclined at an angle θ to the horizontal (see Figure 2.2). The particle starts from rest at the point A, and slides down to the point B, which is a vertical distance h below A. The displacement of the particle from A, measured down the slope, is denoted by x. The point B is to be taken as the datum for the potential energy function.

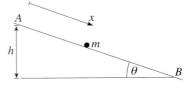

Figure 2.2

(a) Show that the total mechanical energy of the particle can be written as

$$E = \tfrac{1}{2}mv^2 + mg(h - x\sin\theta),$$

where v is the speed of the particle.

(b) Obtain, in terms of h, an expression for the speed of the particle at B, and comment on your result.

(c) Apply the result from part (b) to the specific case of a crate of empty bottles that slides 2 metres down a smooth ramp set at an angle of $\pi/6$ radians to the horizontal, starting from rest.

This problem was considered in Example 3.2 of *Unit 6*.

*Exercise 2.2

A particle of mass 0.5 kg moves along a horizontal straight frictionless track. The particle is attached to an end of a model spring of stiffness $2\,\mathrm{N\,m^{-1}}$, the other end of the spring being fixed (see Figure 2.3).

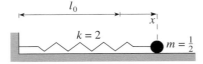

Figure 2.3

Initially the extension of the spring is 2 m and the particle's velocity is $3\,\mathrm{m\,s^{-1}}$, directed towards the spring. What is the particle's maximum speed during the subsequent motion, and at what positions is it momentarily at rest? (Assume that the natural length l_0 of the model spring is greater than 2.5 metres.)

Exercise 2.3

A particle of mass m is attached to the lower end of a model spring of natural length l_0 and stiffness $k = 10mg/l_0$, where g is the acceleration due to gravity. The spring is hung vertically, with its upper end fixed (see Figure 2.4). The particle is pulled vertically downwards until the spring's length is $\tfrac{5}{4}l_0$ and then released from rest. By using the law of conservation of energy, find the speed of the particle when the spring is of length l_0 in the subsequent motion.

Figure 2.4

(*Hint*: The potential energy function is the sum of a gravity term and a spring term.)

Energy in oscillating systems

As you have seen in the above example and exercises, the law of conservation of mechanical energy,

$$E = \tfrac{1}{2}mv^2 + U(x), \tag{1.4}$$

provides a convenient method for finding the relationship between the velocity $v\mathbf{i}$ and the position $x\mathbf{i}$ whenever the force acting on a particle is a function of position. Since the term $\tfrac{1}{2}mv^2$ can never be negative, the same must be true of the quantity $E - U(x)$, which means that motion is possible only in regions for which $E - U(x) \geq 0$. Also, the particle will be momentarily at rest $(v = 0)$ at points for which $E - U(x) = 0$. At such points, called **turning points**, the particle changes its direction of motion; this is illustrated in Figure 2.5. A particle moving under the action of a force that gives rise to the illustrated potential energy function $U(x)$, and with total mechanical energy E, will oscillate backwards and forwards between the two turning points A and B, changing its direction of motion each time it reaches one of these points.

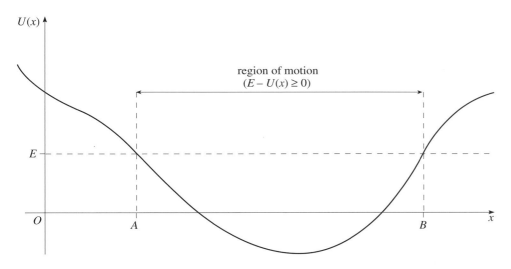

Figure 2.5

*Exercise 2.4

A particle of mass $m = 2$ moves under the influence of a force that has x-component $F(x) = 2 - 2x$.

(a) Find a potential energy function $U(x)$ for this force.

(b) If the particle is released from rest at $x = -1$, find the total mechanical energy of the particle in the subsequent motion.

(c) Use the law of conservation of mechanical energy to find an expression for the velocity $v\mathbf{i}$ of the particle at position $x\mathbf{i}$.

(d) Find the region of motion of the particle, and its speed at the midpoint of this region.

Throughout this question, all quantities are measured in the appropriate SI units.

We now analyse one of the most important oscillating systems: the pendulum. Figure 2.6 shows a pendulum which consists of a particle (called the pendulum bob) connected to a model rod (called the pendulum stem) of length l pivoted at O. This mechanical system is a little different to the systems studied so far, in that to specify the position of a pendulum, it is natural to specify the angle, θ, that the pendulum makes with the vertical rather than a distance from a fixed origin.

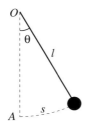

Figure 2.6

When analysing the pendulum we shall need to relate the position and speed of the pendulum bob to the angle θ. A standard result from geometry relates the arc length s, shown in Figure 2.6, to the angle θ (measured in radians) by the formula

$$s = l\theta.$$

The speed of the pendulum is the magnitude of the rate of change of this arc length, i.e. $v = |\dot{s}|$. Since the length of the model rod l is constant, this gives the following relationship between the speed of the pendulum bob, v, and the rate of change of angle, $\dot{\theta}$:

$$v = |l\dot{\theta}|. \tag{2.2}$$

Before we proceed to analyse the pendulum, we need to extend the range of applicability of a result from Section 1, where we derived the following result for the gravitational potential energy:

$$U(x) = mg \times \text{height above datum}.$$

This equation holds not only for motion in a straight line, but for any motion in space. This result is applied in the following example.

This result is proved in *Unit 24*.

Example 2.2

A particle of mass m is attached to a model rod of length l, which is in turn attached to a pivot at O, as shown in Figure 2.6. Initially the pendulum is at rest at an angle ϕ to the vertical. After the pendulum is released from rest, let the angle between the pendulum stem and the vertical be θ. Use conservation of mechanical energy to derive a relationship between θ and $\dot{\theta}$ (which also involves ϕ, l and g).

Solution

The pendulum is shown in Figure 2.6.

◀Draw picture▶

Choose O for the datum of potential energy.

◀Choose datum▶

The distance of the bob below O is $l\cos\theta$, so

◀Find potential energy▶

$$U(\theta) = -mgl\cos\theta.$$

Adding this to the kinetic energy of the bob gives the total mechanical energy

$$E = \tfrac{1}{2}mv^2 - mgl\cos\theta.$$

Initially the pendulum bob is at rest (so $v = 0$) at an angle ϕ to the vertical (so $\theta = \phi$). So the initial energy of the bob is ◀Find E▶

$$E = -mgl\cos\phi.$$

By conservation of mechanical energy, the total mechanical energy of the bob is always $-mgl\cos\phi$, so ◀Find x or v▶

$$\tfrac{1}{2}mv^2 - mgl\cos\theta = -mgl\cos\phi. \tag{2.3}$$

This is the point at which we use Equation (2.2) to relate the speed of the pendulum to the angle θ. Substituting $v = |l\dot\theta|$ into Equation (2.3) gives ◀Interpret solution▶

$$\tfrac{1}{2}ml^2\dot\theta^2 - mgl\cos\theta = -mgl\cos\phi,$$ Note that $|l\dot\theta|^2 = l^2\dot\theta^2$.

which simplifies to give the desired relationship

$$\tfrac{1}{2}l\dot\theta^2 - g\cos\theta = -g\cos\phi. \quad \blacksquare \tag{2.4}$$

Equation (2.4) is a non-linear first-order differential equation, and we do not try to solve it directly. Differentiating the equation with respect to t gives

$$\tfrac{1}{2}l \times 2\dot\theta\ddot\theta + g\sin(\theta)\dot\theta = 0.$$

Dividing by $\dot\theta$ (the solution $\dot\theta = 0$ represents the pendulum constantly at rest and is not interesting) and simplifying gives

$$\ddot\theta + \frac{g}{l}\sin\theta = 0.$$

At first sight this does not seem to have helped. This equation is a non-linear second-order equation, which is no easier to solve than Equation (2.4). However, we can now use what is called the **small angle approximation**, which states that if θ is small (and measured in radians), then

This approximation is very good, leading to only 10% inaccuracy for an angle of $\frac{\pi}{4}$.

$$\sin\theta \simeq \theta.$$

Making the small angle approximation leads to the differential equation

$$\ddot\theta + \frac{g}{l}\theta = 0.$$

This is the simple harmonic motion (SHM) equation, whose solution is given by

$$\theta = A\cos(\omega t + \phi_0),$$

where A and ϕ_0 are constants to be determined from the initial conditions, and $\omega = \sqrt{g/l}$ is the angular frequency. This gives the following important result.

Period of a pendulum undergoing small oscillations

When a pendulum moves through small angles, the period, T, of the oscillations is $T = 2\pi\sqrt{l/g}$.

Notice that this does not depend on the initial angle or the mass of the pendulum bob, suggesting that the period of a pendulum depends only on its length.

The approach used above to analyse the oscillations of a pendulum can be applied to many other oscillating systems, for example the bead on a wire considered in the following exercise.

*Exercise 2.5

Consider a bead moving on a smooth wire bent upwards into the shape of a parabola, as shown in Figure 2.7. Choose the origin O to be the lowest point on the wire, with the x-axis pointing right.

(a) Write down the total energy, E, of the bead when its x-coordinate is x and its velocity along the wire is v.

(b) Consider small oscillations of the bead. (Note that for small oscillations, $v \simeq dx/dt$.) Differentiate your expression for E to obtain a second-order differential equation for x.

(c) You should arrive at a familiar second-order linear differential equation. By inspection, write down the angular frequency of small oscillations of the bead.

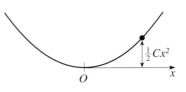

Figure 2.7

For small oscillations, the distance the bead travels along the wire is approximately the horizontal distance x. So the velocity of the bead is approximately dx/dt.

The argument outlined in the above exercise holds for a particle with a general potential energy function, $U(x)$, with a local minimum. Choose the origin, O, at the minimum to simplify the notation. Expanding $U(x)$ as a Taylor series about the origin gives

$$U(x) = U(0) + U'(0)x + \tfrac{1}{2!}U''(0)x^2 + \tfrac{1}{3!}U'''(0)x^3 + \cdots.$$

Choosing the origin as the datum of potential energy gives $U(0) = 0$. Since $U(x)$ has a local minimum at the origin, we have $U'(0) = 0$. So the Taylor series simplifies to

$$U(x) = \tfrac{1}{2!}U''(0)x^2 + \tfrac{1}{3!}U'''(0)x^3 + \cdots.$$

Now we make the approximation that x is small, so that the first term of the above series will dominate the remainder if $U''(0) \neq 0$; if $U''(0) = 0$, then the quadratic term disappears and the following discussion does not hold.

The case where $U''(0) = 0$ is not considered further.

So the potential energy is approximately quadratic:

$$U(x) \simeq \tfrac{1}{2}U''(0)x^2.$$

From the above arguments it is sensible to construct a model of the behaviour of the small oscillations where the potential energy is exactly quadratic, i.e.

$$U(x) = \tfrac{1}{2}U''(0)x^2.$$

So the total mechanical energy of the particle is

$$E = \tfrac{1}{2}mv^2 + \tfrac{1}{2}U''(0)x^2.$$

Differentiating this (using first the small oscillations assumption $v \simeq \dot{x}$ as in Exercise 2.5, then using the fact that energy is conserved and E is constant) and simplifying gives

$$0 = m\ddot{x} + U''(0)x.$$

This is the SHM equation, so the motion is simple harmonic with angular frequency $\omega = \sqrt{U''(0)/m}$. You will appreciate from this general argument that this kind of motion occurs frequently. Hence we give a mechanical system of this kind a name: it is called a **harmonic oscillator**.

Note that for the angular frequency to be real, we must have $U''(0) \geq 0$, which *is* the case if $U(x)$ has a local minimum at the origin.

End-of-section Exercises

Exercise 2.6

A particle of mass $m = 3$ moves along a straight line and experiences a force that repels it from the origin of position $x = 0$. This force has x-component $F(x) = 2/x^2$ for $x > 0$. Initially the particle is moving towards the origin, being at the position $x = 10\mathbf{i}$ with velocity $v = -\mathbf{i}$.

All quantities here are measured in the appropriate SI units.

(a) Find a potential energy function for this force for $x > 0$, stating the datum you use.

(b) Find the total mechanical energy of the particle.

(c) What is the closest point to the origin that is reached by the particle?

(d) Sketch the graph of the potential energy function, and indicate the region of motion.

Exercise 2.7

The system in Figure 2.8 can be used to model the motion of a railway truck while in contact with buffers. The mass of the truck is $m = 2000\,\text{kg}$ and the combined stiffness of the (model) buffer springs is $k = 10^5\,\text{N}\,\text{m}^{-1}$. If the truck comes to rest at a position where the springs are compressed by 0.1 metres, find the speed of the truck when it first came into contact with the buffers. (You should neglect friction, and assume that the springs have their natural length when the truck first touches the buffers.)

This is not a realistic model, since the truck would bounce off such buffers.

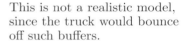

Figure 2.8

Exercise 2.8

A bead of mass m is threaded onto a frictionless horizontal wire. The bead is attached to a model spring of stiffness k and natural length l_0, whose other end is fixed to a point A at a vertical distance h from the wire (where $h > l_0$). The position x of the bead is measured from the point on the wire closest to A, as shown in Figure 2.9.

(a) Find the potential energy function $U(x)$.

(b) The bead is released from rest at $x = h\sqrt{3}$. Describe its subsequent motion, and find the speed with which it passes through its equilibrium position.

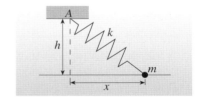

Figure 2.9

*Exercise 2.9

A particle of mass $0.5\,\text{kg}$ is supported on a vertical model spring of natural length 0.4 metres and stiffness $100\,\text{N}\,\text{m}^{-1}$. The lower end of the spring is fixed, as shown in Figure 2.10. Initially the spring has its natural length and the particle is moving downwards with speed $2\,\text{m}\,\text{s}^{-1}$.

(a) Find the initial total mechanical energy of the system, taking the lower end of the spring as the datum for the gravitational potential energy.

(b) Show that the velocity v of the particle when the length of the spring is x is given by

$$v^2 = -200x^2 + (160 - 2g)x + (0.8g - 28).$$

(c) Find the amplitude of the oscillatory motion of the particle.

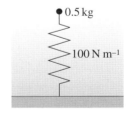

Figure 2.10

3 Unit 5 consolidation

As described in the Introduction, this section contains additional exercises to help consolidate your study of *Unit 5*. As mentioned in the Introduction, italic markers in the margin indicate where a particular topic is first mentioned.

Exercise 3.1

A particle subject to certain forces $\mathbf{F}_1, \mathbf{F}_2, \ldots, \mathbf{F}_n$ is in equilibrium (that is, it does not move). What condition must the forces satisfy?

Equilibrium condition for particles

In each of the figures below, the arrows show the directions of forces acting on a particle. In each case, state whether or not the particle could be in equilibrium if the magnitudes of the forces were chosen suitably.

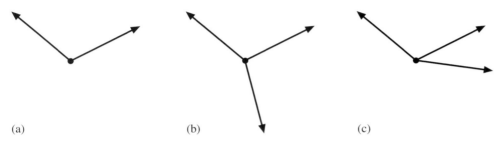

(a)   (b)   (c)

Suppose that a particle is subject to four forces, $\mathbf{F}_1$, $\mathbf{F}_2$, $\mathbf{F}_3$ and $\mathbf{F}_4$, three of which are known:

$$\mathbf{F}_1 = 3\mathbf{i} - 2\mathbf{j} + \mathbf{k}, \quad \mathbf{F}_2 = -2\mathbf{i} - 2\mathbf{j} + 3\mathbf{k}, \quad \mathbf{F}_3 = \mathbf{i} + 4\mathbf{j} - 2\mathbf{k},$$

with respect to given Cartesian unit vectors $\mathbf{i}$, $\mathbf{j}$, $\mathbf{k}$. Find $\mathbf{F}_4$ if the particle is in equilibrium.

Exercise 3.2

A block rests on a rough slope inclined at an angle α and is subject to a horizontal force $\mathbf{P}$, as shown in Figure 3.1. Assume that the magnitude of $\mathbf{P}$ is large enough for friction to act down the slope.

Resolving forces

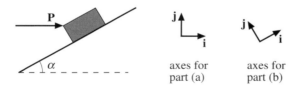

axes for   axes for
part (a)   part (b)

Figure 3.1

(a) If the $\mathbf{i}$- and $\mathbf{j}$-directions are aligned horizontally and vertically, as shown in Figure 3.1, resolve the four forces acting on the block.

(b) If the $\mathbf{i}$- and $\mathbf{j}$-directions are aligned up the slope and perpendicular to the slope, as also shown in Figure 3.1, resolve the four forces acting on the block.

Exercise 3.3

What do we call the gravitational force acting on a body, and how is it related to the body's mass?

Gravitational force

The value of g, the acceleration due to gravity, at the Earth's equator is slightly less than it is at the North Pole. How do the mass and the weight of a particle change if it is transported from the equator to the North Pole?

Exercise 3.4

In each of the examples shown in Figure 3.2, state where, and in what direction, any normal reaction on the body B acts.

Normal reaction

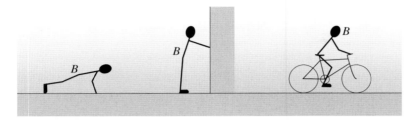

Figure 3.2

*Exercise 3.5

A ball-bearing lies between, and in contact with, two planes, as shown in Figure 3.3. The planes are smooth and are fixed at right-angles to each other, and the angle between the lower plane and the horizontal is $\pi/6$. The mass of the ball-bearing is 0.1 kg. Find the magnitudes of the normal reactions exerted by the planes on the ball-bearing.

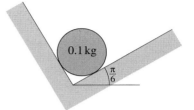

Figure 3.3

Exercise 3.6

Figure 3.4 shows a baby in a baby-bouncer. Assuming that the baby is stationary, and can be modelled as a particle (perhaps both rather unlikely assumptions, but never mind), draw diagrams showing the forces acting on the baby (a) when the baby is not in contact with the floor and (b) when the baby is standing on the floor.

Tension

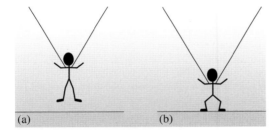

Figure 3.4

*Exercise 3.7

Tarzan is hanging from a liana (or, less exotically, from a rope), as shown in Figure 3.5. The ends of the liana are secured to trees (out of sight in the diagram). One part of the liana makes an angle of $\frac{\pi}{3}$ with the horizontal, the other an angle of $\frac{\pi}{6}$ with the horizontal. Tarzan's mass is 100 kg. Find the tensions in the two parts of the liana, given that Tarzan is in equilibrium.

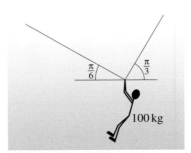

Figure 3.5

151

Exercise 3.8

Friction

A paperback book lies on the horizontal plane surface of a table. Someone pushes the book, very gently at first but with increasing strength, so that it is subject to a horizontal force (through the centre of mass of the book) in a fixed direction and with magnitude that increases from zero. The surface is rough; that is, there can be a friction force between the surface and objects in contact with it. The book stays at rest initially.

What is the direction of the friction force acting on the book? How is the magnitude of the friction force related to that of the applied force while the book is in equilibrium? What happens to the book eventually as the magnitude of the applied force increases?

How, if at all, will the magnitude of the force required to make the book begin to move differ in the following situations?

(a) The table is given a good polish.

(b) The book is replaced by another of the same mass, also a paperback, which has a larger surface area.

(c) A second book is placed on top of the first (but the force continues to be applied to the lower book).

(d) The person doing the pushing presses down on the book with the other hand.

You should give explanations for your answers.

Exercise 3.9

A book lies on a rough table; one end of the table is slowly lifted, so that the plane surface of the table becomes inclined increasingly steeply. What is the largest angle that the table can make with the horizontal without the book slipping, if the mass of the book is 0.5 kg and the coefficient of static friction between the table and the book cover is 0.3?

How could the results of your analysis of this situation be used to give a method of measuring coefficients of static friction?

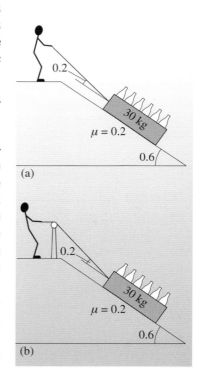

Figure 3.6

*Exercise 3.10

(a) A crate of empty bottles of total mass 30 kg is to be hauled by rope up a ramp from the cellar of a pub. The rope is not parallel to the ramp, since the person doing the pulling is standing upright; as shown in Figure 3.6(a), it makes an angle of 0.2 radians (just over 10°) with the ramp, which itself makes an angle of 0.6 radians (about 35°) with the horizontal. The coefficient of static friction between the plastic crate and the wooden ramp is 0.2. What is the tension in the rope when the crate is on the point of moving upwards?

(b) Yet another crate of empty bottles of total mass 30 kg is to be hauled by rope up a ramp from the cellar of a pub. This time the rope is arranged to pass over a pulley, so that the rope can be pulled horizontally as shown in Figure 3.6(b). Otherwise, the data for this part of the question are the same as those for part (a). How hard must the rope be pulled to start the crate moving upwards?

Exercise 3.11

Torque

The measure of the turning effect of a force about a fixed point is the product of the magnitude of the force and the perpendicular distance from the point to the line of action of the force.

(a) What is meant by the phrase 'line of action' of a force?

(b) Consider a rod pivoted at its centre that is in horizontal balance. Write down a relation between the magnitudes of the two vertical forces acting on the rod and the distances of their points of action from the pivot. How does this illustrate the equality of turning effects of forces in equilibrium?

(c) What is the torque of a force about a fixed point? Explain how the magnitude of the torque gives the turning effect of the force about the fixed point, according to the definition given in the first sentence of this question. What is the significance of the direction of a torque?

(d) State the conditions for equilibrium of a rigid body acted on by forces $\mathbf{F}_1, \mathbf{F}_2, \ldots, \mathbf{F}_n$.

Exercise 3.12 _____

Jack and Jill, Pat and Bill are all on the same see-saw. Jill has mass $\frac{5}{6}$ that of Jack, Pat has mass $\frac{3}{4}$ that of Jack, and Bill has mass $\frac{2}{3}$ that of Jack. Jack and Jill are on the same side of the see-saw: Jack is sitting a distance l from the pivot (at the see-saw's centre), and Jill a distance $\frac{3}{5}l$. Pat is sitting on the other side, also a distance l from the centre. Where must Bill sit in order to balance the see-saw?

*Exercise 3.13 _____

(a) A uniform ladder stands on rough horizontal ground and leans against the wall of a house, which can be taken to be smooth. A person whose mass is half that of the ladder wants to climb to the top of the ladder (in order to clean out the gutter of the house, perhaps). The coefficient of static friction between the ground and the ladder is $\frac{2}{3}$. Call the angle between the ladder and the horizontal α. Find the smallest value that α can take such that the person can stand at the top of the ladder without it slipping.

(b) What difference does it make if a bag of cement, whose weight is equal to the weight of the person, is placed on the bottom rung of the ladder (which can be taken to be at ground level)?

4 Unit 6 consolidation

As described in the Introduction, this section contains additional exercises to help consolidate your study of *Unit 6*.

Exercise 4.1 _____

A ball rolls up, and then down, the slope of an inclined plane. Its position at time $t \geq 0$ is given by   *Velocity and acceleration*

$$\mathbf{r}(t) = (4t - 2t^2)\mathbf{i},$$

where $\mathbf{i}$ is a unit vector pointing up the slope of the plane.

(a) Find the velocity and acceleration of the ball.

(b) How far up the plane from its position at $t = 0$ does the ball travel before it instantaneously stops and then begins to move down the plane?

(c) The motion of the ball at any time can be described in everyday terms as either accelerating or decelerating, either forwards or backwards. Choose the appropriate description that applies before, and the one that applies after, the instant when the ball changes from moving up to moving down the plane. (Here 'forwards' means 'in the direction determined by **i**', i.e. up the plane.)

Exercise 4.2

A particle is moving along a straight line, which is taken to be the x-axis. Its acceleration at time t is given by

$$\mathbf{a}(t) = \cos 2t\,\mathbf{i} \quad (t \geq 0).$$

Initially (at $t = 0$) the particle is at rest at the point whose position vector is $-\mathbf{i}$. Find the velocity and position of the particle at time t. Find the point furthest from its initial point that the particle can reach in its motion.

Exercise 4.3

A particle moves along the x-axis with constant acceleration $A\mathbf{i}$. It is initially at the origin, and its initial velocity is $V\mathbf{i}$. Its position and velocity functions are represented by $x(t)\mathbf{i}$ and $v(t)\mathbf{i}$. Select the correct expressions for $x(t)$ and $v(t)$ from the following alternatives.

Constant acceleration

(a) $V + At$ (b) $V + At^2$ (c) $V + \frac{1}{2}At^2$ (d) $V^2 + 2At$

(e) Vt (f) $Vt + A$ (g) $Vt + At^2$ (h) $Vt + \frac{1}{2}At^2$

Exercise 4.4

A particle moves along a straight line. It starts from rest and travels with a constant acceleration of $2\,\mathrm{m\,s^{-2}}$ for 5 seconds. It then moves at the speed it has attained for 10 seconds. Finally, it decelerates uniformly to rest. The total distance covered is 200 metres. Calculate the magnitude of the particle's (constant) deceleration in the final phase of its motion.

Exercise 4.5

When solving problems concerning a particle moving along a straight line with (varying) acceleration $a\mathbf{i}$, it is often necessary to express the acceleration function a as a derivative. This can be done in any one of three ways: write down the three possible expressions for a. Which of the three expressions is likely to be the best to use in each of the following cases?

Acceleration as a derivative

(a) a is given in terms of t, and it is required to find v in terms of t.

(b) a is given in terms of x, and it is required to find v in terms of x.

(c) a is given in terms of x and v, and it is required to find x in terms of t.

How would you proceed to solve the problem in each case?

Exercise 4.6

(a) The fundamental laws on which Newtonian mechanics is based are Newton's laws of motion. In *Units 5–8* we have concentrated on Newton's first two laws of motion. What are they?

Newton's laws

Newton's third law is used in Unit 19.

(b) In many applications of Newton's laws, the object whose motion is under investigation is modelled as a particle. What is a particle?

(c) What is meant by the term mass? How is the mass of a compound object (one which is made up by sticking together several pieces) related to that of its component parts?

Mass

(d) Give examples of the kinds of forces that might act on ordinary-sized objects moving in ordinary situations — such as tennis balls in play, toboggans running downhill, and crates being drawn up ramps out of cellars. When an object is acted on by more than one force, how must the forces be combined in order to calculate the total force acting?

Force

(e) The SI unit of force is the newton. How is the newton defined? If a body whose mass is 5 kg experiences a total force of 3 N, what is the magnitude of its resulting acceleration?

(f) Express Newton's second law as a vector equation relating force, mass and acceleration.

Exercise 4.7

A train approaches a station at which it is to stop. At the instant when the engine passes one end of the platform, it is travelling at 36 km per hour. At that instant, the driver applies the brakes, which produce a constant deceleration just sufficient to bring the train to a halt when the engine is at the other end of the platform. The platform is 200 metres long. The mass of the train is 40 tonnes. Calculate the magnitude of the force exerted by the brakes.

1 tonne = 1000 kg

Exercise 4.8

The first step in solving a problem in mechanics should always be to draw a picture of the situation being modelled. The next step is to draw a force diagram: what information should this diagram contain? The purpose of the force diagram is to help one write down the equation of motion: how is this done? What is the procedure for solving the problem after one has obtained the equation of motion?

Solving problems in mechanics

*Exercise 4.9

A bad-tempered professional tennis player, in a fit of annoyance when his first serve is judged out though he thought it was good, commits an act of 'ball abuse': he takes a swipe with his racket at the ball he is holding, and hits it as hard as he can vertically up into the air. When the ball is struck by the racket it is 1 metre above the ground. The ball leaves the racket with a speed of $20\,\mathrm{m\,s^{-1}}$. How high above the ground does the ball go, how long is it in the air, and what is its speed when it reaches the ground on its return journey? You should ignore air resistance.

Motion under gravity in one dimension

This problem was solved using conservation of energy in Exercise 1.8. Compare the amount of effort needed to solve problems using the different approaches.

*Exercise 4.10

A girl is sledging down an icy hill. The hill can be modelled as a sloping plane making an angle of $\pi/6$ with the horizontal. The sledge weighs 10 kg, and the girl weighs 40 kg. The girl runs and pushes the sledge to set it going, and then jumps on; at that instant the speed of the sledge is $5\,\mathrm{m\,s^{-1}}$. Ignore air resistance in this question.

Friction

Find the speed of the sledge with the girl on it after it has run for 30 metres down the slope from the point at which she jumped aboard:

(a) assuming that there is no friction between the runners of the sledge and the ice on the hillside;

(b) assuming that there is friction between the runners of the sledge and the ice, the coefficient of sliding friction being 0.02.

Exercise 4.11

A particle slides down a plane whose slope makes an angle α with the horizontal. Ignore air resistance, and find a formula for the time the particle takes to travel a distance d along its path down the plane in terms of its initial velocity v_0, the angle α, and g, the acceleration due to gravity:

(a) if the plane is smooth;

(b) if the plane is rough and the coefficient of sliding friction is μ', where $\mu' < \tan\alpha$.

Exercise 4.12

Everyday experience — of cycling, for example — makes the following three features of air resistance familiar to everyone: it acts so as to slow one down; its effect is more noticeable the faster one is going; its effect is reduced if one presents a smaller profile in one's direction of motion. How are these features incorporated into simple models of objects moving under the influence of air resistance, as well as, say, gravity?

Air resistance

Exercise 4.13

A cannonball is dropped from the top of the Leaning Tower of Pisa. For all but the first few millimetres of its motion, the effects of air resistance on the cannonball can be modelled by means of a resistive force of magnitude kv^2, where k is a positive constant (in fact $k = c_2 D^2$, where D is the diameter of the cannonball and $c_2 = 0.20$ is a constant, but we use k to save writing) and v is the speed of the cannonball. The mass of the cannonball is m.

Derive the equation of motion of the cannonball, for the period when the quadratic model for air resistance applies, with respect to an x-axis whose origin is at the point from which the ball is released and which points vertically down, expressing your answer in terms of k, m and such other symbols as are required. Find the specific equation of motion if the mass of the cannonball is $0.5\,\text{kg}$ and $k = 5 \times 10^{-4}$ in SI units.

*Exercise 4.14

A downhill skier is modelled as a particle of mass m sliding down a slope at constant angle α. The skier is subject to two resistive forces: the sliding friction between the skis and the snow, and a force due to air resistance. Use the quadratic model of air resistance in the form: magnitude of force is kv^2, where v is the skier's speed and k is a positive constant (in fact $k = c_2 D^2$, where D is the skier's effective diameter, but we use k to save writing). Use Newton's second law to express the skier's acceleration in terms of k, v, α, m, g (the acceleration due to gravity) and μ' (the coefficient of sliding friction between the skis and the snow).

Terminal velocity

In *Unit 6*, terminal velocity was defined only for falling objects. But it can be defined for objects sliding down slopes too. The *terminal velocity* of an object sliding down a slope is the constant velocity the object will acquire as time tends to infinity. Because the terminal velocity of an object is constant, the object's acceleration when travelling at terminal velocity is zero. Use this fact and the expression you obtained for the skier's acceleration to deduce that the skier's terminal velocity v_T is given by

$$v_T = \sqrt{\frac{mg}{k}(\sin\alpha - \mu'\cos\alpha)} \quad \text{(provided that } \mu' \le \tan\alpha\text{)}.$$

Find the value of the terminal velocity of a skier (and skis) of total mass $80\,\text{kg}$ on a slope of angle $\frac{\pi}{6}$ radians for which $\mu' = 0.03$, if $k = 0.5$ in SI units.

Exercise 4.15

A particle of mass 10^{-3} kg moves in a vertical line under the action of gravity and a resistive force that depends on the particle's velocity. The magnitude of this resistive force (in newtons) when the particle's velocity is v (in metres per second) is

$$10^{-4}|v| + 2 \times 10^{-6}|v|^2,$$

and the direction of the force is always opposite to the direction of the particle's motion. (This is a refinement to the two models of air resistance described in *Unit 6*, which approaches the linear model when v is small, and is approximated more closely by the quadratic model for larger v.) The x-axis is chosen to point vertically upwards.

(a) By applying Newton's second law, show that when the particle is moving upwards, its acceleration a is given in terms of its velocity by

$$a = -10^{-3}(2v^2 + 100v + 1000g),$$

and find the corresponding expression for the particle's acceleration when it is moving downwards.

(b) Determine the terminal velocity of the particle when it is moving downwards.

Exercise 4.16

The purpose of this question is to model the motion of a person diving from a diving board into a deep swimming pool. The whole motion can be split into two phases.

Water resistance

In the first phase the diver, who can be modelled as a particle moving under gravity alone, jumps upwards off the board with a certain initial speed, and travels up and down in a vertical line before entering the water immediately below the board. (You should, of course, assume that the diver does not hit the board on the way down. In a better model this stipulation would not be necessary, but here we must think of the motion as taking place in a straight line so that we may apply the methods of the unit.)

The second phase of the motion occurs while the diver is underwater. Here the diver experiences two forces in addition to the force of gravity. The first is a resistance due to the water, opposing the motion, and of magnitude proportional to the square of the diver's speed. The second is buoyancy, which is modelled as a constant upward force (of magnitude greater than the magnitude of the weight of the diver).

(a) Find the speed of the diver on entering the water, in terms of the initial speed, the height of the diving board above the water level, and any other relevant quantities.

(b) Obtain the equation of motion of the diver while moving downwards in the water, and hence find a formula from which you can derive the answer to the following question. How deep will a diver whose mass is 75 kg submerge when diving from the 2.5-metre board, with initial upwards speed $2\,\mathrm{m\,s^{-1}}$, if the constant of proportionality in the expression for the water resistance is 50 (in SI units) and the magnitude of the buoyancy force is 850 newtons?

5 Unit 7 consolidation

As described in the Introduction, this section contains additional exercises to help consolidate your study of *Unit 7*.

Exercise 5.1

(a) A model spring has natural length l_0 and stiffness k. One end of it is fixed, and the other has a particle attached to it; matters are so arranged that the spring and particle remain in a horizontal line, as shown in Figure 5.1. Describe, in magnitude and direction, the force exerted by the spring on the particle if the length of the spring is l, for the cases $l > l_0$, $l < l_0$, $l = l_0$.

(b) Calculate the magnitude of the force, and state its direction, if the stiffness of the spring is $150 \, \text{N m}^{-1}$ and the spring is compressed from its natural length by 0.5 metres.

(c) Explain how the force **H** exerted by a model spring at either one of its ends is related to the unit vector $\hat{\mathbf{s}}$ from the centre of the spring to that end.

Force law for a model spring

Figure 5.1

Exercise 5.2

In order to find the stiffness of a certain model spring, particles of various masses are suspended from it. When a particle of mass 5 kg is suspended from the spring, its length is 1.3 metres. When a particle of mass 9 kg is suspended from the spring, its length is 1.5 metres.

Statics problems involving springs

(a) What are the stiffness and natural length of the spring?

(b) If the length of the spring is 2 metres when another particle is suspended from it, what is the mass of this particle?

Exercise 5.3

This question concerns the design of a simple spring balance for use as kitchen scales. It will consist in its essentials of a model spring supporting a pan, as shown in Figure 5.2. The balance is to be used to weigh (i.e. measure the mass of) ingredients up to 2 kg. The measuring scale should be not more than about 0.2 metres long. The pan to be used has a mass of about 0.1 kg. What should the stiffness of the spring be (roughly)?

When a balance has been constructed, containing a spring of the appropriate stiffness, it will be necessary to calibrate it, i.e. fix the scale marks. How should this be done?

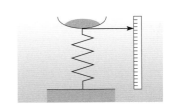

Figure 5.2

Exercise 5.4

An object of mass 2 kg is lying on a horizontal table. The coefficient of static friction between the object and the table is 0.3. The object is attached to a horizontal spring whose other end is attached to a fixed point, as shown in Figure 5.3. This spring has stiffness $100 \, \text{N m}^{-1}$ and natural length 0.5 metres. What is the maximum distance from the fixed end of the spring at which the object can remain at rest?

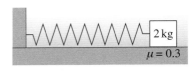

Figure 5.3

Exercise 5.5

A model spring has natural length l_0 and stiffness k. One end of it is fixed, and the other has a particle attached to it; matters are so arranged that the spring and mass remain in a horizontal line, as shown in Figure 5.4.

Equation of motion of particle attached to spring

Derive the equation of motion of the particle, in the form of a second-order differential equation for the x-coordinate of the particle as a function of time, where the x-axis points along the line of the spring to the right in the figure, and its origin is taken:

Figure 5.4

(a) at the equilibrium position of the particle;

(b) at the fixed end of the spring.

Write down the general solution of the differential equation you obtain, for each case.

*Exercise 5.6

A particle moves so that its position $x(t)$ at time t is given by

Simple harmonic motion

$$x(t) = 4\cos 8t - 3\sin 8t.$$

(a) Show that the particle's motion is periodic.

(b) What is the period τ of its motion?

(c) What is the average position of the particle, about which the oscillations take place?

(d) Where is the particle when its velocity is zero?

(e) What is the amplitude of the oscillations?

(f) Think of the x-axis as horizontal and pointing to the right. Is the particle to the right or the left of its average position when $t = 0$? What is the direction of the velocity of the particle at $t = 0$?

(g) What is the smallest positive value of t at which the particle passes through its average position?
     (Give your answer in the form $t = a \arctan b$, for some numbers a and b.)

(h) Using your answers to the previous parts of the question, sketch the graph of x against t for $0 \leq t \leq \tau$.

(i) For each of the following values of t, state whether the particle is to the right or to the left of the average position, and whether it is moving to the right or to the left: $t = \frac{1}{4}\tau$, $t = \frac{1}{2}\tau$, $t = \frac{3}{4}\tau$, $t = \tau$.

Exercise 5.7

A particle moves so that its position $x(t)$ at time t is given by

$$x(t) = x_0 + A\cos(\omega t + \phi).$$

Its position and velocity at time $t = 0$ are given by $x(0) = 1$ and $\dot{x}(0) = -1$; it oscillates between the points whose coordinates are $x = -1 \pm 2\sqrt{2}$. Find: the particle's average position during its motion; the amplitude, angular frequency, frequency and period with which it oscillates; and the smallest positive value of the time t at which it passes through its average position.

Exercise 5.8

(a) Find constants B and C such that

$$3\cos(\omega t + \tfrac{\pi}{3}) = B\cos \omega t + C\sin \omega t \quad \text{(for all } t).$$

(b) Find constants A $(A > 0)$ and ϕ $(-\pi < \phi \leq \pi)$ such that

$$0.2\cos \omega t - 0.1\sin \omega t = A\cos(\omega t + \phi) \quad \text{(for all } t).$$

Exercise 5.9

There are two standard ways of representing simple harmonic motion with angular frequency ω: $x(t) = B\cos\omega t + C\sin\omega t$ for any constants B and C, not both zero; and $x(t) = A\cos(\omega t + \phi)$ for constants A and ϕ such that $A > 0$ and $-\pi < \phi \leq \pi$. Some of the following expressions represent simple harmonic motion, but not necessarily in standard form, whereas others represent motion that is not simple harmonic. Decide in each case whether or not the motion is simple harmonic; if it is simple harmonic, give the appropriate standard representation.

(a) $x(t) = -A\cos(\omega t + \phi)$, where $A > 0$, $0 < \phi \leq \pi$

(b) $x(t) = B\cos\omega t + C\sin 2\omega t$

(c) $x(t) = B\sin\omega t + C\cos\omega t$

(d) $x(t) = A\sin(\omega t + \phi)$, where $A > 0$, $-\frac{\pi}{2} < \phi \leq \pi$

(e) $x(t) = B\cos\omega t + C\tan\omega t$

Exercise 5.10

A particle of mass m moves on a smooth (i.e. frictionless) plane inclined at an angle α to the horizontal. It is attached to one end of a model spring, whose other end is fixed in such a position that the force exerted by the spring on the particle always acts parallel to the surface of the plane, as shown in Figure 5.5. The spring has stiffness k. Ignore air resistance. Show that the particle executes simple harmonic motion, and find its period.

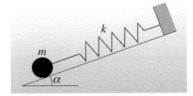

Figure 5.5

Exercise 5.11

A second model spring is attached to the particle of the previous exercise, and the other end is fixed down the plane from the particle, as shown in Figure 5.6. The stiffness of the new spring is k'. What is the period of the simple harmonic motion of the new system?

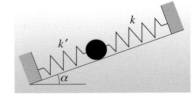

Figure 5.6

*Exercise 5.12

A particle of mass m is attached to two model springs, both of natural length l_0, whose stiffnesses are k_1 and k_2. The other ends of the springs are attached to the same fixed point, and the particle oscillates in a vertical line below it. Find the distance of the equilibrium position of the particle below the point of suspension, and the period of the particle's oscillatory motion about its equilibrium position.

Exercise 5.13

A particle of mass m is attached to two model springs, of natural lengths l_1 and l_2, and stiffnesses k_1 and k_2, respectively. The other ends of the springs are attached to two fixed points, one vertically above the other and a distance L apart, as shown in Figure 5.7, so that the upper spring has stiffness k_1. Find the distance of the equilibrium position of the particle below the upper fixed point, and the period of the particle's oscillatory motion about its equilibrium position.

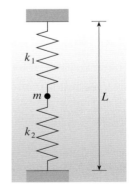

Figure 5.7

Outcomes

After studying this unit you should be able to:

- understand and explain the concepts of kinetic energy, potential energy and total mechanical energy;
- apply the equation for gravitational potential energy of a particle of mass m ($U = mg \times$ height above datum);
- apply the equation for the energy stored in a spring of stiffness k ($U = \frac{1}{2}k \times$ (deformation)^2);
- apply, in appropriate circumstances, the law of conservation of mechanical energy;
- understand that the above formula for the gravitational potential energy applies to motion in two or three dimensions, and apply this in certain situations;
- identify the turning points and region of motion for a particle with given potential energy and total mechanical energy.

Appendix: Potential energy for a step function

In the argument leading from the potential energy function for constant forces to the general case, we considered the intermediate step of finding the potential energy function for a succession of constant forces. This appendix shows how we can define a potential energy function for these forces so that conservation of energy applies.

To illustrate the argument that applies to a succession of any number of constant forces, we consider the case of two constant forces shown in Figure A.1, which corresponds to the force $F(x)\mathbf{i}$, where

$$F(x) = \begin{cases} F_0, & 0 \leq x < h, \\ F_1, & h \leq x \leq 2h. \end{cases}$$

On the subinterval $[0, h)$ the force is constant, so we can apply Equation (1.4) to obtain

$$E = \tfrac{1}{2}mv^2 - F_0 x \quad (0 \leq x < h), \tag{A.1}$$

where the constant E can be determined by taking $x = 0$ as the datum for potential energy.

On the subinterval $[h, 2h]$ we have $F(x) = F_1$, a constant. So again Equation (1.4) applies, giving

$$E' = \tfrac{1}{2}mv^2 - F_1 x \quad (h \leq x \leq 2h), \tag{A.2}$$

where E' is another constant. Our goal is to choose a suitable datum so that we can relate E' to E.

To choose the datum for the second subinterval, we shall use the fact that for physical problems the velocity of a particle is a continuous function (otherwise we would have infinite — or undefined — accelerations). As a consequence of this, the kinetic energy function $T(x) = \frac{1}{2}mv(x)^2$ is also a continuous function of position.

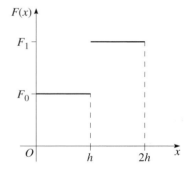

Figure A.1

So we now rearrange Equations (A.1) and (A.2) to make $T(x)$ the subject:

$$T(x) = \begin{cases} E + F_0 x, & 0 \le x < h, \\ E' + F_1 x, & h \le x \le 2h. \end{cases}$$

Now, since $T(x)$ is continuous at $x = h$, we obtain

$$E + F_0 h = E' + F_1 h.$$

So $E' = E + F_0 h - F_1 h$, which we can substitute into Equation (A.2) to obtain

$$E + F_0 h - F_1 h = \tfrac{1}{2} m v^2 - F_1 x \quad (h \le x \le 2h).$$

This can be rearranged to give

$$E = \tfrac{1}{2} m v^2 - F_0 h - F_1 (x - h) \quad (h \le x \le 2h).$$

So if we define the potential function as

$$U(x) = \begin{cases} -F_0 x, & 0 \le x < h, \\ -F_0 h - F_1 (x - h), & h \le x \le 2h, \end{cases}$$

then we have

$$E = \tfrac{1}{2} m v^2 + U(x)$$

for the whole of the interval $[0, 2h]$. This is the equation that corresponds to Equation (1.4) for the constant force case. So energy is conserved on the interval $[0, 2h]$, and the potential energy at the end of the interval is $U(a) = -F_0 h - F_1 h$.

Solutions to the exercises

Section 1

1.1 (a)

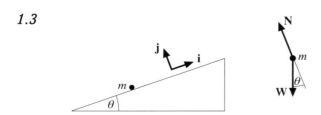

Using the origin as the datum with a downward-pointing x-axis, we have $\mathbf{F} = \mathbf{W} = mg\mathbf{i}$. Substituting $F = mg$ into Equation (1.3), we have

$$E = \tfrac{1}{2}mv^2 - mgx.$$

The initial condition is $v = 0$ when $x = 0$, so $E = 0$. Hence we have

$$0 = \tfrac{1}{2}v^2 - gx, \quad \text{or} \quad v^2 = 2gx,$$

throughout the motion. So when $x = 77$, we find that

$$|v| = \sqrt{2 \times 9.81 \times 77} \simeq 38.9.$$

Hence the speed of the marble just before it hits the water is $38.9\,\mathrm{m\,s^{-1}}$.

(The same answer was obtained by direct application of Newton's second law in *Unit 6*.)

Further, when $v = 20$, we have

$$x = 20^2/(2 \times 9.81) \simeq 20.4.$$

So the marble has fallen $20.4\,\mathrm{m}$ when its speed reaches $20\,\mathrm{m\,s^{-1}}$.

(b) The force of air resistance is a function of velocity. Hence the total force acting on the particle is not dependent on position alone, and the law of conservation of mechanical energy is not applicable.

1.2 With the given x-axis, the force due to gravity has x-component $F = -mg$. Using the definition of the potential energy function (1.6), we have

$$U(x) = -\int F(x)\,dx = \int mg\,dx = mgx + c.$$

The given datum is the origin, so $U(0) = 0$ thus $c = 0$, and we obtain

$$U(x) = mgx.$$

So, for the force due to gravity, the potential energy function is mg times the height above the chosen datum.

1.3

Choose the unit vectors $\mathbf{i}$ and $\mathbf{j}$ as shown above.

Then the forces acting on the particle are the normal reaction $\mathbf{N}$ (in the $\mathbf{j}$-direction) and the weight

$$\mathbf{W} = -mg\sin\theta\,\mathbf{i} - mg\cos\theta\,\mathbf{j}.$$

The motion (and hence the resultant force) is along the slope. The total force acting on the particle along the slope, $F(x)$, is given by

$$F(x) = (\mathbf{N} + \mathbf{W}) \cdot \mathbf{i} = -mg\sin\theta.$$

Using the definition of the potential energy function (1.6), we have

$$U(x) = -\int F(x)\,dx = \int mg\sin\theta\,dx$$
$$= mgx\sin\theta + c.$$

The given datum is the origin, so $U(0) = 0$ thus $c = 0$, and we obtain

$$U(x) = mgx\sin\theta.$$

(Since $x\sin\theta$ is the vertical height of the particle as measured from the datum, the potential energy function is again mg times the height above the chosen datum.)

1.4 With the given choice of origin, the force due to the spring will be

$$\mathbf{H} = -k(l - l_0)\,\mathbf{i} = -kx\mathbf{i},$$

whose x-component is $F(x) = -kx$. Hence the potential energy function is

$$U(x) = -\int F(x)\,dx = \int kx\,dx = \tfrac{1}{2}kx^2 + c.$$

The given datum is $x = 0$, so $U(0) = 0$ thus $c = 0$, and we have

$$U(x) = \tfrac{1}{2}kx^2.$$

So, for the force due to the spring, the potential energy function is

$$\tfrac{1}{2} \times \text{stiffness} \times (\text{deformation})^2.$$

1.5 (a) For $F(x) = -ax^2$, we have

$$U(x) = -\int F(x)\,dx = \int ax^2\,dx = \tfrac{1}{3}ax^3 + c.$$

Choosing $x = 0$ as the datum, so $U(0) = 0$, gives $c = 0$. Hence the potential energy function is

$$U(x) = \tfrac{1}{3}ax^3.$$

(b) For $F(x) = bx^{-2}$ $(x > 0)$, we have

$$U(x) = -\int F(x)\,dx = -\int bx^{-2}\,dx = bx^{-1} + c.$$

Choosing $x = \infty$ as the datum, so $U(\infty) = 0$, gives $c = 0$. Hence the potential energy function is

$$U(x) = b/x \quad (x > 0).$$

(You may have chosen a different datum. However, your answer should differ from the above only by the addition of a constant.)

1.6 **(a)** From the definition of potential energy, if $U(x)$ is the potential energy function corresponding to the force $F(x)$, then

$$U(x) = -\int F(x)\,dx$$

$$= -\int \left[F_1(x) + F_2(x) \right] dx$$

$$= -\int F_1(x)\,dx - \int F_2(x)\,dx$$

$$= U_1(x) + U_2(x).$$

(b) If $F_1(x) = -ax^2$ and $F_2(x) = bx^{-2}$ $(x > 0)$, then, from Exercise 1.5, we have

$$U_1(x) = \tfrac{1}{3}ax^3, \quad U_2(x) = bx^{-1} \ (x > 0).$$

Now the given force is $F(x) = F_1(x) + F_2(x)$, so its potential energy function is

$$U(x) = U_1(x) + U_2(x)$$

$$= \tfrac{1}{3}ax^3 + bx^{-1} \quad (x > 0).$$

(Your answer could differ from the above by a constant if you chose a different datum for either F_1 or F_2; see the paragraph that follows Exercise 1.7.)

1.7 As noted on page 138, differentiating both sides of the equation

$$U(x) = -\int F(x)\,dx$$

gives

$$F(x) = -\frac{dU}{dx}.$$

Hence if

$$U(x) = ax^2 + bx^{-2} \quad (x > 0),$$

then

$$F(x) = -\frac{dU}{dx} = -2ax + 2bx^{-3} \quad (x > 0).$$

1.8 Choose an x-axis directed upwards, with origin at ground level immediately below the point at which the ball is hit. The only force acting on the ball is its weight. The ball's potential energy at height x, with the origin as datum, is mgx, where m is its mass. The law of conservation of mechanical energy states that the ball's total mechanical energy $\tfrac{1}{2}mv^2 + mgx$ remains constant. (We could, but need not, denote this constant value by E.) Since the total mechanical energy is constant, it retains the value it has initially, which is $\tfrac{1}{2}mv_0^2 + mgx_0$, where v_0 is the initial velocity and x_0 is the initial position. Thus

$$\tfrac{1}{2}mv^2 + mgx = \tfrac{1}{2}mv_0^2 + mgx_0.$$

At the highest point of its path, the ball's velocity is 0; so h, the height of this point above ground level, is given by $mgh = \tfrac{1}{2}mv_0^2 + mgx_0$, thus $h = \tfrac{1}{2}v_0^2/g + x_0$. Using the data from the question, we obtain

$$h = \tfrac{1}{2} \times 20^2/9.81 + 1 \simeq 21.39,$$

so the height attained is about 21 m.

When the ball reaches the ground, $x = 0$, so its velocity is given by $\tfrac{1}{2}mv^2 = \tfrac{1}{2}mv_0^2 + mgx_0$, thus

$$v = -\sqrt{v_0^2 + 2gx_0}$$

(it will be moving downwards). Using the data from the question, we obtain

$$v = -\sqrt{400 + 2g} \simeq -20.48,$$

so the ball's speed when it hits the ground is about $20.5\,\mathrm{m\,s^{-1}}$.

Section 2

2.1 **(a)**   ◄Draw picture►

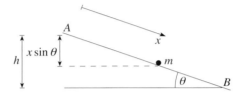

◄Choose datum►

The point B is chosen as the datum.

◄Find potential energy►

At position x, the height of the particle above point B is $h - x\sin\theta$. So the potential energy function is $U(x) = mg(h - x\sin\theta)$, and the total mechanical energy of the particle is therefore

$$E = \tfrac{1}{2}m\dot{x}^2 + mg(h - x\sin\theta).$$

(b)   ◄Find E►

At A we have $x = 0$ and $\dot{x} = 0$, so $E = mgh$ and

$$\tfrac{1}{2}m\dot{x}^2 + mg(h - x\sin\theta) = mgh$$

throughout the motion.

◄Find x or v►

At B we have $x\sin\theta = h$, so $\tfrac{1}{2}m\dot{x}^2 = mgh$. Since $\dot{x} > 0$, this gives

$$\dot{x} = \sqrt{2gh}.$$

◄Interpret solution►

The speed of the particle at B is therefore $\sqrt{2gh}$.

This result depends on the height h, but not on the angle θ at which the slope is inclined. For a less steep slope, the acceleration of the particle will be less, but then the particle has further to travel down the slope in order to descend a given vertical distance h. The result depends on the assumption of no friction between the particle and the surface, but does not depend on the mass of the particle.

(c) For the given data, we obtain a value at B of

$$\dot{x} = \sqrt{2gh} = \sqrt{2 \times 9.81 \times 2\sin\tfrac{\pi}{6}} \simeq 4.4,$$

so the crate of empty bottles reaches the bottom of the slope with speed $4.4\,\mathrm{m\,s^{-1}}$. (This agrees with the answer obtained in Example 3.2 of *Unit 6*.)

2.2 ◀Draw picture▶

A picture is given alongside the question as Figure 2.3.

◀Choose datum▶

Take the datum at $x = 0$ (the point of zero deformation).

◀Find potential energy▶

For the force exerted by a spring with deformation x, the potential energy function is $U(x) = \frac{1}{2}kx^2$, so the law of conservation of mechanical energy gives

$\frac{1}{2}mv^2 + \frac{1}{2}kx^2 = E$.

◀Find E▶

Since $m = 0.5$ and $k = 2$, this becomes

$\frac{1}{4}v^2 + x^2 = E$.

Initially $v = -3$ when $x = 2$, so

$E = \frac{9}{4} + 4 = \frac{25}{4}$.

◀Find x or v▶

Hence we have

$v^2 + 4x^2 = 25$.

From this equation, $|v|$ will take its maximum value when $4x^2$ takes its minimum value, which is zero. So the maximum speed is $|v| = \sqrt{25} = 5$.

The particle is at rest when $v = 0$, i.e. at $x = \pm\frac{5}{2}$.

◀Interpret solution▶

Summarizing, the maximum speed of the particle is $5\,\mathrm{m\,s^{-1}}$, and it is momentarily at rest at $\pm\frac{5}{2}$ m from the equilibrium position.

2.3 ◀Draw picture▶

A picture is given alongside the question as Figure 2.4.

◀Choose datum▶

We choose the fixed top of the spring as the datum for gravitational potential energy. We choose the point of zero deformation as the datum for the spring potential energy.

◀Find potential energy▶

Let x be the length of the spring. The potential energy function is the sum of two contributions, one due to gravity and one due to the spring. The height above the datum is $-x$, since we are taking the top of the spring as a datum. So the gravitational potential energy is $mg \times (\text{height above datum}) = -mgx$. The extension of the spring is $x - l_0$, so the spring contributes a term $\frac{1}{2}k(x - l_0)^2$ to the potential energy. So the potential energy of the particle is

$U(x) = \frac{1}{2}k(x - l_0)^2 - mgx$.

So by the law of conservation of energy,

$E = \frac{1}{2}mv^2 + \frac{1}{2}\frac{10mg}{l_0}(x - l_0)^2 - mgx$, (S.1)

where we have substituted in the given value of k.

◀Find E▶

Initially the particle is at rest at a depth of $\frac{5}{4}l_0$, so

$E = \frac{1}{2}m0^2 + \frac{1}{2}\frac{10mg}{l_0}(\frac{5}{4}l_0 - l_0)^2 - mg\frac{5}{4}l_0$

$= 0 + \frac{5}{16}mgl_0 - \frac{5}{4}mgl_0$

$= -\frac{15}{16}mgl_0$.

◀Find x or v▶

We wish to find $|v|$ when the spring has its natural length. Substituting $x = l_0$ into (S.1) gives

$-\frac{15}{16}mgl_0 = \frac{1}{2}mv^2 + \frac{1}{2}\frac{10mg}{l_0}(l_0 - l_0)^2 - mgl_0$.

This leads to $|v| = \sqrt{gl_0/8}$.

◀Interpret solution▶

The speed of the particle as it passes the point where the spring is undeformed is $\sqrt{gl_0/8}$.

2.4 (a) We choose the origin as the datum (you may have made a different choice). The potential energy function is then

$U(x) = -\int F(x)\,dx$

$= -\int (2 - 2x)\,dx = -2x + x^2$.

(b) The total mechanical energy of the particle is

$E = \frac{1}{2}mv^2 + U(x) = v^2 - 2x + x^2$,

since the mass of the particle is $m = 2$. Now $v = 0$ when $x = -1$, so

$E = 0 + 2 + 1 = 3$.

(If you used a different datum for the potential energy, so that $U(x) = -2x + x^2 + c$, then your answer for the total mechanical energy will be $E = 3 + c$.)

(c) By the law of conservation of mechanical energy,

$3 = v^2 - 2x + x^2$,

so

$v = \pm\sqrt{3 + 2x - x^2}$.

(d) The region of motion is given by

$3 + 2x - x^2 \geq 0$,

which factorizes to give

$(1 + x)(3 - x) \geq 0$,

that is,

$-1 \leq x \leq 3$.

At the midpoint, $x = 1$, the particle's speed is

$|v| = \sqrt{3 + 2 - 1} = 2$.

2.5 (a) The only contribution to the potential energy of the bead is the gravitational potential energy. The height above the datum when the bead is at position x is $\frac{1}{2}Cx^2$. So the gravitational potential energy is $mg \times \frac{1}{2}Cx^2$. If the velocity of the bead is v, then the total mechanical energy, E, of the bead is given by

$E = \frac{1}{2}mv^2 + \frac{1}{2}mgCx^2$.

(b) Making the small oscillations assumption gives $v = \dot{x}$, so the total mechanical energy can be written as

$$E = \tfrac{1}{2}m\dot{x}^2 + \tfrac{1}{2}mgCx^2.$$

For this system the total mechanical energy is conserved, so E is a constant, i.e. $dE/dt = 0$. So we can differentiate the total mechanical energy to obtain

$$0 = m\dot{x}\ddot{x} + mgCx\dot{x}.$$

Discounting the solution $\dot{x} = 0$ and simplifying gives the desired second-order differential equation

$$\ddot{x} + gCx = 0.$$

(c) The above equation is the SHM equation. So the solution is oscillatory with angular frequency $\sqrt{gC}$.

2.6 (a) We choose $x = \infty$ as the datum. The potential energy function is then

$$U(x) = -\int F(x)\,dx = -\int \frac{2}{x^2}\,dx = \frac{2}{x}.$$

(If you chose a different datum, then your answer should be $U(x) = 2x^{-1} + c$.)

(b) The law of conservation of mechanical energy is

$$\tfrac{1}{2}mv^2 + U(x) = E, \quad \text{or} \quad \tfrac{3}{2}v^2 + \frac{2}{x} = E.$$

Initially $v = -1$ when $x = 10$, which leads to

$$E = \tfrac{17}{10} \text{ (in joules)}.$$

(If you used a different datum for the potential energy function, as above, then you should have found $E = \tfrac{17}{10} + c$.)

(c) At the point of closest approach, the particle must be stationary, so that $v = 0$. Then, from the law of conservation of mechanical energy, the corresponding value of x is given by

$$\tfrac{3}{2} \times 0^2 + \frac{2}{x} = \tfrac{17}{10}.$$

Hence the point of closest approach is $x = \tfrac{20}{17}$, i.e. about 1.18 m.

(d)

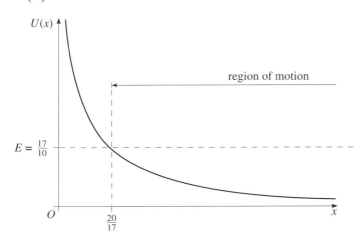

The region of motion is $x \geq \tfrac{20}{17}$.

(The particle is initially at $x = 10$, moving in the direction of decreasing x. It comes instantaneously to rest at $x = \tfrac{20}{17}$, and changes its direction of motion. It then

continues to move in the direction of increasing x. For large values of x, its velocity will approach $v = \sqrt{\tfrac{17}{15}}$, i.e. about $1.06\,\mathrm{m\,s^{-1}}$.)

2.7 When the buffers are at maximum compression, the spring potential energy is

$$\tfrac{1}{2} \times \text{stiffness} \times (\text{deformation})^2$$
$$= \tfrac{1}{2} \times 10^5 \times (0.1)^2 = 500,$$

and the kinetic energy of the truck is zero. So the total mechanical energy of the system is 500 J.

When the truck first comes into contact with the buffers, the spring potential energy is zero and the kinetic energy of the truck is $\tfrac{1}{2} \times 2000v^2$, where v is the velocity of the truck. Using conservation of energy, we have

$$1000v^2 = 500,$$

so $|v| = 1/\sqrt{2}$, i.e. the speed of the truck when it first hits the buffers is about $0.707\,\mathrm{m\,s^{-1}}$.

2.8 (a) The length of the spring is $(h^2 + x^2)^{\frac{1}{2}}$, so its extension is $(h^2 + x^2)^{\frac{1}{2}} - l_0$. Hence the potential energy function is

$$U(x) = \tfrac{1}{2}k\left((h^2 + x^2)^{\frac{1}{2}} - l_0\right)^2.$$

(b) The total mechanical energy is

$$E = \tfrac{1}{2}mv^2 + U(x)$$
$$= \tfrac{1}{2}mv^2 + \tfrac{1}{2}k\left((h^2 + x^2)^{\frac{1}{2}} - l_0\right)^2.$$

The bead is released from rest ($v = 0$) at $x = h\sqrt{3}$, so

$$E = \tfrac{1}{2}k\left(\left(h^2 + (h\sqrt{3})^2\right)^{\frac{1}{2}} - l_0\right)^2 = \tfrac{1}{2}k(2h - l_0)^2,$$

hence

$$mv^2 + k\left((h^2 + x^2)^{\frac{1}{2}} - l_0\right)^2 = k(2h - l_0)^2$$

throughout the motion. We have $v = 0$ at $x = \pm h\sqrt{3}$, so the bead oscillates between these two turning points, about the mean (equilibrium) position $x = 0$.

At $x = 0$, we have

$$mv^2 + k(h - l_0)^2 = k(2h - l_0)^2,$$

so $v = \pm\sqrt{kh(3h - 2l_0)/m}$. Thus the speed of the bead at the equilibrium position is $\sqrt{kh(3h - 2l_0)/m}$.

(Note that although the motion is oscillatory, it is not simple harmonic motion because the force on the bead is not simply $-cx$, for any constant c.)

2.9 Take an x-axis directed upwards, with origin at the base of the spring.

(a) The total mechanical energy of the system when the particle is at the point x is

$$\tfrac{1}{2}mv^2 + mgx + \tfrac{1}{2}k(x - l_0)^2$$

(mgx for the particle's gravitational potential energy and $\tfrac{1}{2}k(x - l_0)^2$ for the potential energy of the spring). Initially, $v = -2\,\mathrm{m\,s^{-1}}$ and $x = l_0 = 0.4\,\mathrm{m}$, so the initial value of the total mechanical energy is

$$\tfrac{1}{2} \times 0.5 \times (-2)^2 + 0.5 \times g \times 0.4 + 0 = 1 + 0.2g$$
$$= 2.962 \text{ J}.$$

(b) By the law of conservation of mechanical energy, using the given data,

$$\tfrac{1}{4}v^2 + \tfrac{1}{2}gx + 50(x - \tfrac{4}{10})^2 = 1 + 0.2g,$$

which gives

$$v^2 = 4(-\tfrac{1}{2}gx - 50(x^2 - \tfrac{4}{5}x + \tfrac{4}{25}) + 1 + 0.2g)$$
$$= -200x^2 + (160 - 2g)x + (0.8g - 28).$$

(c) The extreme points of the motion are those at which $v = 0$, so they are the roots of the equation $-200x^2 + (160 - 2g)x + (0.8g - 28) = 0$, which are $x \simeq 0.50$ and $x \simeq 0.20$. The amplitude of the particle's oscillations is half the distance between the extremities, which is about $0.15\,\mathrm{m}$.

Section 3

3.1 If the particle is in equilibrium, the vector sum of the forces acting on it must be zero, i.e.

$$\mathbf{F}_1 + \mathbf{F}_2 + \cdots + \mathbf{F}_n = \mathbf{0};$$

alternatively, the total force acting on the particle must be zero. (Conversely, if the total force acting on a particle is zero, then the particle will be in equilibrium or moving with constant speed in a straight line, by Newton's first law.)

(a) No   (b) Yes   (c) No

Since the particle is in equilibrium, we must have $\mathbf{F}_1 + \mathbf{F}_2 + \mathbf{F}_3 + \mathbf{F}_4 = \mathbf{0}$, so

$$\mathbf{F}_4 = -(\mathbf{F}_1 + \mathbf{F}_2 + \mathbf{F}_3) = -2\mathbf{i} - 2\mathbf{k}.$$

3.2 (a) It is useful to draw a force diagram showing all the forces acting on the block.

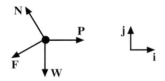

We can see, by inspection, that two of the forces are aligned with the **i**- and **j**-directions and hence can be resolved immediately to give

$$\mathbf{P} = |\mathbf{P}|\,\mathbf{i} \quad \text{and} \quad \mathbf{W} = -|\mathbf{W}|\,\mathbf{j}.$$

For the other two forces we use the dot product formula from *Unit 4*. For this we need to know the angles between the forces and the unit vectors. It is useful to have in your mind which angles are equal to α, and for that the following diagram is useful.

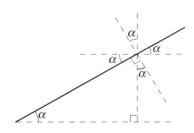

For **N** we have

$$\mathbf{N} = (\mathbf{N} \cdot \mathbf{i})\,\mathbf{i} + (\mathbf{N} \cdot \mathbf{j})\,\mathbf{j}$$
$$= |\mathbf{N}| \cos(\tfrac{\pi}{2} + \alpha)\,\mathbf{i} + |\mathbf{N}| \cos\alpha\,\mathbf{j}.$$

But $\cos(\tfrac{\pi}{2} + \alpha) = \cos\tfrac{\pi}{2}\cos\alpha - \sin\tfrac{\pi}{2}\sin\alpha = -\sin\alpha$. So

$$\mathbf{N} = -|\mathbf{N}|\sin\alpha\,\mathbf{i} + |\mathbf{N}|\cos\alpha\,\mathbf{j}.$$

For **F** we have

$$\mathbf{F} = |\mathbf{F}| \cos(\pi + \alpha)\,\mathbf{i} + |\mathbf{F}| \cos(\tfrac{\pi}{2} + \alpha)\,\mathbf{j}.$$

But $\cos(\pi + \alpha) = \cos\pi\cos\alpha - \sin\pi\sin\alpha = -\cos\alpha$ and $\cos(\tfrac{\pi}{2} + \alpha) = -\sin\alpha$, as before. So

$$\mathbf{F} = -|\mathbf{F}| \cos\alpha\,\mathbf{i} - |\mathbf{F}| \sin\alpha\,\mathbf{j}.$$

(b) For this part the force diagram is the same, but now with new axes.

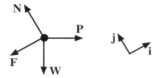

Again, two of the forces are aligned with the **i**- and **j**-directions and can be written down by inspection to obtain

$$\mathbf{F} = -|\mathbf{F}|\,\mathbf{i} \quad \text{and} \quad \mathbf{N} = |\mathbf{N}|\,\mathbf{j}.$$

For the other forces we use the dot product formula from *Unit 4*. (The diagram showing the angles equal to α given in part (a) is again very useful.) For **W** we have

$$\mathbf{W} = |\mathbf{W}| \cos(\tfrac{\pi}{2} + \alpha)\,\mathbf{i} + |\mathbf{W}| \cos(\pi + \alpha)\,\mathbf{j}$$
$$= -|\mathbf{W}|\sin\alpha\,\mathbf{i} - |\mathbf{W}|\cos\alpha\,\mathbf{j}.$$

For **P** we have

$$\mathbf{P} = |\mathbf{P}| \cos\alpha\,\mathbf{i} + |\mathbf{P}| \cos(\tfrac{\pi}{2} + \alpha)\,\mathbf{j}$$
$$= |\mathbf{P}| \cos\alpha\,\mathbf{i} - |\mathbf{P}| \sin\alpha\,\mathbf{j}.$$

3.3 The gravitational force acting on a body is its weight; the magnitude of this force is mg, where m is the body's mass and g is the acceleration due to gravity.

A particle's mass never changes merely as a result of a change in the particle's position. The particle's weight, however, will have a larger magnitude at the North Pole than at the equator. It will also act in a different direction.

3.4 The normal reactions act as shown.

3.5 The ball-bearing is subject to two normal reaction forces, one from each plane. Modelling it as a particle, the forces acting on it are as shown below, where $\mathbf{N}_1$ is the normal reaction due to the left-hand plane and $\mathbf{N}_2$ is the normal reaction due to the right-hand plane.

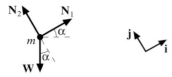

The angle between the lower plane and the horizontal has been denoted by α and the mass of the ball-bearing by m.

The three forces acting on the ball-bearing are

$$\mathbf{N}_1 = |\mathbf{N}_1|\mathbf{i},$$
$$\mathbf{N}_2 = |\mathbf{N}_2|\mathbf{j},$$
$$\mathbf{W} = mg\cos(\tfrac{\pi}{2}+\alpha)\mathbf{i} + mg\cos(\pi+\alpha)\mathbf{j}$$
$$= -mg\sin\alpha\,\mathbf{i} - mg\cos\alpha\,\mathbf{j}.$$

The equilibrium condition is

$$\mathbf{W} + \mathbf{N}_1 + \mathbf{N}_2 = \mathbf{0}.$$

Resolving in the **i**-direction gives

$$|\mathbf{N}_1| - mg\sin\alpha = 0,$$

hence $|\mathbf{N}_1| = mg\sin\alpha$. Resolving in the **j**-direction gives

$$|\mathbf{N}_2| - mg\cos\alpha = 0,$$

hence $|\mathbf{N}_2| = mg\cos\alpha$. Taking $m = 0.1\,\mathrm{kg}$ and $\alpha = \frac{\pi}{6}$ we find that the magnitudes of $\mathbf{N}_1$ and $\mathbf{N}_2$ are $0.49\,\mathrm{N}$ and $0.85\,\mathrm{N}$, respectively (to two significant figures).

(We have used symbols to represent the angle of slope and the mass of the ball-bearing, rather than the numerical values given in the question, for two reasons: when one does so it is actually easier to avoid making errors of calculation, and also the principles underlying the solution are more clearly revealed. We shall often use similar procedures in subsequent solutions, and we suggest that you do likewise when solving mechanics questions.)

3.6 (a)   **(b)**

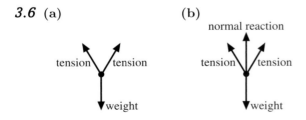

3.7 Modelling Tarzan as a particle, the tension forces in the two parts of the liana act as shown.

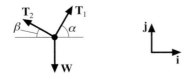

The equilibrium condition is

$$\mathbf{W} + \mathbf{T}_1 + \mathbf{T}_2 = \mathbf{0}.$$

With the angles as marked in the figure, resolving in the **i**-direction gives

$$|\mathbf{T}_1|\cos\alpha - |\mathbf{T}_2|\cos\beta = 0;$$

resolving in the **j**-direction gives

$$-mg + |\mathbf{T}_1|\sin\alpha + |\mathbf{T}_2|\sin\beta = 0.$$

Thus $|\mathbf{T}_2| = |\mathbf{T}_1|(\cos\alpha/\cos\beta)$, so

$$|\mathbf{T}_1| = \frac{mg\cos\beta}{\sin(\alpha+\beta)}$$

(since $\sin\alpha\cos\beta + \cos\alpha\sin\beta = \sin(\alpha+\beta)$) and

$$|\mathbf{T}_2| = \frac{mg\cos\alpha}{\sin(\alpha+\beta)}.$$

In this case $\alpha + \beta = \frac{\pi}{2}$. The magnitudes of $\mathbf{T}_1$ and $\mathbf{T}_2$ are therefore $850\,\mathrm{N}$ and $490\,\mathrm{N}$, respectively (to two significant figures).

(In fact, the answer can be deduced more or less immediately from Solution 3.5: the force diagram is the mirror image of that in Solution 3.5, and Tarzan's mass is 1000 times that of the ball-bearing.)

3.8 The friction force acts horizontally, in the opposite direction to the direction of the applied force or push; so long as the book is in equilibrium, the magnitude of the friction force will be equal to that of the applied force. This follows from the equilibrium condition: the vector sum of the forces acting on a particle in equilibrium is zero.

Modelling the book as a particle, let $\mathbf{W}$ be the book's weight (acting vertically downwards), let $\mathbf{N}$ be the normal reaction between the book and the table (acting vertically upwards on the book), let $\mathbf{P}$ be the applied force (acting horizontally), and let $\mathbf{F}$ be the friction force (also acting horizontally). By resolving horizontally, we see that $\mathbf{F}$ opposes $\mathbf{P}$, and $|\mathbf{F}| = |\mathbf{P}|$. The forces acting are shown below.

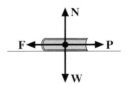

The book can remain in equilibrium only so long as the magnitude of the friction force $\mathbf{F}$ does not exceed a certain fraction of the magnitude of the normal reaction $\mathbf{N}$; that is, only so long as $|\mathbf{F}| \leq \mu|\mathbf{N}|$, where μ, the coefficient of static friction, is a constant, characteristic of the two materials in contact. This condition is stated in terms of $\mathbf{F}$ and $\mathbf{N}$, but we have no direct experience of these two forces: it is necessary to replace this condition by an equivalent one involving the applied force $\mathbf{P}$ and the book's weight $\mathbf{W}$. But $|\mathbf{F}| = |\mathbf{P}|$, and $|\mathbf{N}| = |\mathbf{W}| = mg$, where m is the mass of the book.

So, as the magnitude of the applied force increases, the book remains in equilibrium until $|\mathbf{P}| = \mu mg$; the instant that the magnitude of the applied force exceeds μmg, the book begins to move.

(a) The effect of polishing the table is to reduce the value of μ, so a smaller applied force will move the book.

(b) The limiting value of $|\mathbf{F}|$ does not depend on the area of contact between the book and the table. Furthermore, the values of μ and m are unchanged (the new book is another paperback, of the same mass). So changing the book for the one with larger area has no effect.

(c) Placing a second book on top of the first will have the effect of increasing m — doubling it, if the two books are identical, for example. The applied force required to make the book move is proportional to the mass, so it will increase when the second book is added; it will double if the second book is identical to the first.

(d) Suppose that the person doing the pushing exerts an additional force $\mathbf{Q}$ vertically downwards on the book. Then the equilibrium condition becomes

$$\mathbf{W} + \mathbf{N} + \mathbf{Q} + \mathbf{F} + \mathbf{P} = \mathbf{0},$$

so the equation determining the magnitude of the normal reaction changes to $|\mathbf{N}| = mg + |\mathbf{Q}|$. It remains true that $|\mathbf{F}| = |\mathbf{P}|$ and that the slipping condition is $|\mathbf{F}| = \mu|\mathbf{N}|$. So the condition on $\mathbf{P}$ for slipping to occur is $|\mathbf{P}| = \mu(mg + |\mathbf{Q}|)$; that is, the magnitude of the applied force required to make the book move increases.

These results are all in accord with experience.

3.9 Suppose that the angle that the table makes with the horizontal is α. The forces acting on the book, modelled as a particle, are shown below.

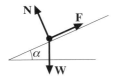

So long as the book is in equilibrium, $\mathbf{W} + \mathbf{N} + \mathbf{F} = \mathbf{0}$, hence $|\mathbf{F}| \cos \alpha = |\mathbf{N}| \sin \alpha$, thus $|\mathbf{F}| = |\mathbf{N}| \tan \alpha$. But the book can remain in equilibrium without slipping only if $|\mathbf{F}| \le \mu|\mathbf{N}|$. So equilibrium can occur only if $\tan \alpha\, |\mathbf{N}| \le \mu|\mathbf{N}|$, or $\tan \alpha \le \mu$, thus the largest value of α is $\arctan \mu$. In the case given in the question, the largest value of α is $\arctan 0.3$.

(Note that the answer does not depend on the mass of the book. To solve the problem you have to resolve only horizontally. Resolving vertically gives $mg = |\mathbf{N}| \cos \alpha + |\mathbf{F}| \sin \alpha$, but this is not of any interest so far as this question is concerned. If several books of different sizes were placed on the table, they would all begin to slip together when the angle reached $\arctan 0.3$ — assuming, of course, that the coefficient of static friction is 0.3 for each pair of surfaces in contact.)

The general result is that the maximum angle for which a particle can remain at equilibrium on a rough inclined plane is $\arctan \mu$, where μ is the coefficient of static friction. So measuring that angle gives a way of measuring μ.

To find the value of μ for two materials, take a plane made of one and an object made of the other — say a small cube. Put the cube on the plane, and tip the plane until the cube just begins to slip (assuming it does not tip). Measure the angle that the plane then makes with the horizontal, and find its tangent. (Of course, to make this into a decent experimental method, one would have to think up mechanisms for changing the slope of the plane and for measuring the angle accurately; but the principle is clear.)

3.10 (a) Modelling the crate as a particle, the forces act as shown. It is good practice to use symbols for the mass of the crate and for the angles: m is the mass of the crate, α is the angle of the ramp, and β is the angle between the ramp and the rope.

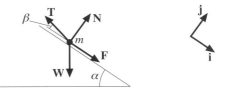

Use axes aligned along and perpendicular to the slope. Writing down the equilibrium condition and resolving in the **i**-direction gives

$$|\mathbf{F}| = |\mathbf{T}| \cos \beta - mg \sin \alpha;$$

resolving in the **j**-direction gives

$$|\mathbf{N}| = mg \cos \alpha - |\mathbf{T}| \sin \beta.$$

(The advantage of using unit vectors **i** and **j** in the directions shown, rather than horizontal and vertical ones, is that resolving leads to equations that give $|\mathbf{F}|$ and $|\mathbf{N}|$ directly.)

The crate will remain in equilibrium if

$$|\mathbf{T}| \cos \beta - mg \sin \alpha \le \mu(mg \cos \alpha - |\mathbf{T}| \sin \beta),$$

i.e. if

$$|\mathbf{T}| \le mg \left(\frac{\mu \cos \alpha + \sin \alpha}{\cos \beta + \mu \sin \beta} \right).$$

The tension in the rope when the crate is on the point of moving upwards is given by the term on the right-hand side of this inequality. In the case specified in the question, this takes the value 210.58, so the tension in the rope is just over 210 N.

(b) Modelling the pulley as a model pulley, the magnitude of the force with which the rope must be pulled is equal to the tension in the rope on either side of the pulley, which in turn is equal to the tension in the rope where it is attached to the crate. So the magnitude of the force with which the rope must be pulled is just the tension found in part (a) (since the geometry is the same).

3.11 (a) When we are considering the equilibrium of a rigid body, we have to take into account not just the direction of each force acting on it but also the point of the body at which the force acts. The line of action of a force is the straight line through this point of action in the direction of the force.

(b) The magnitude of the turning effect of a force $\mathbf{F}$ about a point is $|\mathbf{F}|l$, where l is the perpendicular distance from the point to the line of action of the force. When a pivoted rod remains in horizontal equilibrium under the action of vertical forces, the perpendicular distance from the pivot to the line of action of each force is the distance from the pivot to the point of action of the force, since the line of action is perpendicular to the rod. Thus the condition of balance, which for two forces is

$$|\mathbf{F}_1|l_1 = |\mathbf{F}_2|l_2,$$

says precisely that the turning effects of the two forces about the pivot are equal in magnitude. (The turning effects also have to be opposite in direction.)

(c) The torque of a force $\mathbf{F}$ about a fixed point O is $\mathbf{r} \times \mathbf{F}$, where $\mathbf{r}$ is the position vector, relative to O, of a point on the line of action of the force. (It does not matter which point on the line of action is taken, because to take a different point involves adding to $\mathbf{r}$ a vector parallel to $\mathbf{F}$, which does not affect the value of $\mathbf{r} \times \mathbf{F}$.)

The magnitude of $\mathbf{r} \times \mathbf{F}$ is $|\mathbf{r}|\,|\mathbf{F}|\sin\theta$, where θ is the angle between the directions of $\mathbf{r}$ and $\mathbf{F}$; $|\mathbf{r}|\sin\theta$ is the perpendicular distance from O to the line of action of $\mathbf{F}$.

The direction of this torque is given by a unit vector perpendicular to both $\mathbf{r}$ and $\mathbf{F}$, in the direction determined by the screw rule. This vector, located at the fixed point O, gives the axis about which the force is tending to turn the body on which it acts, and also (because of the screw rule) the sense in which it tends to turn it.

(d) For a rigid body to be in equilibrium, the forces acting on it must satisfy two equations: $\sum_{i=1}^{n} \mathbf{F}_i = \mathbf{0}$ and $\sum_{i=1}^{n} \mathbf{r}_i \times \mathbf{F}_i = \mathbf{0}$. The first of these is the equilibrium condition if the body is considered as a particle. The second says that the vector sum of the torques of the forces acting, about any fixed point, must be zero. The fixed point with respect to which the torques are calculated may be chosen to be a point that is convenient for the problem at hand.

3.12 Suppose that Bill sits a distance d from the pivot, on the same side as Pat. Then the rule for balancing a rod, or equivalently the torque equilibrium equation, gives

$$(\tfrac{5}{6}mg)(\tfrac{3}{5}l) + mgl = (\tfrac{3}{4}mg)l + (\tfrac{2}{3}mg)d,$$

where m is the mass of Jack. Thus $\tfrac{2}{3}d = (\tfrac{1}{2} + 1 - \tfrac{3}{4})l$, so $d = \tfrac{9}{8}l$: Bill must sit a distance $\tfrac{9}{8}l$ from the pivot, on the same side as Pat.

(If we had started with the (less plausible) assumption that Bill sits on the same side as Jack and Jill, then we would have obtained $d = -\tfrac{9}{8}l$.)

3.13 (a) Modelling the ladder as a model rod, the forces acting on the ladder are as shown below. ($\mathbf{W}_1$ is the weight of the ladder, $\mathbf{W}_2$ is the weight of the person, etc.)

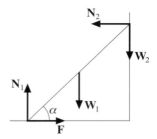

Using the equilibrium condition for forces gives

$$\mathbf{W}_1 + \mathbf{W}_2 + \mathbf{N}_1 + \mathbf{N}_2 + \mathbf{F} = \mathbf{0}.$$

Denote the mass of the person by m, so that the mass of the ladder is $2m$; this avoids having to write down a lot of halves. On resolving vertically, we obtain

$$|\mathbf{N}_1| = (2m + m)g = 3mg.$$

In questions like this it is often possible to save time and effort by making a good choice of origin for the calculation of torques. In this case, the choice of the top of the ladder as the origin with respect to which to calculate torques eliminates $\mathbf{N}_2$, the normal reaction at the top of the ladder, from consideration, and makes it unnecessary to resolve the force equilibrium equation in the horizontal direction. (In fact, resolving horizontally gives simply $|\mathbf{F}| = |\mathbf{N}_2|$.) The equilibrium condition for torques about the top of the ladder gives

$$(2l\sin\alpha)|\mathbf{F}| + (l\cos\alpha)(2mg) = (2l\cos\alpha)|\mathbf{N}_1|,$$

where the length of the ladder is taken to be $2l$ (again to save writing halves). Substituting for $|\mathbf{N}_1|$ and rearranging gives

$$|\mathbf{F}| = 2mg\cot\alpha.$$

The ladder will be able to remain in equilibrium provided that $|\mathbf{F}| \le \mu|\mathbf{N}_1|$, i.e. provided that

$$2mg\cot\alpha \le 3\mu mg = 2mg$$

(using $\mu = \tfrac{2}{3}$), which gives $\tan\alpha \ge 1$. So the smallest angle at which the ladder can remain in equilibrium is $\tfrac{\pi}{4}$.

(b) The force diagram with the bag of cement (of mass m) included is shown below.

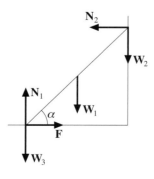

We use the same method. The equations become

$$|\mathbf{N}_1| = (2m + m + m)g = 4mg$$

and

$$(2l \sin\alpha)|\mathbf{F}| + (l\cos\alpha)(2mg) + (2l\cos\alpha)mg$$
$$= (2l\cos\alpha)|\mathbf{N}_1|.$$

Thus

$$|\mathbf{F}| = 2mg\cot\alpha,$$

as before.

The condition for equilibrium is

$$2mg\cot\alpha \le 4\mu mg,$$

giving $\tan\alpha \ge \frac{3}{4}$. The smallest angle is now $\arctan\frac{3}{4}$. (Note that $\arctan\frac{3}{4} < \frac{\pi}{4}$, so weighting the bottom of the ladder allows it to stand at smaller angles to the horizontal without slipping, as we should expect.)

Section 4

4.1 The motion is one-dimensional.

We have $\mathbf{r}(t) = x(t)\mathbf{i}$, where $x(t) = 4t - 2t^2$.

(a) $\mathbf{v}(t) = \dot{x}(t)\mathbf{i}$ and $\dot{x}(t) = 4 - 4t$, so $\mathbf{v}(t) = 4(1-t)\mathbf{i}$; $\mathbf{a}(t) = \ddot{x}(t)\mathbf{i} = -4\mathbf{i}$.

(b) The ball comes instantaneously to rest when $t = 1$ (for then $\mathbf{v} = \mathbf{0}$); at that instant $x = 2$, whereas initially $x = 0$; the point where the ball comes instantaneously to rest is therefore distant 2 units up the plane from the initial position.

(c) The ball is speeding up when its velocity and acceleration vectors are in the same direction, or in other words when $\dot{x}$ and $\ddot{x}$ have the same signs; it is slowing down when the vectors are in opposite directions, or in other words when $\dot{x}$ and $\ddot{x}$ have opposite signs. We have $\ddot{x} < 0$ for all t. For $0 < t < 1$, $\dot{x} > 0$: the ball is moving forwards and slowing down, i.e. decelerating forwards. For $t > 1$, $\dot{x} < 0$: the ball is moving backwards and speeding up, i.e. accelerating backwards.

4.2 We have $\mathbf{a}(t) = a(t)\mathbf{i}$ where $a(t) = \cos 2t$. Thus

$$v(t) = \int \cos 2t\, dt = \tfrac{1}{2}\sin 2t + A,$$

where A is a constant. But we are given that the particle is at rest when $t = 0$, i.e. $v(0) = 0$; so $A = 0$ and $v(t) = \frac{1}{2}\sin 2t$. So the velocity of the particle is

$$\mathbf{v} = \tfrac{1}{2}\sin 2t\,\mathbf{i}.$$

It follows that

$$x(t) = \tfrac{1}{2}\int \sin 2t\, dt = -\tfrac{1}{4}\cos 2t + B.$$

We are given that the particle is initially at the point $-\mathbf{i}$, i.e. $x(0) = -1$. Thus $B = -\frac{3}{4}$ and $x(t) = -\frac{1}{4}\cos 2t - \frac{3}{4}$. So the position of the particle is

$$\mathbf{r} = -\tfrac{1}{4}(\cos 2t + 3)\,\mathbf{i}.$$

The motion is oscillatory, the extreme points being given by $x = -1$ (when $\cos 2t = 1$) and $x = -\frac{1}{2}$ (when $\cos 2t = -1$). Thus the point of the motion furthest from the initial point is $-\frac{1}{2}\mathbf{i}$.

4.3 $x(t) = Vt + \frac{1}{2}At^2$, option (h);
$v(t) = V + At$, option (a).

4.4 It is helpful to record the information — and the unknowns — for each phase of the motion. Denote by t_i, x_i, u_i, v_i, a_i the elapsed time, distance covered, initial velocity, final velocity, and acceleration, for the ith phase of the motion ($i = 1, 2, 3$). The data and unknowns are summarized in the table below.

i	t_i	x_i	u_i	v_i	a_i
1	5	x_1	0	v_1	2
2	10	x_2	u_2	v_2	0
3	t_3	x_3	u_3	0	a_3

We have to find a_3. Since the acceleration in phase 2 is 0, $v_2 = u_2$; and since the initial velocity of one stage is the final velocity of the preceding one, $u_3 = v_2 = u_2 = v_1$. Since the total distance covered is 200 metres, $x_1 + x_2 + x_3 = 200$. We now proceed to calculate the unknowns, using the formulae for motion with constant acceleration:

$$x_1 = \tfrac{1}{2}a_1 t_1^2 = 25;$$
$$v_1 = a_1 t_1 = 10;$$
$$x_2 = u_2 t_2 = v_1 t_2 = 100;$$
$$x_3 = 200 - 25 - 100 = 75;$$
$$u_3^2 + 2a_3 x_3 = 0, \quad \text{so} \quad a_3 = -\frac{10^2}{2\times 75} = -\tfrac{2}{3}.$$

So the deceleration magnitude in phase 3 is $\frac{2}{3}\,\mathrm{m\,s^{-2}}$.

4.5 The three possible expressions are

$$\frac{dv}{dt}, \quad \frac{d^2x}{dt^2}, \quad v\frac{dv}{dx}.$$

(a) Use $a = dv/dt$, and integrate.

(b) Use $a = v\,dv/dx$, and solve a first-order differential equation by separating the variables.

(c) Use $a = d^2x/dt^2$, write dx/dt for v, and solve a second-order differential equation.

4.6 (a) Newton's first law states that if the force acting on a particle is zero, then the particle remains at rest or moves with constant velocity (that is, with constant speed in a straight line). Newton's second law states that a particle with constant mass, which is subject to a force, moves such that the product of its mass and its acceleration is equal to the total force acting.

Here 'total force' means the total of all the forces, summed as vectors; the particle's acceleration is a vector, its mass a scalar, and the mass and acceleration are combined by scalar multiplication. The first law can be regarded as a consequence of the second, in that motion with zero acceleration is motion with constant, possibly zero, velocity.

(b) A particle is a material object whose size and structure may be neglected. (Structure is intended to include shape and composition; later in the course you will see how these features may be taken into account when modelling the motion of a material object. Other features of material objects, such as colour, are neglected throughout mechanics.)

In deciding to treat a material object as a particle, we are saying that for the purposes at hand it is enough to know the motion of one representative point of it.

(c) The mass of an object is usually defined as the amount of matter in it. The important point to remember is that each object — in particular, each particle — has associated with it a scalar quantity, its mass, which is intrinsic to that object, being for example indifferent to the object's location in the universe and its position in relation to any other objects. In this course we deal only with particles whose masses are constant in time.

The mass of a compound object is the sum of the masses of its component parts.

(d) The kinds of forces that you have met in *Units 5 to 8* are: gravitational force, or weight; the normal reaction exerted by a surface on an object in contact with it; tension force due to a string; friction; air resistance; water resistance; the force exerted by a stretched or compressed spring trying to return to its natural state.

Forces are vectors, and are combined by vector addition.

(e) A force has magnitude one newton if, when it acts on a particle of mass one kilogram, it produces in the particle an acceleration of one metre per second per second (in the direction in which it acts).

A force of magnitude $3\,\mathrm{N}$ produces in a body of mass $5\,\mathrm{kg}$ an acceleration of magnitude $\frac{3}{5}\,\mathrm{m\,s^{-2}}$.

(f) $\mathbf{F} = m\mathbf{a}$

4.7 The engine's initial speed is given in km per hour, which must be converted to $\mathrm{m\,s^{-1}}$: since there are 1000 metres in a kilometre and 60×60 seconds in an hour, the initial speed is $(36 \times 1000)/(60 \times 60) = 10\,\mathrm{m\,s^{-1}}$. The engine comes to rest in 200 metres, so the magnitude of its constant deceleration (acceleration) is $10^2/(2 \times 200) = \frac{1}{4}\,\mathrm{m\,s^{-2}}$. The mass of the train is $40\,000\,\mathrm{kg}$. The magnitude of the force exerted by the brakes is therefore $40\,000 \times \frac{1}{4} = 10\,000$ newtons.

4.8 The diagram should contain a dot to represent the particle, arrows to represent all the forces acting on the particle, and possibly a symbol for the mass of the particle. To obtain the equation of motion, take the vector sum of the forces, and set the result equal to the mass times the acceleration. Substitute the values of the forces. Choose which direction you are going to use for the positive x-axis, and resolve in that direction in order to obtain the equation of motion. Express the acceleration as a derivative in the appropriate way (see Solution 4.5), and solve the resulting differential equation or equations, using any given information about initial conditions.

4.9

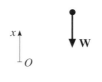

The equation of motion is $\mathbf{W} = m\mathbf{a}$. With the x-axis chosen to point vertically upwards, with its origin at the point at which the ball is struck, this gives $-mg\mathbf{i} = ma\mathbf{i}$, whence $a = -g$. The ball moves with constant acceleration, so the problem may be solved by using the constant acceleration formulae; alternatively, the equation of motion can be solved from scratch, which is the method we shall use here for extra practice.

Integration of $a = dv/dt = -g$ gives
$$v = -gt + A,$$
and $A = 20$ since 'the ball leaves the racket with a speed of $20\,\mathrm{m\,s^{-1}}$'. So
$$x = -\tfrac{1}{2}gt^2 + 20t + B,$$
and $B = 0$ because of the choice of origin. The ball rises until $v = 0$, i.e. until $t = 20/g$; the corresponding value of x is
$$-\tfrac{1}{2}g(20/g)^2 + 20 \times 20/g = \tfrac{1}{2} \times 20^2/g \simeq 20.39,$$
so the height of the ball above the ground at its highest point (remembering that it starts 1 metre above the ground) is approximately 21 metres.

The time taken for the ball to reach the ground, where $x = -1$, is obtained by solving the quadratic equation $-\tfrac{1}{2}gt^2 + 20t = -1$. The relevant root (the positive one) is 4.127 (to four significant figures), so the ball is in the air for just over 4 seconds.

The ball's velocity on reaching the ground is given by $v = -4.127g + 20 \simeq -20.48$, so its speed is about $20.5\,\mathrm{m\,s^{-1}}$ (just a little more than the speed with which it was launched).

4.10 **(a)** Model the sledge and girl together as a single particle of mass m.

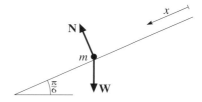

Newton's second law gives $m\mathbf{a} = \mathbf{W} + \mathbf{N}$, where $\mathbf{W}$ is the total weight of the sledge and the girl, and $\mathbf{N}$ is the normal reaction.

Resolving in the direction of increasing x yields
$$ma = mg\sin\tfrac{\pi}{6},$$
whence $a = \tfrac{1}{2}g$. Since this is constant, we can use the formula $v^2 = v_0^2 + 2ax$ to find that the speed v is
$$\sqrt{5^2 + g \times 30} \simeq 17.9\,\mathrm{m\,s^{-1}}.$$

(This is about 40 mph, which seems dangerously fast!)

(b)

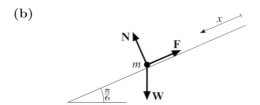

Newton's second law now gives $m\mathbf{a} = \mathbf{W} + \mathbf{N} + \mathbf{F}$, where $\mathbf{F}$ is the friction force. Resolving perpendicular to the slope gives $|\mathbf{N}| = mg\cos\frac{\pi}{6}$. The magnitude of the friction force is $\mu'|\mathbf{N}| = \mu'mg\cos\frac{\pi}{6}$, and the friction force acts up the slope. Thus resolving in the direction of increasing x yields $ma = mg\sin\frac{\pi}{6} - \mu'mg\cos\frac{\pi}{6}$, whence $a = (\frac{1}{2} - 0.02 \times \frac{\sqrt{3}}{2})g \simeq 4.735$. The speed of the sledge is $\sqrt{5^2 + 2 \times 4.735 \times 30} \simeq 17.6\,\mathrm{m\,s}^{-1}$. This is a little less than the answer obtained in part (a), as is to be expected.

4.11 By reasoning similar to that in the previous solution, we obtain the equation of motion $a = g\sin\alpha$ if the plane is smooth, or $a = g(\sin\alpha - \mu'\cos\alpha)$ if the plane is rough. The acceleration is constant in either case. Thus $v = v_0 + at$ (using the initial condition), and $x = v_0 t + \frac{1}{2}at^2$, if the origin is taken at the initial point. The time to travel a distance d is the positive root of the equation $v_0 t + \frac{1}{2}at^2 = d$, which is

$$\frac{-v_0 + \sqrt{v_0^2 + 2ad}}{a}.$$

Thus the time of travel is:

(a) $\dfrac{-v_0 + \sqrt{v_0^2 + 2gd\sin\alpha}}{g\sin\alpha}$

for a smooth plane;

(b) $\dfrac{-v_0 + \sqrt{v_0^2 + 2gd(\sin\alpha - \mu'\cos\alpha)}}{g(\sin\alpha - \mu'\cos\alpha)}$

for a rough plane. The condition $\mu' < \tan\alpha$ ensures $\sin\alpha - \mu'\cos\alpha > 0$, so the formula in the square root is non-negative (regardless of the value of v_0) and the denominator is non-zero. (The formula also works for $\mu' > \tan\alpha$ provided that v_0 is sufficiently large, or d is sufficiently small, to ensure that the term in the square root is non-negative.)

These formulae are not important in themselves: what is important is the method. It is worth noting that the acceleration is constant in both cases. If you can solve a problem like this, with its abstract setting, then you will be able to solve any similar problem set in a specific context such as sledging or skiing.

4.12 Air resistance is modelled as a force whose direction is opposite to that of the motion (that is, so as to slow one down), and whose magnitude is an increasing function of speed (that is, its effect is more noticeable the faster one is going) and of effective diameter (that is, its effect is reduced if one reduces one's profile).

In fact, the force of air resistance on a sphere depends on $D|\mathbf{v}|$, where D is the sphere's diameter. There are two common models: the linear one, where the magnitude of air resistance is proportional to $D|\mathbf{v}|$, and the

quadratic one, where its magnitude is proportional to $(D|\mathbf{v}|)^2$. The direction of the resistive force is given by $-\hat{\mathbf{v}}$, so the force is $-c_1 D\mathbf{v}$ in the linear case, and $-c_2 D^2|\mathbf{v}|\mathbf{v}$ in the quadratic case, where c_1 and c_2 are constants. The two models are appropriate for different ranges of values of $D|\mathbf{v}|$.

4.13 The equation of motion is $ma = mg - kv^2$, where a is the acceleration. The equation in the specific case is $a = 9.81 - 10^{-3}v^2$.

4.14

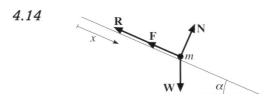

Newton's second law gives

$$m\mathbf{a} = \mathbf{W} + \mathbf{N} + \mathbf{F} + \mathbf{R},$$

where $\mathbf{W}$ is the skier's weight, $\mathbf{N}$ is the normal reaction, $\mathbf{F}$ is the friction force, and $\mathbf{R}$ is the air resistance force. Resolving in the direction of increasing x gives

$$ma = mg\sin\alpha - |\mathbf{F}| - kv^2.$$

Resolving perpendicular to the x-axis gives

$$|\mathbf{N}| = mg\cos\alpha.$$

Since $|\mathbf{F}| = \mu'|\mathbf{N}|$, we have

$$ma = mg\sin\alpha - \mu'mg\cos\alpha - kv^2,$$

hence

$$a = g(\sin\alpha - \mu'\cos\alpha) - kv^2/m.$$

Putting $a = 0$, as suggested in the question, gives the terminal velocity

$$v_{\mathrm{T}} = \sqrt{(mg/k)(\sin\alpha - \mu'\cos\alpha)}.$$

With the given data, the terminal velocity is just over $27\,\mathrm{m\,s}^{-1}$ down the slope.

4.15 (a) When the particle is moving upwards, v is positive, and the resistive force acts downwards. Thus the equation of motion is

$$10^{-3}a = -10^{-3}g - (10^{-4}v + 2 \times 10^{-6}v^2),$$

so

$$a = -10^{-3}(2v^2 + 100v + 1000g).$$

When the particle is moving downwards, on the other hand, v is negative, so $|v| = -v$, and the resistive force acts upwards. The equation of motion in this case is

$$10^{-3}a = -10^{-3}g + (-10^{-4}v + 2 \times 10^{-6}v^2),$$

so

$$a = 10^{-3}(2v^2 - 100v - 1000g).$$

(b) The terminal velocity is that velocity for which $a = 0$. The values of v for which $a = 0$ when the particle is moving downwards are the roots of

$$2v^2 - 100v - 1000g = 0,$$

which are approximately 99.36 and -49.36. We must take the negative root (since the particle is moving downwards), so the terminal velocity is about $49\,\mathrm{m\,s}^{-1}$ downwards.

173

4.16 (a)

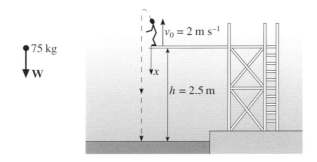

In the first phase the diver moves with constant acceleration g. If the initial speed is v_0 and the height of the board is h, then the speed v_1 with which the diver enters the water is given by $v_1^2 = v_0^2 + 2gh$, so $v_1 = \sqrt{v_0^2 + 2gh}$.

(b)

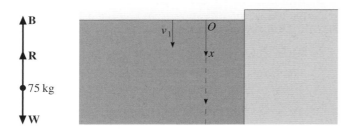

Relative to an x-axis pointing vertically downwards, with origin at the point where the diver enters the water, the equation of motion is $ma = mg - kv^2 - b$, where k is the constant of proportionality in the water resistance, b is the magnitude of the buoyancy force, and m, a, g and v have their usual meanings. To solve the problem we need to find the value of x when $v = 0$, so we set $a = v\,dv/dx$ and obtain the equation

$$mv\frac{dv}{dx} = mg - b - kv^2.$$

This can be solved by separation of variables. Write c for $b - mg$, for convenience (note that $b > mg$); then

$$x + A = -m \int \frac{v}{c + kv^2}\,dv = -\frac{m}{2k}\ln(c + kv^2).$$

The value of A can be determined by using v_1 from part (a) as the initial value of v. Thus

$$A = -\frac{m}{2k}\ln(c + kv_1^2),$$

so

$$x = \frac{m}{2k}\ln\left(\frac{c + kv_1^2}{c + kv^2}\right).$$

The problem is then solved by setting $v = 0$ to determine the lowest point the diver can reach:

$$x = \frac{m}{2k}\ln\left(1 + \frac{kv_1^2}{c}\right).$$

With the data given in the question, we have

$$v_1^2 = 2^2 + 2 \times 9.81 \times 2.5 = 53.05$$

and $c = 850 - 75 \times 9.81 = 114.25$, hence

$$x = \frac{75}{2 \times 50}\ln\left(1 + \frac{50 \times 53.05}{114.25}\right) \simeq 2.39,$$

so the diver submerges to a depth of about 2.4 metres.

Section 5

5.1 (a) The magnitude of the force is the stiffness times the amount by which the spring is extended or compressed, i.e. $k|l - l_0|$. The direction of the force is towards the centre of the spring if the spring is extended, i.e. if $l > l_0$, and away from the centre of the spring if the spring is compressed, i.e. if $l < l_0$. When $l = l_0$, the magnitude of the force is zero, so its direction is undetermined.

(b) The force has magnitude $75\,\mathrm{N}$, and its direction is away from the centre of the spring.

(c) The force is given by $\mathbf{H} = -k(l - l_0)\widehat{\mathbf{s}}$. This force certainly has the correct magnitude. If $l > l_0$, then the direction of $\mathbf{H}$ is the same as the direction of $-\widehat{\mathbf{s}}$, i.e. towards the centre of the spring. If $l < l_0$, then the direction of $\mathbf{H}$ is the same as the direction of $\widehat{\mathbf{s}}$, i.e. away from the centre of the spring. If $l = l_0$, then $\mathbf{H} = \mathbf{0}$. This is all in agreement with the descriptions given in the first part of the solution.

5.2 (a) Take the $\mathbf{i}$-direction to be vertically downwards, so $\widehat{\mathbf{s}} = \mathbf{i}$. Then the model spring provides a force

$$\mathbf{H} = -k(l - l_0)\widehat{\mathbf{s}} = -k(l - l_0)\mathbf{i},$$

where k is the stiffness and l_0 is the natural length of the spring. For each particle of mass m, the weight is

$$\mathbf{W} = mg\mathbf{i}.$$

Since the particle is in equilibrium, we have

$$\mathbf{W} + \mathbf{H} = \mathbf{0}, \quad \text{so} \quad mg - k(l - l_0) = 0.$$

Now $l = 1.3\,\mathrm{m}$ when $m = 5\,\mathrm{kg}$, and $l = 1.5\,\mathrm{m}$ when $m = 9\,\mathrm{kg}$, so we have the simultaneous equations

$$5g - k(1.3 - l_0) = 0,$$
$$9g - k(1.5 - l_0) = 0.$$

Subtraction of the first equation from the second gives

$$4g - 0.2k = 0,$$

so $k = 20g = 196.2\,\mathrm{N\,m^{-1}}$. Substituting the value $20g$ for k back into the first equation provides

$$5g - 20g(1.3 - l_0) = 0,$$

so $l_0 = 1.05\,\mathrm{m}$.

Thus the model spring has stiffness about $200\,\mathrm{N\,m^{-1}}$ and natural length $1.05\,\mathrm{m}$.

(b) With the values just found for k and l_0, the equation $mg - k(l - l_0) = 0$ from part (a) becomes

$$mg - 20g(l - 1.05) = 0.$$

Hence, if $l = 2\,\mathrm{m}$, the corresponding mass of the particle is

$$m = 20(2 - 1.05) = 19\,\mathrm{kg}.$$

5.3 We want the spring to compress by about 0.2 m on the addition of a mass of 2 kg to the scale pan, i.e. when it is subject to an additional force of magnitude $2g$. The stiffness should therefore be about $2g/0.2 = 98.1\,\mathrm{N\,m^{-1}}$, or say $100\,\mathrm{N\,m^{-1}}$. The mass of the pan is irrelevant, since the pan is present for every weighing; it is the difference in mass between full pan and empty pan that one measures.

Since the compression of the spring is a linear function of the mass in the pan, the scale will be linear, i.e. equal divisions of the scale will represent equal masses. To calibrate the balance, therefore, it is enough to mark two points on the scale, corresponding to two accurately known masses (say 0.5 kg and 1.5 kg), and then mark off suitable equal divisions.

5.4 Assume that the object is a particle and that the spring is a model spring. Take the x-axis to point from left to right, with origin at the fixed end of the spring, as shown in part (a) of the figure below.

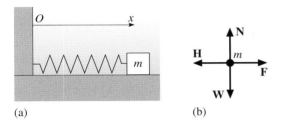

(a)   (b)

If the particle is in equilibrium at a position where the spring is extended, then there will be a friction force **F** acting on the particle, as shown in part (b) of the figure above. The largest magnitude that this force can take is $|\mathbf{F}| = \mu|\mathbf{N}|$, where μ is the coefficient of static friction and **N** is the normal reaction from the table. Resolving in the **j**-direction gives $|\mathbf{N}| = |\mathbf{W}|$, so

$$|\mathbf{F}| = \mu|\mathbf{N}| = \mu|\mathbf{W}| = \mu mg,$$

where m is the mass of the particle. From the data given, we have

$$|\mathbf{F}| = 0.3 \times 2 \times g = 0.6g.$$

With the spring extended, this force will be directed to the right, to prevent the spring from pulling the particle to the left, so $\mathbf{F} = 0.6g\mathbf{i}$. By Hooke's law, we have

$$\mathbf{H} = -k(l - l_0)\hat{\mathbf{s}} = -100(x - 0.5)\mathbf{i},$$

so resolving in the **i**-direction gives

$$-100(x - 0.5) + 0.6g = 0.$$

We conclude that $x \simeq 0.56$, so the furthest distance from the fixed end of the spring at which the object can remain at rest is about 0.56 m.

5.5 The vector $\hat{\mathbf{s}}$ is **i**, the unit vector in the positive x-direction.

(a) Here x is the current extension or compression of the spring: $x = l - l_0$, so $\mathbf{H} = -kx\mathbf{i}$.

The equation of motion is

$$m\ddot{x}\mathbf{i} = \mathbf{H} = -kx\mathbf{i},$$

or equivalently

$$m\ddot{x} + kx = 0,$$

and its general solution is

$$x = B\cos\omega t + C\sin\omega t,$$

where $\omega = \sqrt{k/m}$.

(b) Here, on the other hand, x is the current length of the spring: $x = l$, so $\mathbf{H} = -k(x - l_0)\mathbf{i}$. The equation of motion is

$$m\ddot{x}\mathbf{i} = \mathbf{H} = -k(x - l_0)\mathbf{i},$$

or equivalently

$$m\ddot{x} + kx = kl_0,$$

and its general solution is

$$x = l_0 + B\cos\omega t + C\sin\omega t,$$

where $\omega = \sqrt{k/m}$ as before.

5.6 (a) To say that the particle's motion is periodic is to say that it repeats the same pattern over and over again. To see that this is so, note that, for any t,

$$\cos(8(t + \tfrac{\pi}{4})) = \cos(8t + 2\pi) = \cos 8t$$

and

$$\sin(8(t + \tfrac{\pi}{4})) = \sin(8t + 2\pi) = \sin 8t.$$

Thus, for $x(t) = 4\cos 8t - 3\sin 8t$, $x(t + \tfrac{\pi}{4}) = x(t)$ for any t. So the motion that takes place in any one time interval $t_0 \le t \le t_0 + \tfrac{\pi}{4}$ establishes the pattern for the motion at all times; that same pattern is repeated exactly over and over again at intervals of $\tfrac{\pi}{4}$.

(b) The period is $\tau = \tfrac{\pi}{4}$.

(c) The average position is given by $x = 0$, i.e. the oscillations take place about the origin.

(d) The particle's velocity is given by

$$\dot{x} = -8 \times 4\sin 8t - 8 \times 3\cos 8t,$$

so $\dot{x} = 0$ when $\tan 8t = -\tfrac{3}{4}$. Since $\sqrt{3^2 + 4^2} = 5$, for these values of t we must have $\sin 8t = \pm\tfrac{3}{5}$, $\cos 8t = \mp\tfrac{4}{5}$, and the corresponding values of x are $\mp(\tfrac{16}{5} + \tfrac{9}{5}) = \mp 5$. So the points at which $\dot{x} = 0$ are $x = -5$ and $x = 5$.

(Notice that it is not necessary to find the values of t for which $\dot{x}(t) = 0$ explicitly; all we want is the corresponding values of $\cos 8t$ and $\sin 8t$ to substitute into the formula for $x(t)$.)

(e) The points found in part (d) are the extreme points of the motion; its amplitude is therefore 5. (The amplitude may also be found by expressing $x(t)$ in the form $A\cos(8t + \phi)$.)

(f) At $t = 0$, $x = 4$, so the particle is to the right of its average position; and $\dot{x} = -24$, so the particle is moving to the left.

(g) The particle passes through its average position, the origin, when $0 = 4\cos 8t - 3\sin 8t$, that is, when $\tan 8t = \tfrac{4}{3}$; the smallest positive solution of this equation is $t = \tfrac{1}{8}\arctan\tfrac{4}{3}$.

(h) Your graph should look like this.

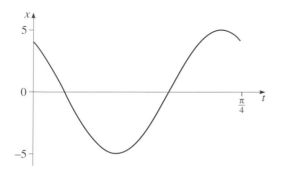

(i) The answers are given in the table.

t	$\frac{1}{4}\tau$	$\frac{1}{2}\tau$	$\frac{3}{4}\tau$	τ
Position	L	L	R	R
Motion	L	R	R	L

5.7 We have to find the values of x_0, A, ω and ϕ from the data in the question. From the initial conditions,

$$x_0 + A\cos\phi = 1 \quad \text{and} \quad -\omega A\sin\phi = -1.$$

The position x_0 is the mean position of the particle and is halfway between the extremes of the motion, so

$$x_0 = \left[(-1 - 2\sqrt{2}) + (-1 + 2\sqrt{2})\right]/2 = -1.$$

The amplitude of the motion is the absolute value of the distance between an extreme point and x_0, so

$$A = \left|(-1 - 2\sqrt{2}) - (-1)\right| = 2\sqrt{2}.$$

Thus $2\sqrt{2}\cos\phi = 2$, so $\cos\phi = \frac{1}{\sqrt{2}}$, and $\phi = \pm\frac{\pi}{4}$, since $-\pi < \phi \leq \pi$. Moreover, $\omega\sin\phi = \frac{1}{2\sqrt{2}}$. Since ω must be positive, this rules out $\phi = -\frac{\pi}{4}$; thus $\phi = \frac{\pi}{4}$, $\sin\phi = \frac{1}{\sqrt{2}}$, and $\omega = \frac{1}{2}$.

The interpretation of these results is as follows. The average position of the particle in its motion is determined by x_0: it is the point $x = -1$. The amplitude of the motion is $A = 2\sqrt{2}$. The angular frequency is $\omega = \frac{1}{2}$; the frequency is therefore $\frac{1}{4\pi}$, and the period is 4π. The particle passes through its average position when $A\cos(\omega t + \phi) = 0$, i.e. when $\omega t + \phi = \frac{\pi}{2} + N\pi$, where N can be any integer. But $\phi = \frac{\pi}{4}$ and $\omega = \frac{1}{2}$, so the smallest positive value of t satisfying this equation is $\frac{\pi}{2}$.

5.8 (a) $3\cos(\omega t + \frac{\pi}{3}) = 3(\cos\omega t\cos\frac{\pi}{3} - \sin\omega t\sin\frac{\pi}{3})$

$$= \tfrac{3}{2}\cos\omega t - \tfrac{3\sqrt{3}}{2}\sin\omega t,$$

so $B = \frac{3}{2}$ and $C = -\frac{3\sqrt{3}}{2}$.

(b) Expanding the right-hand side of the equation gives

$$0.2\cos\omega t - 0.1\sin\omega t = A\cos\phi\cos\omega t - A\sin\phi\sin\omega t.$$

Equating the coefficients of $\cos\omega t$ and $\sin\omega t$ gives the equations

$$A\cos\phi = 0.2 \quad \text{and} \quad A\sin\phi = 0.1.$$

Squaring and adding the equations (to eliminate ϕ) gives

$$A = \sqrt{0.2^2 + 0.1^2} = \sqrt{0.05}.$$

Substituting this into the first equation gives

$$\phi = \arccos(0.2/\sqrt{0.05})$$

(since $\cos\phi$ and $\sin\phi$ are both positive, ϕ satisfies $0 < \phi < \frac{\pi}{2}$).

The answer so far is sufficient, but if you want to check the numerical values, they are $A \simeq 0.224$ and $\phi \simeq 0.464$.

5.9 (a) The motion is simple harmonic; we may write $x(t) = A\cos(\omega t + \phi')$ where $\phi' = \phi - \pi$. (Note that ϕ' is within the permitted range. If ϕ satisfies $-\pi < \phi \leq 0$ instead, then we have to take $\phi' = \phi + \pi$.)

(b) The motion is not simple harmonic.

(c) The motion is simple harmonic; interchange B and C in the standard expression.

(d) The motion is simple harmonic; we may write $x(t) = A\cos(\omega t + \phi')$ where $\phi' = \phi - \frac{\pi}{2}$. (Note that ϕ' is within the permitted range. If ϕ satisfies $-\pi < \phi \leq -\frac{\pi}{2}$ instead, then we have to take $\phi' = \phi + \frac{3\pi}{2}$.)

(e) The motion is not simple harmonic.

5.10 ◄Draw picture► ◄Choose axes►

In this case a picture is shown alongside the question on page 160. Take the x-axis along the slope of the plane, pointing downwards, with origin at the point of attachment of the spring. Take the **j**-direction perpendicular to the slope, pointing upwards.

◄Draw force diagram►

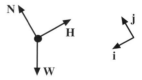

From the diagram we can resolve the normal reaction directly to give $\mathbf{N} = |\mathbf{N}|\,\mathbf{j}$, and the weight can be resolved using the dot product formula from *Unit 4*:

$$\mathbf{W} = |\mathbf{W}|\cos(\tfrac{\pi}{2} - \alpha)\,\mathbf{i} + |\mathbf{W}|\cos(\pi + \alpha)\,\mathbf{j}$$
$$= mg\sin\alpha\,\mathbf{i} - mg\cos\alpha\,\mathbf{j}.$$

The force due to the spring can be written down using the vector form of Hooke's law as

$$\mathbf{H} = -k(x - l_0)\,\mathbf{i},$$

where l_0 is the natural length of the spring.

◄Apply Newton's 2nd law►

Applying Newton's second law to the particle gives

$$m\mathbf{a} = \mathbf{N} + \mathbf{W} + \mathbf{H}.$$

Resolving in the **i**-direction gives

$$m\ddot{x} = mg\sin\alpha - k(x - l_0),$$

which can be rearranged to give

$$m\ddot{x} + kx = mg\sin\alpha + kl_0.$$

◄Solve differential equation▶ ◄Interpret solution▶

This is the SHM equation, so the particle executes simple harmonic motion, with angular frequency $\sqrt{k/m}$, and period $2\pi\sqrt{m/k}$.

(Note that the fact that the spring is at an angle to the horizontal makes no difference to the period of the oscillations; the period is determined completely by the mass of the particle and the stiffness of the spring, and is the same however the spring is oriented.)

5.11   ◄Draw picture▶ ◄Choose axes▶

A picture of the system is shown alongside the question on page 160. Choose the same axes as in the previous exercise.

◄Draw force diagram▶

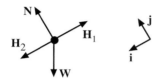

As before we have $\mathbf{N} = |\mathbf{N}|\mathbf{j}$, $\mathbf{H}_1 = -k(x - l_0)\mathbf{i}$ and $\mathbf{W} = mg\sin\alpha\,\mathbf{i} - mg\cos\alpha\,\mathbf{j}$.

For the force due to the second spring we need to introduce the distance between the fixed points of attachment of the springs. Let this distance be d. (As this distance is not given in the exercise, you can expect that the final answer will be independent of d.) Using the vector form of Hooke's law, we can write down the force exerted on the particle due to the second spring as

$$\mathbf{H}_2 = -k'((d - x) - l_0)(-\mathbf{i}) = k'(d - x - l_0)\mathbf{i}.$$

◄Apply Newton's 2nd law▶

Applying Newton's second law to the particle gives

$$m\mathbf{a} = \mathbf{N} + \mathbf{W} + \mathbf{H}_1 + \mathbf{H}_2.$$

Resolving in the $\mathbf{i}$-direction gives

$$m\ddot{x} = mg\sin\alpha - k(x - l_0) + k'(d - x - l_0),$$

which can be rearranged to give

$$m\ddot{x} + (k + k')x = mg\sin\alpha + kl_0 + k'(d - l_0).$$

◄Solve differential equation▶ ◄Interpret solution▶

This is the SHM equation, so we can write down the period of oscillations as $2\pi\sqrt{m/(k + k')}$. (Again, the period does not depend on the angle of slope of the plane.)

5.12 Take an x-axis with origin at the point of suspension and directed downwards, as shown in the figure below.

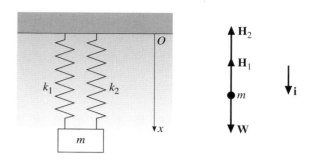

The total force acting on the particle is

$$\mathbf{F} = \mathbf{H}_1 + \mathbf{H}_2 + \mathbf{W},$$

where the two spring forces are given by

$$\mathbf{H}_1 = -k_1(x - l_0)\mathbf{i} \quad\text{and}\quad \mathbf{H}_2 = -k_2(x - l_0)\mathbf{i}.$$

The equation of motion is

$$m\ddot{x}\mathbf{i} = \mathbf{H}_1 + \mathbf{H}_2 + \mathbf{W};$$

since $\mathbf{W} = mg\mathbf{i}$, this gives

$$m\ddot{x} + (k_1 + k_2)x = (k_1 + k_2)l_0 + mg.$$

At equilibrium $\ddot{x} = 0$, so the equilibrium position is given by

$$x_{\text{eq}} = l_0 + \frac{mg}{k_1 + k_2}.$$

The general solution of the equation of motion is

$$x = x_{\text{eq}} + B\cos\omega t + C\sin\omega t,$$

where $\omega^2 = (k_1 + k_2)/m$, so the period of oscillations about the equilibrium position, given by $2\pi/\omega$, is $2\pi\sqrt{m/(k_1 + k_2)}$.

5.13 Take an x-axis with origin at the upper fixed point and directed downwards. The total force acting on the particle is

$$\mathbf{F} = \mathbf{H}_1 + \mathbf{H}_2 + \mathbf{W},$$

where $\mathbf{H}_1$ is the force exerted by the upper spring and $\mathbf{H}_2$ is the force exerted by the lower one. We have $\mathbf{H}_1 = -k_1(x - l_1)\mathbf{i}$, while $\mathbf{H}_2 = -k_2(L - x - l_2)(-\mathbf{i})$. Since $\mathbf{W} = mg\mathbf{i}$, the equation of motion is

$$m\ddot{x} + (k_1 + k_2)x = k_1l_1 + k_2(L - l_2) + mg.$$

The equilibrium position is given by

$$x_{\text{eq}} = \frac{k_1l_1 + k_2(L - l_2) + mg}{k_1 + k_2}.$$

The general solution of the equation of motion is

$$x = x_{\text{eq}} + B\cos\omega t + C\sin\omega t,$$

where $\omega^2 = (k_1 + k_2)/m$, so the period of oscillations about the equilibrium position is $2\pi\sqrt{m/(k_1 + k_2)}$, just as in the previous exercise.

Index